D1072507

Indiana University
Northwest Campus Library

SCHIZOPHRENIA
Conditional Reflex Studies

Publication Number 471

AMERICAN LECTURE SERIES®

A Monograph in

The BANNERSTONE DIVISION *of*
AMERICAN LECTURES IN OBJECTIVE PSYCHIATRY

Edited by

W. HORSLEY GANTT, M.D.
Director. Pavlovian Laboratory
The Johns Hopkins University
Baltimore, Maryland
and
Chief Scientist, V. A. Hospital
Perry Point, Maryland

Schizophrenia
Conditional Reflex Studies

By

CHRISTIAN ASTRUP, M.D.

Gaustad Hospital
Oslo, Norway

CHARLES C THOMAS • PUBLISHER
Springfield • Illinois • U.S.A.

Published and Distributed Throughout the World by

CHARLES C THOMAS • PUBLISHER
BANNERSTONE HOUSE
301-327 East Lawrence Avenue, Springfield, Illinois, U.S.A.

This book is protected by copyright. No
part of it may be reproduced in any manner
without written permission from the publisher.

© *1962, by* CHARLES C THOMAS • PUBLISHER

Library of Congress Catalog Card Number: 61-17007

*With THOMAS BOOKS careful attention is given to all details of
manufacturing and design. It is the Publisher's desire to present books
that are satisfactory as to their physical qualities and artistic possibilities
and appropriate for their particular use. THOMAS BOOKS will be true
to those laws of quality that assure a good name and good will.*

RC 514
.A8

Printed in the United States of America

13.75

Dedicated

to

W. HORSLEY GANTT

Pioneer in the Field

of

Objective Psychiatry

21,737

This study has been made possible by Grants from the Norwegian Research Council for Science and the Humanities.

FOREWORD

Since the turn of the century, there have been two main assaults upon the psyche, from the concepts of two Europeans—Sigmund Freud and Ivan Pavlov. The former is well known and occupies a chief role in American psychiatry, while the work of the latter, though well known in Eastern Europe, is only slightly known or understood in our midst. The causes for this discrepancy are complex. An abundance of experimental material, however, exists, based upon the experiments and theories of Pavlov, both as regards the human and the dog. Most of this is buried in the Russian language.

Dr. Astrup presents in this volume much material having to do with conditional reflexes and related to the psychoses, both conceptual and experimental from the laboratory. Dr. Astrup is well fitted for this task. He is one of the leading young psychiatrists in Europe; with a background of solid Norwegian clinical experience, he has worked in the clinics of Russia, of Leipzig and at the Maudsley Hospital, London. His material is presented from a factual point of view and is remarkably free from prejudice.

To those who are willing to look at the experimental facts obtained and to consider their relevance to the concepts that have been elaborated around Pavlov's fundamental experiments, the book will be very rewarding and will occupy a unique position in an English psychiatric library.

Mrs. Maria Simonson and Miss Priscilla Beach, members of the Pavlovian Laboratory at The Johns Hopkins University, have given valuable help in the editing of the manuscript.

W. Horsley Gantt
V. A. Hospital
Psychophysiological Laboratory
Perry Point, Maryland

INTRODUCTION

THE PURPOSE of this investigation was to analyze to what extent schizophrenia resembles or differs from other psychiatric disorders with regard to experimental disturbances of the higher nervous functions. A survey of studies of the higher nervous activity in mental disorders is given, with extensive bibliography, which the author believes will be useful for research in this field.

The present study is mainly concerned with the group of schizophrenias. In follow-up studies of acute schizophrenias and affective psychoses treated in Gaustad Hospital (Oslo), Holmboe, Fossum and Astrup analyzed the relations between clinical symptomatology and recovery. The experiences of these investigations have been the basis of a detailed clinical study. An analysis is made to the extent the experimental findings might contribute to differential diagnosis, more precise sub-grouping, prognosis and understanding of the pathophysiological foundation of the schizophrenic "process" (64, 331).

CONTENTS

Contents

xiv

Contents

ILLUSTRATIONS

TABLES

SCHIZOPHRENIA
Conditional Reflex Studies

Chapter I

THEORETICAL BACKGROUND
OF REFLEXOLOGICAL STUDIES
IN MENTAL DISORDERS

Wᴵᵀᴴ exception of the psychiatric diseases with known etiology and pathogenesis, the subjective experiences of the patients give the most important information in clinical psychiatry. This does not mean that the clinical symptomatology is an entirely subjective phenomenon which cannot be objectivized. On the contrary, the tendency to similar experiences in the various types of clinical syndromes makes it likely that the subjective experiences may reflect various types of physiological disturbances in the nervous process. With the theoretical conceptions of Hughlings Jackson and Sechenov neuropsychiatric disorders were explained from reflexological principles (379, 985). In recent years Ey and others have tried to interpret psychiatric disorders according to principles of Hughlings Jackson (77, 212). Through experimental psychology, especially in the laboratory of Wundt, objective methods were worked out for the study of psychic activity. Kraepelin introduced the experimental method in the study of psychopathological phenomena (485). Modern reflexological research is predominantly built upon the behaviorist theory of Watson and the reflexological theories of Bekhterev and Pavlov.

The present study is carried out with conditional and unconditional reflex methods, and the results are interpreted according to Pavlovian theories. The theoretical basis of the application of these theories in psychiatry will be discussed. As to the basic laboratory experiments and general theories of conditional reflexes, references are made to the works of Pavlov, Bekhterev, Gantt, Ivanov-Smolensky, Ischlondsky, Masserman, Hilgard, Marquis and others (102, 103, 104, 270, 328, 344, 371, 491, 589, 660, 672, 673, 674, 750, 751, 904, 1053, 1066). The special problems

3

of reflexological research in psychiatry have been dealt with by Pavlov, Gantt, Villars Lunn, and others (126, 266, 270, 271, 273, 274, 279, 371, 564, 673, 753, 988, 990, 1059). In reflexological psychiatry an attempt is made to describe objectively and quantitatively by experimental methods, the physiological basis of abnormal behavior. Because of the complexity of the phenomena met with in psychiatry, there seems still to be a wide gap between the aims and the actual knowledge. The complex psychic activity of man is considerably more difficult to study in exact experiments than is the behavior of animals. The existing experimental methods are also primitive and probably only in the very beginning of their development. Clinical psychiatry, in spite of long traditions, has widely divergent opinions about the pathogenesis of mental disorders, and especially for the group of schizophrenias. The dependence of the subjective experiences upon objectively measurable nervous activity even in normal persons is only partly known. It is possible that severely abnormal subjective experiences and behavior in some mental disorders may be related to gross impairment of nervous functions, which can more easily be demonstrated than the subtle connections of the subjective and the objective in normal states.

In the interpretation of data, one is sailing between the Scylla of idealism and the Charybdis of mechanical materialism in explaining the relationships between consciousness and brain physiology. Some simplifications and mechanical interpretations seem unavoidable in approaching such a complex field. It will be a task of further research to correct such inadequacies. Beside the general problem of relating subjective experiences to objective measurements, there is the great problem of the significance of subjective factors in the test performances. Obviously the person's attitude towards the experiment is of great importance. Especially for schizophrenics, lack of interest in the experiment and great distractability can be considered as the cause of poor performances in many tests. Even such subjective factors may equally be considered to result from changes in nervous activity as the ultimate cause. Through the combination of voluntary, semi-voluntary and involuntary reflexological methods, response patterns are obtained, which fit in well with the hypothesis that abnormal attitudes are usually related to general disturbances of nervous functions. In individual cases with great discrepancies in performances of voluntary and involuntary tests, a clinical judgment can help to evaluate the significance of the subjective factor. In the chronic schizophrenias, there are some types of patients, who obviously according to their generally well integrated behavior should be able to perform tests, but who refuse to carry out the tasks adequately.

If patients were willing to do the tests, the impression was that they did their best. Of very great importance was the estimation of how far poor performances were related to conscious or unconscious misunderstanding of the test. These factors are considered more in detail in the description of the applied experimental methods and the results in a sample of normals, who were eager to explain why they misunderstood some tests.

It became evident during the International Congress of Psychiatry in Zurich in 1957 that schizophrenia is the great puzzle of psychiatry, where numerous and quite opposite theories without any generally convincing data have been unable to establish the nature of the disease. We have to accept that the pathogenesis of schizophrenia is entirely unknown. The theories about psychogenesis, based upon psychoanalytical or existentialist concepts, can hardly be expected to provide any experimental quantitative data to prove the theories. The hereditary factors are obviously of great importance, and possibly sociological factors. In the individual cases such factors cannot give exhaustive descriptions of the pathogenesis. Seen in extensive surveys of the literature, experimental research has provided no pathognomonic pathological factors for schizophrenia. The numerous somatic studies have failed signally to find any specific metabolic disturbances of schizophrenia, although it is generally agreed that several somatic functions show greater intergroup variations than in normal persons (106, 109, 333, 759). Though somatic disturbances can be found to be more frequent in schizophrenia than in normal persons, it can be questioned whether such factors cause the psychic disorder. They may be secondary to the psychic disturbances, or correlated changes due to a general biological failure in adaptation.

The achievements of Gjessing in demonstrating relationship between somatic factors and periodic catatonia indicate that studies of distinctly separated homogeneous groups of schizophrenia are most likely to bring to light correlations between the clinical picture and experimentally observed deviations of mental and somatic functions (295). The author has laid great stress on dividing the clinical material into homogeneous and precisely defined subgroups. If it is assumed that the human organism is built up by increasingly complex levels of integration from basic biochemical processes to the most complicated psychic functions, there is a wide chasm from studies of biochemical changes to the clinical pictures as analyzed by the psychic symptomatology. It is a possibility that reflexological research might help to bridge the gap between biochemical and psychological studies. With exclusively psychological studies, especially with the projective techniques, it is difficult to interpret the factors determining abnormal reactions in physiological terms. Demonstrated by Gantt, experimental studies with the conditional reflex method give hope of establishing the physiological basis of psychiatric disorders. With regard to the conditional reflexes, the view ranges from that expressing complete dependence on the cortex (early work of Pavlov) to those who claim that conditional reflexes can be formed in the spinal animal.

Practically all the experiments show that the conditional reflex function is grossly impaired by cortical damage, and that the higher we go on the zoological scale, the greater the impairment. For human beings it can safely be assumed that the conditional reflex can be taken as a measure of cortical function. Among the cortical functions one can distinguish between the lower level of the first signaling system common to animal and man, and the higher level of the specific human verbal functions, which Pavlov designated as the second signaling system (274, 673). The subcortical functions represent the instinctual life, mainly the affective and emotional aspects of the psyche. The first signaling system is composed of the psychic factors depending upon concrete experiences, under direct influence of the external and internal milieu of the organism—in other words all the nonverbal conditional reflex activity. The second signaling system is characterized by the higher forms of thinking, the verbal functions, which support abstractions and generalizations. Pavlov and Ivanov-Smolensky emphasized that the studies of the higher nervous functions in man in health and disease must take into account the functions at all three levels. It is impossible to find a nervous disturbance confined to one of the three levels mentioned; the pathophysiological mechanisms of one sympton or a syndrome cannot be elucidated unless all three levels are taken into consideration.

Although Asratyan and others have demonstrated that unconditional reflexes are to a great extent dependent upon the cerebral cortex (49, 985), we will in the following, as an oversimplification, in accordance with Traugott and others, consider the unconditional reflexes as measures mainly of the subcortical activity (985). In the second signaling system as well as in the first, the reactions are not entirely dependent upon the cerebral cortex, but also upon the subcortex. Within the first signaling system one can discriminate between the simple and the more complex connections. This applies as well to the degrees of complexity of stimuli and reactions as to reflexes of the first, second and third order (139). Also in the second signaling system one can discriminate between primitive and higher reaction forms (351, 356, 360). When we consider in the following pages the reactions in the first and second signaling systems as measures of lower and higher cortical functions, this is also a hypothetical simplification and abstraction. As to the theoretical problems introduced by a consideration of the first and the second signaling system, it is only necessary here to refer to the literature (366, 369, 370, 371, 452, 573, 673, 754, 905, 974, 984, 985).

In this investigation, experimental data concerning the disturbances of the higher nervous functions at the three levels of unconditional subcortical functions and the cortical functions of the first and second signaling systems are available. An attempt will be made to analyze to what extent different types of clinical syndromes can be correlated to the experimental findings. Some relations should be expected, as the abnormal psychic experiences and behavior are phenomena which can be described in terms of the three studied levels of integration. It is stressed that the group of schizophrenics is subdivided according to clinical symptoms. This is because the clinical entities have already been defined during the long history of clinical research, whereas the experimental studies are only in their infancy and have not given sufficient valid information as the detailed clinical investigation. The experimental chemically produced psychoses give possibilities of relating mental symptoms to physiological changes in the nervous system, and the treatment with ataraxic drugs has increased the need for quantitative evaluation of the physiological effect of such drugs. Animal studies give increasing knowledge about the actions of ataraxic drugs on various properties and integrative levels of the nervous system. If this study should lead to a better knowledge about how nervous processes are affected in schizophrenia, it is a small contribution to the difficult problems of finding adequately directed physiological methods of treatment.

Chapter II

EXPERIMENTAL METHODS IN THE STUDY OF
HIGHER NERVOUS ACTIVITY

1. SELECTION OF EXPERIMENTAL METHODS

THE FIRST PROBLEM is which dimensions of the higher nervous functions should be measured. According to Pavlov the nervous processes are characterized by the strength of the excitatory and inhibitory processes, the equilibrium and the mobility of such processes. The stronger the excitatory processes, the shorter are the reaction times and the stronger the reflex responses. Pavlov divided the inhibitory phenomena into two main groups, the internal or active inhibition depending upon the strength of cortical inhibitory processes, and the external or passive inhibition, which has an unconditional character. In the experimental animal neuroses the interactions of inhibitory and excitatory processes are often disturbed, giving undue weight either to excitation or to inhibition. With a weakening of the active cortical inhibition, the excitatory processes predominate, and we shall choose methods which can measure such changes. With a weakening of the excitatory processes, there will be a predominance of passive inhibition, which it is also important to register through changes of reaction times and responses. The inhibition is usually associated with changes of reactivity as equivalent, paradoxical or ultraparadoxical phases (371). A pathological mobility of the nervous processes occurs either in the form of pathological lability or pathological inertia. As most studies of pathological nervous mobility have been concerned with pathological inertia, only this dimension of mobility will be analyzed. Further methods are needed, which can measure the three levels of unconditional reactions and reactions in the first and second signaling systems. Normally the interactions of these levels are well integrated. Gantt, however, has pointed out that there may often be a split or dissociation in the

9

interactions of the nervous functions, which he calls schizokinesis (275, 280, 282). For obvious reasons we deem it very important to have measures of the dissociation in the study of the higher nervous functions of schizophrenics. As discussed in the section on pathodynamic structures, it is also important to investigate the more localized disturbances of the higher nervous activity.

Before going into the various methods of the study of unconditional and conditional reflexes, some general principles of selection will be mentioned. In order to be able to study a sufficiently large number of patients with various clinical pictures, only a few methods could be selected. Primarily it seemed advantageous to apply methods which had been extensively used earlier, and could be considered to be well elaborated and giving data for comparisons. It is important the technique should not be too complicated. The methods should give fairly objective, quantitative measures for the disturbances of the higher nervous functions, which could be described in terms of the physiology of the higher nervous activity. Also the experimental setting should not be too time consuming for patient and examiner. Gantt and Bykov stress that a variety of somatic, autonomous and biochemic functions can be conditioned (146, 274). In studies of human persons, and especially in psychiatric disorders, only a few of the reflex studies have been widely used.

In previous studies of disturbances of the second signaling system, the author has used a battery of association tests after the principles of Jung and Zurabashvili (388, 887, 1101), the Bourdon test, the calculation test of Kraepelin, the Wordsplit test of Müller-Hegemann (632), and the word-pair method of Ranschburg. It was found that the association test gave the most valuable information, and that the other tests were more difficult to interpret in physiological terms. As the association test has also been widely used formerly, this test was selected for measuring the disturbances of the second signaling system (50, 51, 52).

In the animal studies, the experimental setting can be well controlled, so that the subjective factors (conscious, emotional and voluntary elements) do not interfere with the results. In the human being it is otherwise. Hilgard and Marquis classify the types of conditional reflexes generally used in human studies according to the voluntary component (328). In the first group are reflexes which are mainly regulated by the autonomic nervous system. Here are the changes in salivary excretion, in the cutaneous electrical activity, the reactions of the pupils, the cardiac and vasomotor reactions. Although the salivary reactions were the principal basis of the studied of Pavlov, they have not been extensively applied in psychiatric disorders. Krasnogorsky has elaborated a method which has been used for children (489). Finesinger has used a similar method in a study of psychoneuroses and others in schizophrenia. (230, 291, 769). Salivary conditional reflexes are rather complicated to work with, and for this reason, this method was not chosen. The galvanic skin responses have been widely applied in the study of normal and abnormal psychic reactions. Landis and De Wick referred to 301 publications and three years later Landis added 247 more (507, 508). Merlin has especially evaluated the characteristics of conditional psychogalvanic reflexes in man (596). The author applied the psychogalvanic reflex in studies of neuroses. It seemed that this reflex was also very sensitive to stimuli not related to the experiments, just as pointed out by Villars Lunn (564). As the physiological interpretation of this reflex is difficult, it was not selected for the present study. It might be that this method could have given useful data relative to the studies of complexes, as pointed out by Ås (29). Studies and interpretations of conditional and unconditional pupillary reflexes according to Tatarenko are promising, but not widely used (68, 69, 540, 848, 952, 954, 957).

The vasomotor reflexes, as measured by the plethysmographic reactions, have been frequently used for the study of the higher nervous activity. As it was desired to measure involuntary reactions to various stimuli, this method was selected. EKG has also been used to study unconditional and conditional reflexes (83, 85, 87, 90, 91, 631, 985).

In a second group are the relatively involuntary reactions, where the reaction is carried out by the striated muscles. Most important are the eyelid movement, the patellar reflex and changes of respiration.

The patellar reflex has been rather difficult to condition. In psychiatric disorders only a few investigations have been carried out with this method (695, 906). According to the literature, the eyelid method seems to give valuable information about unconditional and conditional reflexes, also in psychiatric disorders (239, 654, 902, 903, 1025, 1032). This method seems to be useful for the study of complex reactions, and could be applied in a polygraph study combined with respiratory, vasomotor, psychogalvanic, electrocardiographic and other autonomic or semi-voluntary reactions. For the present study, one restricts the complex factors to the vasomotor and respiratory components in order to limit the many variables in an already complex investigation.

The changes of respiration are easily measured and widely studied, so that it was advantageous to include this reflex component in the studies. The respiratory responses could be easily registered in severely disturbed patients, who otherwise could not actively cooperate with the examiner.

In a third group are the semi-voluntary and voluntary reactions. Here motor conditional reflexes with verbal commands and withdrawal responses have mostly been used. Both of these methods have been selected for this study. The withdrawal reflex has the advantage of giving a simple measure of unconditional motor reflexes. In combination with plethysmographic and respiratory unconditional reflexes, one can obtain indices of the motor as well as of the vegetative unconditional responses, which mainly depend upon subcortical structures. The conditional reflexes with verbal command have been extensively used for the study of higher nervous activity. This method gives information primarily about the functions in the first system and the interactions of the two signalling systems. With this method motor conditional reflexes are studied, which are more rapidly developed than the autonomic and relatively involuntary reflexes. In the course of one or two sessions one can obtain information about the before mentioned properties of the nervous processes. With other methods these would demand long series of experiments, exhausting for patients as well as for experimenter. Discussed in another part of this chapter, the motor reflexes must be carefully evaluated because of the voluntary factors. Even the voluntary conditional behavior is so characteristic of the human being that this method may give important information about the physiological basis of abnormal behavior. Some authors have combined the measuring of motor reflexes with electromyographic recording, which can give additional information and especially for schizophrenia (190, 191, 1076, 1078). As mentioned in the previous part of this chapter, the functions of the second signaling system are the most important neurophysiological differences between animals and men. It is obvious that the study of the second signaling system will be of particular interest for the psychiatric disorders.

When Ivanov-Smolensky in his monograph (1928) described the methods for study of the higher nervous activity in man, he tried to modify the already existing psychological test methods for the physiological study of the higher nervous activity (356). In spite of the tremendous development of psychological tests since that time, there have not been any further systematic attempts to coordinate psychological tests with Pavlovian physiology. It is noted that Marinesco, Shipkovenski and others compared the Rorschach test with conditional reflex studies (172, 579, 858). The general impression is that reflexological and psychological research followed different directions. Studies of Eysenck and others seem to bridge some of the gaps between reflexology and objective psychology (214, 850). According to the studies of Eysenck and co-workers objective perception tests may be valuable for the differential diagnosis of clinical states. But the conditional reflex studies of schizophrenic patients have hitherto been little concerned with studies of perception, although there is a considerable literature about this problem in animals as well as in normal men (28, 72, 73, 74, 97, 98, 214, 286, 371, 824, 895, 914, 1072).

In recent years vestibular functions and chronaximetric studies have been used for studies of conditional reflex activity (7, 8, 559, 651, 787, 788, 1062, 1063, 1064, 1065, 1071). In the case of EEG an extensive literature of conditioning has also developed (68, 69, 166, 167, 233, 394, 395, 396, 397, 676, 763, 776, 1067). These methods seem to be promising for the future, but at present are not widely used in conditional reflex studies of psychiatric patients. Combinations of conditional reflex studies with various biochemic, pharmacological and immunological studies are advocated by several authors (729, 915, 957, 1086). It is not unlikely that patient groups with similar clinical symptomatologies and disturbances of the higher nervous activity reveal similar biological and biochemic changes of etiological importance.

In the following parts of this chapter the methodological problems of the selected methods will be discussed. Also given is a survey of findings with these methods not only for schizophrenics, but also for other bodily and mental disorders and normals. This is done so as to evaluate to what extent the disturbances of the higher nervous system in groups of schizophrenics resemble or differ from normals and other mental disorders. In Chapter V a summarization of present knowledge about disturbances of the higher nervous activity in schizophrenia is presented.

2. THE APPLICATION OF THE WORD ASSOCIATION TECHNIQUE FOR THE ANALYSIS OF THE DISTURBANCES OF THE SECOND SIGNALING SYSTEM

A. Theoretical Background and Methodological Problems

According to Pavlov the conditional reflexes are dependent upon cortical processes. Common to men and animals is the ability to form conditional reflexes with motor or vegetative reactions to direct sensory stimuli. Those reflexes occur in the first signaling system. Specifically human are language and the combined thinking processes. Pavlov designated the speech functions as the second signaling system, which implies that the words are signals for reactions occurring in the first signaling system (673). Through studies of Krasnogorsky, Ivanov-Smolensky, Luria and others the ontogenetical development of the second signaling system has been studied in detail, and the principles of the laws governing the interactions between the two signaling systems have been established (351, 355, 371, 375, 452, 488, 489, 490, 567, 985, 992). The association experiment, being word reactions to word stimuli, predominantly occurs in the second signaling system, and will be used as a technique for analyzing the disturbances of this highest level of the nervous activity. It should be stressed that reactions in the second signaling system are closely dependent upon the first signaling system, so that an isolated study of this level is not possible. The second signaling system is a highly differentiated level, covering all transitions from the simple primitive speech reactions to complicated processes of thought, feelings, and will.

As mentioned previously, the association experiment was chosen because this method has a long tradition in mental testing, and has been applied by several authors for the objective analysis of the functions of the second signaling system. It is not practical to give a complete list of references of all the studies which have been carried out with this technique since it was introduced by Galton in 1879 (261). Long lists of references are, however, given by Jung (388), Wreschner (1061), Bell (105), Murphy (636), symonds (942), (Whipple (1056), Rapaport (747), Warren (1049), and De (182).

In the literature there have been used tests with the numbers of stimulus-words varying between 10 and 400 (182). We have chosen fifty stimulus-words closely resembling those of Smirnov (887). These consisted of nouns selected according to the principles used by Ivanov-Smolensky in the study of the higher nervous functions. This corresponds fairly well to the number of sixty words used by Rapaport (748). Several authors have worked with association tests limiting the answers either to one or two words or to a special type of answers (174, 182, 423, 687, 688, 689, 690).

In the present study the usual free association technique has been applied. This does not imply that the other methods might not give better information about certain aspects of associative processes. The free association technique has been the most widely used, and provides for several measures concerning the properties of the nervous processes. Stressed by Jung and Ivanov-Smolensky the association test is actually not so much the measure of the association of ideas as argued in the classical works of the Wundt school, but principally a measure of word reactions.

An important index of the association experiments is the reaction time (from the time the stimulus-word is given until the answer follows). Several authors have used the prolongation of reaction time as a measure for inhibition in the second signaling system (318, 356, 511, 887, 976, 1101).

In the classical studies of reaction times complicated apparatus with lip key and chronoscopes measuring 1/1000 of a second have been applied (388). Others have constructed complicated apparatus for the study of word reactions (48, 128). In the earlier studies of Thumb and Marbe (962), Wreschner (1060), Sommer (898, 899), and June (388), it was already claimed that an ordinary stop watch measuring 1/5 of a second gives sufficient exactness and less diversion in the experiment. We measured the reaction times with a stop watch measuring 0.1 second. That this exactness is sufficient becomes quite evident when one has in mind that the same person in a test may give reaction times varying from under one second to several seconds. Noticeable in the pathological materials the dispersions are very great. Buccola, according to Kraepelin, proposed even to regard the dispersion as a measure of the tonus of consciousness (486).

We have used the technique of Jung (388), saying the stimulus-words and recording the reaction time with a stop watch. In mental patients the associative reaction is often preceded by repetition of the stimulus-word or other irrelevant words. In such cases the reaction time is considered to be the period from the stimulus-word until the proper association response follows. Only for patients unable to give associative responses proper is the period between the stimulus-word and the irrelevant answer measured as the reaction time.

For each person the mean reaction time is taken as a measure of the speed. For our purposes, the calculation of the standard error of the mean is unnecessarily cumbersome, and does not give much additional information about the reaction pattern. We have used the median proposed by Kraepelin for association experiments as another measure for our observed means (485). The difference between the mean and the median is mostly due to excessively high values connected with complex influences and other specially disturbing factors in the associative performances. Decreasing speed in the last half of the test can be considered as indicating inhibition of the second signaling system.

The main diffculty met with in the evaluation of the association test is the classification of the response words. The first systematic attempt to classify the associative reactions can be found in the works of Trautscholdt, a pupil of Wundt. His system of classification was further elaborated by Aschaffenburg, Jung and others (36, 147, 389, 993). Other systems of classification, which are summarized by Warren, built upon similar principles, i.e., logical considerations of the connections between stimulus and response words, expressed in outer, inner and a variety of other special forms (1049). The originators of this type of classification were already aware of the extreme difficulties of classifying the individual responses, although the majority of the reactions fitted into the scheme. Kent and Rosanoff have emphasized the subjective character of the scheme of Jung (418). In order to get a more objective criterion for the classification, they based their scheme which gave normal groups of common and individual responses according to tables, on the frequencies of responses found in 1,000 normal people. Their group of unclassified reactions contain the different special forms of the associative reactions, which were already considered by the German investigators to be correlated with mental abnormality. The incoherent reactions, which correspond to the *"mittelbare"* reactions in the German classifications, should be characteristic of dementia praecox (418).

Among later studies mainly based upon the Kent-Rosanoff scheme or modifications of this scheme can be mentioned: Tendler (958, 959), Crown (174), De (182), Eysenck (215) and the majority of the English and American authors. Whipple (1056) has stressed in the Kent-Rosanoff scheme there will also be considerable subjective evaluations. The later modifications of the scheme have not made any essential changes with regard to the criticism of Whipple. It is difficult to ascertain if the individual reactions are of normal or pathological types. The rather complicated scheme of De with 34 diagnostic indices, which also takes the classifications of Jung and Wells into consideration, has not made the classifications easier. Eysenck (215) for such reasons could employ it only in part.

A third principle, distinguishing between formal and content aspects of the responses, has as has been done in such tests as T.A.T. and Rorschach was devised by Rapaport and others (748, 798, 799).

The fourth principle of classification we have in the studies of Ivanov-Smolensky and other investigators who follow his principles (51, 352, 356, 976). The main aim of this classification was to use the association experiment as a measure of the disturbances of the second signaling system. The associative responses were set into relation to the ontogenetic development of speech. The first subdivision was into higher verbal reactions and primitive word reactions. The primitive reactions should then represent ontogenetically lower types of verbal reactions. According to the same functional genetic principle Ivanov-Smolensky divided the higher verbal reactions into individual concrete, general concrete and general abstract reactions, the last mentioned type being the most differentiated type of response. It was assumed that the greater the percentage of general abstract reactions, the greater the predominance of the second system over the first signaling system.

Gakkel thought (254) that the more responses represent generalizations with respect to the stimulus-words, the more the second signaling system is dominating. In an experimental study of the disturbances of the higher nervous activity in fifty-five patients with different forms of psychoneuroses Astrup tried to divide the higher associative reactions into subtypes as proposed by Ivanov-Smolensky and Gakkel. It was rather difficult to divide the responses into the concrete and abstract types, as many words have concrete as well as abstract significance. Principally the distinction between concrete and abstract responses must be decided on the basis of logical analysis in the same way as the distinction between outer and inner associations, and experimental evidence for the justification of such a classification is in fact scarce (52). For such reasons the author will not, in this study, try to separate the higher verbal reactions into subtypes. The higher verbal reactions correspond to a great extent to the outer and inner associations in the classical German studies, the common and normal individual reactions in the Kent-Rosanoff test and the modifications of this test.

For the distinction between higher and primitive verbal reactions there has accumulated considerable experimental evidence. It is supposed that the primitive reactions are called forth by an inhibition which excludes predominantly the complicated and ontogenetically more recently acquired conditional connections, causing the primitive ontogenetically previously obtained reactions to appear. In psychiatric patients it has been shown by Trau-gott, Ivanov-Smolensky (352, 976, 984) and Astrup (51) that primitive reactions predominating during acute psychoses, char-acteristic of clinical severe inhibitions of mental functions, grad-ually become replaced by higher verbal reactions in connection with clinical improvement. In connection with shock-treatment, insulin coma, and sleep treatment, several authors also have dem-onstrated how the primitive reactions during awakening are grad-ually replaced by higher verbal reactions (984, 985).

For reasons mentioned above, the author finds that the distinc-tion between higher and primitive reactions actually represents a biological basis for the classification of associations. This basis might be useful for the analysis of disturbances of the second sig-naling system. The next question is to define precisely which types of verbal reactions should be considered as primitive reac-tions. It is noted that the different forms of primitive reactions are not found uniformly in all clinical conditions. During clinical improvement there is not only a shift from lower to higher reac-tions, but also changes within the types of primitive reactions. During the most severe inhibitions of the second signaling system, the patients are not capable of answering. Instead of words there are often only movements or gestures. Simple echolalia or "yes" answers are also correlated with severe inhibitions (51). As the next step come tautological or vague meaningless answers, which are often anticipated by echolalia or affirmatives. In the transi-tion form between the higher and the primitive ones are complete sentence responses which often begin with echolalia, "yes," or other irrelevant words.

Responses in foreign languages are considered as primitive reac-tions, but cannot always be regarded as abnormal, as they often occur in normal persons, apparently accidental and depending up-on knowledge of other languages. In order to avoid distortions by such factors, a response with a foreign word is always followed by an instruction in our cases to give answers only in the Nor-wegian language. For psychotic patients it is noticed that some patients deliberately have responded with a translation of the stimulus-word in spite of instruction, as in a general pattern of echolalic reactions. For this reason the foreign language reactions phenomenologically are related to the echolalic reactions. Responses in the form of questions are considered as primitive reactions (356). Such reactions, like echolalia, represent the replacement of a new associative content by an irrelevant remark. In normal persons occasionally the subjects say that they did not catch the stimulus-word, and whenever the stimulus-word evidently is not understood, a new stimulus-word is given in order to avoid an incorrect response mainly due to misunderstanding. In severely psychotic patients new stimulus-words do not change the patterns of reactions.

Another group of primitive reactions are the negating responses (356). The most simple type is simply a "no," corresponding merely to an echolalia or "yes" in the former group. More common are sentences beginning with "no." The rejecting responses are considerably less frequent than the reactions in the preceding group, which are the most common primitive reactions.

The third group of primitive reactions embraces the extra-signaling responses (356). They consist of sound associations, incoherent (*"mittelbare"*) reactions, neologisms, inadequate egocentric reactions and delusional responses. From Aschaffenburg and Jung (36, 37, 389) not only sound reactions proper, but also word connections and derivatives of the stimulus-word are considered as sound reactions. The last two types of reactions we classify as primitive reactions, although they are very common in normal persons and neurotics, who otherwise give adequate higher verbal reactions. There seems to be a gradual transition to the next step with sound resembling responses or rhymes, which are predominantly found in psychotics, especially in manic syndromes (51). The most severe disturbances of the sound type are sound-resembling responses, which are not even words of the ordinary speech.

The incoherent or mediate reactions (*"mittelbare"*) do not show any detectable relations to the stimulus words. Sometimes it is observed that the patients respond by mentioning occasional objects in the experimental room. In other cases such reactions represent perseverations. There can be found relations to delusions and other psychotic structures. For such reasons it is evident that the incoherent reactions are not without relation to external or internal stimuli. By questioning the patients about the connections between the stimulus-word and the apparently incoherent reactions, they often can relate the unusual response to some concrete episodes, where the stimulus-word has an unusual associative connection. In normal people, as shown by Kent, Rosanoff, Martin, Murphy (418, 585, 634, 635, 770) and others, the common and popular responses predominate and incoherent reactions are practically never found. This would indicate that in normal, well integrated persons the associative connection of ideas ontogenetically is elaborated in a rather uniform way, and apparently independent of intelligence level, as demonstrated by several authors (174, 182, 958, 959). The unusual and incoherent reactions represent a dissolution of the ontogenetically rather firmly elaborated associative connections, and can be regarded as measures for dissociation in the functions of the second signaling system. There is a grading transition between the incoherent (*"mittelbare"*) reactions and responses with merely incoherent speech, which obviously is a dissociation of the verbal functions. The neologisms are also taken as measures of dissociation. With regard to the incoherent reactions some care must be taken that such reactions are not due to a misunderstanding of the experiment. In the association experiment technique, the instruction is followed by a few examples to ensure that no misunderstanding takes place before the experiment is actually started. After an incoherent response the instruction is repeated with some new examples in order to avoid incoherent reactions due to misunderstanding. In patients with predominant tendencies to incoherent responses such intervention does not change the response pattern.

The inadequate egocentric responses, delusional contents and other psychotically colored responses reflect abnormal psychopathological structures more than general tendencies to dissociation of the second signaling system.

The number of above-mentioned forms of primitive reactions are counted up for each patient's association responses, and regarded as a measure for the inhibition of the second signaling system. The number of each type does not seem to have any special significance, as the different types are usually found together in the same patients without regard to the clinical pictures. The only exception is the primitive reactions indicating dissociation of the second signaling system, which, when found, are grouped separately and designated incoherent responses.

In the second group come reactions with repetition of the stimulus-word or "yes" before giving adequate or multiword responses. Such types of reactions, we, in accordance with Ivanov-Smolensky and Traugott, classify as a transitional group between the higher and the primitive verbal reactions. The remaining group of responses are adequate reactions with one word only according to the instruction, which are classified as higher verbal reactions (356, 976). As described by several authors the normal persons and neurotic patients answer predominantly with higher verbal reactions (51, 182, 887).

The reactions of the middle group seem to predominate in oligophrenia and organic dementia, and the primitive reactions mainly occur in greater numbers in psychotics (51). Kent, Rosanoff, Murphy and others note that normal as well as abnormal persons may respond with all types of verbal reactions. With the possible exception of the extra-signaling reactions no reaction types can be regarded as absolutely pathological and not occurring in normal persons. It may at times be difficult to classify a response. Among reactions classified as higher verbal reactions, unusual responses are frequently found in schizophrenics, which indicate some dissociation of the verbal reactions. These cannot be separated from the ordinary higher responses on the basis of objective criteria.

Reactions starting with echolalia or "yes" are regarded by several authors as signs of inhibition of the verbal reactions, and the number of such reactions are counted up as a measure for the inhibition of the second signaling system and designated echolalic responses (51, 356, 976).

Perseveration in the form of reacting with repetition of previous responses are pointed out by several investigators as pathological reaction types (182, 1050). Gakkel considered such reactions as a measure of the inertia of the verbal processes (254). Lang-Belonogova and Astrup (52, 511) could not find sufficient evidence to regard repetitions of previous responses as reliable criteria for inertia of the second signaling system.

The patients are always instructed to respond only with one word. As already stressed by Wehrlin, Brunnschweiler and Bleuler (122, 142, 1050) some patients are not capable of reacting with one word, in spite of repeated instructions. Ivanov-Smolensky originally considered the multiword responses to be due to lack of active internal inhibition in the second signaling system. Subsequent investigators have been more inclined to regard such reactions as measures for inertia of the nervous processes, especially of the excitatory processes (51, 356, 860, 976).

As previously noted, the number of reactions starting with echolalic responses represents inhibition of verbal reactions. Gakkel and Astrup assume that a great number of such reactions also indicate an inertia of the nervous processes, especially inhibition (52, 254). De had registered separately different forms of incorrect reproductions (182). The author cannot find any principal differences between the various forms of reproductive failures. Most other authors in their quantitative analyses have taken such reactions as a whole group (391, 887). Failure of reproduction is apparently dependent upon several factors, and a rather complex phenomenon. In the experiments of Jung it was regarded as a complex sign. In the work of Harzstein, complex reactions are regarded as due to word stimulation of isolated pathological inert dominants (1018) of psychodynamic nature, being followed by excessive induced inhibition. This inhibition is clearly seen in the prolonged reaction times. The failures of reproduction are not sure signs of external inhibition.

In a study of neurotic patients Astrup found that patients with defective internal inhibition actually tended to have many failures in reproduction. This measure correlated well with other measures of the internal inhibition (52, 318). The author is most inclined to regard the number of defective reproductions as partially a measure for weakness of the active inhibitory processes (51, 52). Only a small proportion of failures in reproductions consist of no answers, notably in the group of neurotics. Usually failures of reproduction come as wrong reproductions, which actually means that there is a deficient active inhibition of the associative connections. This deficient active inhibition is especially seen in psychotics with syndromes of excitation. In the study of De even incorrect reproductions together with unusual vague and incoherent responses were considered as a factor of disorientation. These responses made it possible to distinguish associative reactions of psychotics from the reactions of normals and neurotics at the 1 per cent level of significance (182).

In summarization there are the following signs indicating disturbances of the nervous processes in the second signaling system:

    A. *Signs of external passive inhibition*
        1. Number of primitive responses
        2. Number of echolalic responses
        3. Mean reaction times
        4. Median reaction times
        5. Decreased speed in last half of the test
    B. *Signs of internal inhibition*
        1. Number of defective reproductions
    C. *Signs of inertia of nervous processes*
        1. Number of multiword responses
        2. Number of echolalic responses
    D. *Signs of dissociation*
        1. Number of incoherent responses

The factor of decreased speed in the last half of the test will be confined to the analysis of patients studied repeatedly. The other factors will be used for all comparisons between normals and patients.

The above mentioned factors represent disturbances of specific nervous system qualities, with a certain overlapping, but this is also the case with analogous factors in the animal experiments. This is due to the basic complexity of nervous structures (674).

Changes in the deeper functional levels will affect the verbal reactions. As a general rule, the nervous structures phylogentically and ontogenetically most recently developed tend to be the most affected by overstrain of the nervous processes. Most psychiatric disorders tend to give general disturbances in the functions of the second signaling system.

B. The Influences of Complexes or Pathodynamic Structures

Besides the general disturbances of the functions of the second signaling system, we have more circumscribed functional changes.

Pavlov pointed to the significance of the "weak points" in the experimental neuroses. These "weak points" were considered to be complicated pathological structures, not of anatomical, but of functional dynamic character (673, 674). Ivanov-Smolensky designated the "weak points" pathodynamic structures. He assumed that the neurotic complexes as well as hallucinations, delusions and some other psychotic symptoms were related to "weak points." The pathodynamic structures were considered to be pathological dominants (1018) of the higher nervous activity. These dominants are usually pathologically inert and pathologically excited. There may also be pathological inhibition and phasic states with equivalent, paradoxical and even ultraparadoxical phases.

The pathodynamic structures are closely linked up with disturbances of autonomic functions, which give a pronounced affective anchoring of the psychopathological experiences. Individual life experiences are reflected in complex ways in both signaling systems. Through the autonomic components there are formed conditional-unconditional connections involving the subcortical activity (89, 372, 878, 879, 991). In the following pages the classical term "complex" will be used for neuroses and other psychogenetic disorders. The term "pathodynamic structures" will mainly be used for circumscribed disturbances of nervous activity related to psychotic experiences. Although complexes traditionally imply a psychogenesis, this is not necessarily so for the pathodynamic structures. They may be related to a process or even organic factors, so that the influence of life experiences only are of a pathoplastic significance.

The experimental influences of psychodynamic complexes on associations have since the classical studies of Jung been convincingly demonstrated by several authors. Combinations with psychogalvanic, plethysmographic, respiratory, motor or electroencephalographic reactions have especially contributed to an objective study of complexes (50, 51, 52, 94, 113, 116, 168, 182, 215, 317, 318, 319, 320, 372, 373, 391, 507, 508, 566, 676, 760, 835, 887, 1004).

When some authors denied the significance of complex factors, they were usually working with artificial complexes in normals or criminals (330, 805). In Astrup's experience normals and psychopaths so seldom show reactions with the characteristics of Jung for complex reactions, that such reactions might well be due to other distracting factors (51).

In the next chapter it is shown that complex reactions are especially characteristic of neuroses. Because of the complexity of the psychodynamic complexes, they cannot always be convincingly demonstrated in the association test. Jung thought that complex influences were strong in many schizophrenics (346, 387, 392). Astrup finds that such influences can only with difficulty be demonstrated in schizophrenics. Associative reactions to pathodynamic structures in schizophrenics differ from the complex reactions of neurotics (51,).

C.   The Association Experiment in a Sample of Forty Normal Persons

In the findings of Trautscholdt, Jung, Ivanov-Smolensky, Smirnov, Rapaport, Wreschner and others, the association reaction time lies between 1 and 2.4 seconds in normal persons (352, 388, 748, 887, 993, 1058, 1061).

In a preliminary study Astrup found in nine normal persons the mean as well as median reaction times lower than two seconds (51). This "normal" material consisted of persons with high school education, and for this reason probably is too low. In Gaustad hospital a control material of 40 persons from the nursing staff, twenty male and twenty female nurses, were selected as normal material. In this sample the majority have only elementary school attendance. As to education level this lies close to our patient material. According to some social psychiatric studies, "nervous" traits are present in 30 per cent of the general population (54). With such wide concepts of mental abnormality, even some of our normal persons would reveal nervous traits. As all have been able to work and in absence of well defined nervous symptoms necessitating special treatment, one finds it justified to characterize them as mentally healthy persons. The author did not attempt to analyze the personality structures of the persons in the sample, as intimate personal questions obviously would be felt as intruding. On the average the mean reaction times were 2.7 ± 0.7 seconds and median 2.0 ± 0.4 seconds. There is a slight increase over the usual in the literature. Probably one factor is that most populations studied have higher education than our sample of normals. Another factor is that most normal persons may block for a few words, usually giving an echolalic reaction before the actual answer. In this study the reaction time is measured for the actual answer, which under such circumstances can be delayed to 30 seconds and considerably prolong the mean. It is noted that in the sample the maximum reaction times were 4.7 seconds for the mean and 3.1 seconds for the median, and it was decided only to consider reaction times longer than this as inadequate.

On the average our sample has 6 ± 2.5 defective reproductions. The maximum met with was 12 in defective reproductions, which was considered to be the normal limit. Our previous normal limit was considered to be 10 (51). Four persons of the normal sample have 10 or more inadequate reproductions.

On the average each person of the sample has 1.8 ± 1.5 reactions of the middle type, beginning with echolalic responses followed by an adequate reaction. The maximum is 5, which is considered to be the upper limit of normal variation. Our former limit of 5, being suspect of a pathological reaction, can therefore be maintained. Reactions with more than one word are on the average 0.7 ± 1.3. The maximum was 7, which is close to our previous upper level of 5 (51).

The rule that normals predominantly respond with higher, adequate one-word reactions is confirmed. In averaging there are 46 ± 3.6 adequate reactions out of 50. The minimum was 37 adequate reactions, which was considered to be the limit of normal variation. The average number of primitive reactions was 2.3 ± 2.8 and the maximum 12. In the normal sample most primitive reactions are word combinations and word derivatives. Other primitive reactions are rare, and incoherent reactions were not found. According to De and Eysenck there are several sex differences with the association test. Sex differences are smaller than the resemblances. With our wide limit for the normal variations, there are no sharply defined sex differences. It is known from the literature that the associations of children differ from those of adults (182, 215, 618, 771). For adult persons age seems not to have a great influence. Ranschburg found that even in age above seventy years there are not great differences compared with younger people (746). In the present sample the average age was thirty years with variation between twenty-one and fifty-four years. There were no essential differences between older and younger persons.

Another problem is the factor of intelligence and education. According to De the intelligence has no effect on the ability to carry out the test instructions (182). Recent studies of Crown and Tendler on word association tests have shown the correlation of intelligence with association responses to be very low (174, 958, 959). The influences of education upon association responses were observed by Jung. In the author's experience also, persons with higher education tend to have better associative responses than persons with only elementary school. It is noted that some persons in the normal sample had complex reactions similar to those found in neuroses, but that these reactions occurred so rarely it is possible that other distracting factors are causatives.

For comparisons with pathological materials, the limits of the normal variation are mostly calculated on the basis of the standard error. For the experimental methods applied in this study, several factors can only distinguish between adequate reactions found in normals and inadequate reactions found only in patient groups. Some reactions frequently seen in pathological materials due to occasional misunderstandings of the task, or other irrelevant factors, may be found in normals. It was decided to distinguish between adequate reactions, which definitely occur in normals, and inadequate reactions which possibly are pathological. With the association test, only signs not found in the normal sample will be considered as inadequate.

3. THE APPLICATION OF MOTOR CONDITIONAL REFLEXES FOR THE ANALYSIS OF DISTURBANCES OF THE FIRST SIGNALING SYSTEM AND THE INTERACTIONS OF THE SIGNALING SYSTEMS

A. Theoretical Background and Methodological Problems

The basis of the conditional motor reflexes with verbal reinforcement is the simple motor reflex, which now has been in use for more than 100 years since it was introduced in experimental psychophysiology. During the first experimental studies of conditional reflexes in man, involuntary motor and vegetative reactions were used. This was due to the opinion that only reactions which are not linked up with the higher psychic activity could be regarded as being of reflex character. When Ivanov-Smolensky originally modified the simple motor reflex for studies of conditional motor reflexes in man, he used involuntary movements, which were regarded as elementary, automatic and unconscious reactions (356). Usually the conditional reflexes in animal experiments are worked out by combining the conditional stimulus with an unconditional stimulus. A conditional reflex can also be elaborated on the basis of another well elaborated conditional reflex. Such reflexes Pavlov designated as non-primary conditional reflexes. Among the groups of non-primary conditional reflexes in man are the reactions to verbal stimuli. Through series of experiments Ivanov-Smolensky developed the method using non-primary conditional reflexes with verbal reinforcement (353, 356). The present author has carried out the experiments with this method according to the instructions given by Povorinsky (721). Several authors have worked with modifications of the Ivanov-Smolensky method. For further details about methodological problems see the references (13, 48, 112, 183, 366, 368, 369, 370, 374, 375, 706, 778, 840, 894, 974).

In the present study a reaction apparatus constructed according to the principles described by Povorinsky was used (721). It was built in the Psychological Institute of the University of Leipzig by R. Hartmann (see Fig. 1).

No instructions are given before the experiment. The patient is only informed that his motor reactions will be studied, and that the experiment is a routine examination. Only a few reveal anxiety before the experiment, and are then reassured that it will not be harmful. In the apparatus there is a window through which the patient's behavior can be observed. The patient is seated in front of the apparatus, and puts a finger on a button. Then a sound signal is given, and after one to two seconds the patient is told to press. Often after a few signals the patient will press before he is told, and a motor conditional reflex has been elaborated on the

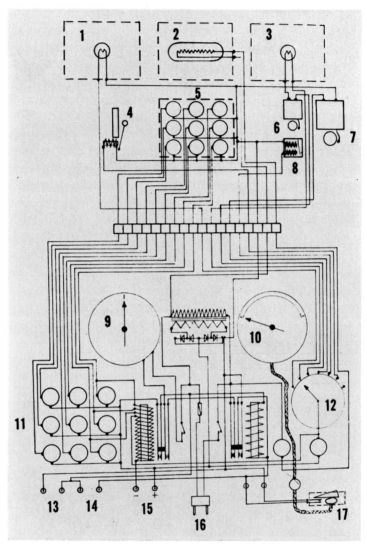

FIGURE 1. Diagram of motor reaction apparatus. 1. For slight visual stimulation and slides. 2. For strong visual stimulation. 3. For slight visual stimulation and slides. 4. For auditory stimulation (gong). 5. For differentiation (9 colored lamps). 6. For slight auditory stimulation (bell). 7. For strong auditory stimulation (bell). 8. For auditory stimulation (buzzer). 9. Synchronized watch. 10. Manometer (for manual tests). 11. Switchboard (for differentiation). 12. Masterswitch. 13. Recording of stimuli. 14. Recording of reactions. 15. For connecting Du Bois-Reymond inductor. 16. 220 A C intake. 17. Button (for manual tests).

basis of verbal reinforcement. The conditional reflex is reinforced with the word "right." If no conditional reflex is obtained after 10 trials, the author gives an instruction to press. The number of reactions until the conditional reflex is formed is mainly a measure for the strength of the excitatory process. The reaction times are also a measure of the strength of the excitatory processes, and long reaction times can be regarded as a measure of passive inhibition.

It has been pointed out by some authors that long reaction times are partly related to inertia of the nervous processes (721). The motor conditional reflex is a direct reaction to direct non-verbal stimuli, and consequently the reactions can give measures of functions predominantly dependent upon the first signaling system (356, 721). Reactions also depend upon the second signaling system, as verbal reinforcement has been applied. It is generally agreed that in the human being the second signaling system normally and also in most pathological conditions predominates over the first signaling system (356, 655, 1001). Although the experiment with motor conditional reflexes is designed so as to minimize the effects of verbal activity and conceptual thinking, such factors will always be present in the study of motor reactions. In the elaboration of the motor conditional reflex, a conscious decision that it is supposed that one will press immediately after the signal will facilitate the development of a conditional reflex.

In normal persons the usual rapid forming of conditional motor reactions indicates strongly the presence of such factors. The person studied may make up his mind that he should not press until he is told. Normal persons who do not give a reflex in the course of ten trials always give this reason for their reactions. For the other more complicated motor reactions, conceptual thinking involving the participation of the second signaling system is also obvious. In order to have objective, comparable data, the measured values are taken as they appear without any attempt to correct for the eventual influence of conceptual thinking in the individual cases. There are no objective criteria to decide how far the motor reactions actually occurred automatically, and the verbal explanations of failure are intellectual rationalizations invented afterwards.

After the conditional reflex is elaborated as a stable reflex, the stimuli are replaced irregularly by other nonreinforced stimuli to study generalization. Then the irradiation from the first to the second signaling system is studied by replacing the signal (sound or light) with the corresponding verbal signal. In our study the conditional reflex was elaborated to a bell signal, and the corresponding word signal was "it rings." The number of signals necessitated in order to have a reflex to stimuli in the second signaling system is considered as a measure for the elective irradiation between the two signaling systems. It is then studied to what extent the irradiation is selective and adequate, by irregularly replacing the adequate stimulus-word by other unrelated words as "it is raining," "the table stands," "it is dark," etc. In contrast to the adequate words, the inadequate words are not reinforced verbally. A generalized irradiation to all kinds of words, should then indicate a dissociation in the interactions of the two signaling systems, and also difficulties of elective irradiation. Those measures have probably only a limited value, as even normal persons often fail in those tasks.

The next step was to extinguish the conditional reflex to direct stimuli. This was obtained by the verbal statement "don't press." The number of reactions until the reflex is extinguished is taken as a measure for the strength of the extinguishing inhibition. Also other authors note a pathological inertia of the nervous processes will decrease the ability of extinction (721), so that the measure cannot be regarded as exclusively a measure of the active cortical inhibition. After five negative reactions have been successively reinforced by the statement "right," the sound signal is again followed by the statement "press" until the motor reflex is restored. Slow restoration indicates that the excitatory processes are weak, and the inhibitory processes predominate, and can be regarded as a measure of the passive inhibition of the first signaling system. Difficulties of restoration also indicate an inertia of the inhibition.

The next step in our experiments was to elaborate a conditional reflex to color stimuli. When a stable reflex had been obtained, it was differentiated against another color stimulus. According to Ivanov-Smolensky and Povorinsky, a simple differentiation between two colors usually is too easy a task for human beings, and following their advice we applied a complex color stimulus consisting of four colored lamps. In the differentiated stimulus one of four colors was changed. The number of differentiated stimuli given until a stable differentiation was obtained was considered as a measure of the differentiating inhibition, and gives a fairly good measure for the strength of the active cortical inhibition. After five successful differential reactions, the differentiated negative response is reversed into a positive reflex by the verbal reinforcement "press." The number of reactions needed to reverse the negative reflex into a positive one is used as a measure of the inertia of the inhibitory processes. When five positive reflexes have been obtained to the formerly differentiated stimulus, alternating with the other stimulus, the originally positive reflex is reversed into a negative one with the verbal statement "don't press." The number of reactions applied to obtain this change, is considered a measure of the inertia of the excitatory processes.

Major signs of inertia are continuous pressing and extra-signaling reactions (492, 777). Extra-signaling reactions have also been interpreted to result partly from deficient internal inhibition (492, 777). By strong inhibitions of the higher nervous activity, motor conditional reflexes cannot be formed, or are unstable. A special type of inhibited motor conditional reflexes are responses with strongly fluctuating reaction times. Some authors have found this type of inhibition characteristic of schizophrenia, possibly associated with some dissociation of the higher nervous activity (55, 56, 409, 977). Often new stimuli are followed by inhibitions of the succeeding reactions. These after-inhibitions are also a sign of passive inhibition.

After each step of the experiment, the patients are asked to tell what they heard or saw, what they did, and what relations there were between the stimuli and their own performances. Ivanov-Smolensky states that an inadequate description of the performances is a measure of the degree of disturbances in the interactions of the two signaling systems. The author has decided to regard inadequate descriptions as a sign of dissociation.

In review, we have the following signs indicating disturbances of motor conditional reflexes.

A. *Signs of external passive inhibition*
   1. No conditional reflexes formed.
   2. Slow conditioning for the first conditional reflex in the first signaling system.
   3. Slow conditioning for the second conditional reflex in the first signaling system.
   4. Slow conditioning in the second signaling system.
   5. Unstable motor conditional reflexes.
   6. Generalization of reflexes in first signaling system.
   7. Generalization of reflexes in second signaling system.
   8. Long reaction times, with fluctuating prolongations.
   9. Slow restoration.
   10. After-inhibitions.

B. *Signs of internal inhibition*
   1. Extinction of reflexes.
   2. Differentiation of reflexes.
   3. Extra-signaling reactions.

C. *Signs of inertia of nervous processes*
   1. Long reaction times.
   2. Extinction of reflexes.
   3. Reversal of negative reflexes.
   4. Reversal of positive reflexes.
   5. Extra-signaling reactions.
   6. Continuous pressing.

D. *Signs of dissociations between the signaling systems*
   1. Deficient elective irradiation from the first to the second signaling system.
   2. Generalized reactions to verbal stimuli.
   3. Inadequate description of motor performances.
      As shown in the section below, generalization of reflexes and deficient irradiation from the first to the second signaling system were so frequent in normals, that these signs could not differentiate possible pathological reaction types. These signs will only be applied for the analysis of patients studied repeatedly. Other signs will be used for

all comparisons between normals and patient groups.

B. Motor Conditional Reflexes in a Sample of Forty Normal Persons

In the vast literature of studies of motor conditional reflexes, there is little information about the reaction types in normals. Povorinsky writes that the reaction times lie about 1.— second. In healthy persons a motor conditional reflex should be elaborated after two to seven trials. O'Connor finds for a normal sample of twenty persons mean values of 6.35 ± 5.98 (654, 721). We have studied the motor conditional reflexes in our normal material of forty female and male nurses. In only sixteen of them did the first motor conditional reflex to a sound signal occur after less than eight trials. In the majority of the normal sample no reflex was obtained after ten reactions. With instructions to press immediately after the sound, all pressed with the first reaction. Rokotova and others have observed that in this experiment several persons believe they should not press until they are ordered to do so (767). Accordingly a slow motor conditioning with this method does not mean that there is an inability to condition in the first signaling system. This is clearly shown by the fact that the second conditioning to colors on the average needs 1.1 ± 0.6 trial. The maximum was four trials.

To overcome misunderstanding due to lack of instruction, Povorinsky recommends the giving of verbal reinforcement rapidly, during the first second of the conditional stimulus (721). This may give a reflex because of involuntary response overcoming the conscious decision not to press. The author has also tried to change the verbal reinforcement and say "just press." With the modification of Protopopov, one does not try to obtain a conditional motor reflex at all, and gives the instruction beforehand in all cases. With the method of Protopopov one can not investigate the inhibitory processes and the inertia of the processes in the first signaling system in a corresponding manner as in the animal experiments (729). A rapid formation of the first as well as the second conditional reflex can be taken as a measure that the excitatory processes are strong. If only the second reflex comes rapidly, this can principally be interpreted in two ways. It can mean that a subjective misunderstanding of the task is the main factor, or it can mean the second signaling system strongly dominates over the first signaling system, so that a tendency to a slow conditioning has been overcome by the instruction. Our experiences with neuroses might indicate that the latter factor is of significance (52). The reaction times for the simple motor reflexes are short and regular and do not exceed 0.6 seconds. A generalized reaction is assumed to mean a weakness of the excitatory processes. We have generalized reactions in 28 normal persons. All are aware of the new signal, and only press because they believe this is right.

There is reason to assume that the tendency to *generalize gives no reliable information* about the properties of the nervous processes. In contrast to pathological material, the new stimuli give no inhibition of the following reactions. Only ten showed selective irradiation to the second signaling system. Twenty-nine needed one reinforcement and one person, four. Lack of selective irradiation is not characteristic of some pathological conditions, as often stated, because this is not less characteristic for normals. O'Connor had similar findings (655). Thirty-one generalized not only to the words "it rings," but also to such words as "it is dark," "it rains." This shows that the generalization in the second signaling system also cannot be regarded as pathological, as some authors have argued (1040). The extinction of the conditional reflex followed after the average 1.3 ± 0.5 trials with a maximum of three trials, which is considered to be the normal limit. Restoration of the reflex needed on the average 2.4 ± 2.1 trials. Here the maximum was eleven trials, which shows that even very slow restoration cannot be regarded as definitely pathological.

The differentiation followed for the total material after 2.3 ± 2.4 trials, with a maximum of thirteen trials. The person with thirteen trials misunderstood the task of differentiation. In the remaining thirty-nine cases the maximum was six trials, which was chosen as the limit of adequate reactions. The reversal from a differentiated negative reflex to a positive reflex needed 2.3 ± 1.5 trials with a maximum of seven. For the reversal of positive reflexes into negative ones, the average was 1.5 ± 0.9, and the maximum five trials. As to the formation of the first conditional reflex, only a rapid formation of the reflex after less than eight trials will be regarded as adequate. One is then aware that the inadequate reactions in pathological cases as in the normal sample are to a great extent related to misunderstanding of the task. For restoration one person in the normal sample, obviously due to misunderstanding, needed eleven trials. In the remaining thirty-nine cases the maximum was six trials, which was considered to be the upper limit of adequate reactions. Extra-signaling reactions, continuous pressing, unstable reflexes and periodic prolongations of reaction times were not found in the normal sample and were considered as inadequate reactions.

It is observed that in normals, even during the change of dynamic stereotype, the reaction times are usually not much prolonged, and no severe after-inhibitions occur. All normals were able to describe adequately their motor performances.

Because of the subjective factors in the formation of conditional motor reflexes with verbal reinforcement, it is impossible to draw a sharp distinction between normal and pathological reactions. For the formation of the first conditional reflex, less then eight trials will be considered as adequate, because slower conditioning probably is due to misunderstanding. Limits of adequate restoration and differentiation were fixed at six trials, as the two persons with more trials obviously misunderstood the task. For the other signs only reactions outside the limits of the normal sample will be considered as inadequate in the pathological materials.

4. THE APPLICATION OF DEFENSIVE REFLEXES FOR THE STUDY OF UNCONDITIONAL REFLEXES AND CORTICAL-SUBCORTICAL INTERACTIONS

A. Theoretical Background and Methodological Problems

The study of unconditional and conditional defensive reflexes was introduced by Protopopov (727, 729, 751). The method is a test for individual adaptation related to the important universal function of defense against pain. The type of defense generally used is withdrawal or avoidance of a mild faradic shock to the hand. As pointed out by Gantt, there are many other similar reactions which one might employ such as the eye wink to a tap on the base of the nose (268).

With conditional reflex methods it has been assumed that the unconditional pain reflexes are mainly dependent upon subcortical structures, but it is not possible to ascertain which of the deeper lying nervous structures are most important. In other studies of men and animals it has been assumed that pain reactions are especially related to hypothalamic centers (289). The author has employed a variation of the method described by Protopopov (729).

The reaction apparatus described in the chapter on motor conditional reflexes was used for marking electrical stimulation and sound signals. The electrical stimulation was derived from a Du Bois-Reymond inductor (type 21825, from Zimmermann, Leipzig) which was supplied with current from the reaction apparatus. The electrical stimulations and the sound signals were marked on a kymograph with magnet writers (type 2084, from Zimmermann, Leipzig). The patient was seated before the apparatus with his right hand fingers on the electrode connected with the reaction apparatus. His second finger was connected with a cord to a vertical writer (type 21128, from Zimmermann, Leipzig), which measured the motor response to the electrical stimulations. The respiratory movements were registered with the Lehmann pheumograph (type 3011). The patients were informed that their reactivity to electrical current should be measured. As this investigation is rather disagreeable for the patient, it is important to have a good knowledge of the clinical picture and good personal contact beforehand with the patient as much as possible. The patient was also informed that one would start with feeble electrical stimulation, which scarcely would be felt, and then gradually increase the current. All patients who displayed fear of the electric current, were also informed they should tell the experimenter to stop if it became painful. In the experience of the author practically all patients collaborated to the best of their ability. With the above precautions, the experiment can safely be carried out without upsetting the patients. After having had a few motor responses as unconditional reactions to electrical stimulation, a sound signal is given before the electrical stimulation. From pre-

liminary studies of neurotics it appeared that the motor component of the conditional reflex to electrical stimulation is *dependent upon the form of instruction* given before the experiment.
This was also the experience of Schnabl, with whom the author
discussed the method (801). In the extensive studies of Gantt
and co-workers with conditional reflexes to electrical stimulation,
autonomic responses have been combined with motor responses
in order to give more complete description of the reactions (752).

As it is rather time consuming to elaborate conditional reflexes
to electrical stimulation, and as we could study various properties
of the conditional responses more rapidly with motor reflexes with
verbal reinforcement, it was not attempted in this study to form
conditional motor responses to electrical stimulation.

According to Kaufman, Chistovich and Traugott, deteriorated
schizophrenics are often incapable of following verbal instructions
to avoid the electrical stimulation, which they suffer through a
pre-stimulation signal. The schizophrenics could often repeat the
instructions and show adequate motor reactions with verbal
reinforcement. But unconditional reinforcement with electrical
stimulation lowered the ability to form new connections. The
unconditional stimuli were also most inadequately reflected in
their reports of the experiments. These data indicated that unconditional stimulation lowers the tonus of the cerebral cortex.
This may be considered as a sign of dissociation between the cortex and subcortex (409, 977). When failure of avoiding electrical
stimulation after instruction is defined as a measure of dissociation
between cortex and subcortex, it is apparent that not only emotional, but also intellectual impairment may give failures. Because
of that one cannot expect failures to be specific of schizophrenia.

In the present study sound signals were applied. The first
sound signal often gives an orienting reaction with withdrawal of
the hand. In such cases the patient is instructed not to raise his
fingers. During five subsequent trials it is ascertained that the
sound signal is not followed by any motor reactions, and then
the sound signal is succeeded by an electrical stimulation. Instead
of forming conditional responses to the signal, the instruction is
given that the sound signal from now on always will be followed
by an electrical stimulation. The patient is told to raise his hand

as soon as he hears the sound, in order to avoid the electrical current. When a patient fails to follow the instruction, it is repeated, several times if necessary in different ways, also by demonstration of the sound, stressing that now a painful electrical stimulation will follow, if the hand is not raised. In this way it is tried as far as possible to avoid failures due to a misunderstanding of the task given.

The next step is to study the unconditional reflex in more detail. Several authors have applied the Hardy-Wolff technique, with cold pressure pain, which implies that the patients tell when they experience the pain (576, 577, 578, 918). It was not possible to use this method for our study, since the material included a great proportion of severely deteriorated schizophrenics. As the respiratory and motor responses probably are also unreliable measures of the pain thresholds for our wide range of psychiatric conditions, any quantitative measure of the pain thresholds was not tried. From the studies of Stengel *et al* with a variety of pain tests, it appeared that the schizophrenics did not differ from other psychiatric patients with regard to pain perception. In this study there were very few schizophrenics and apparently no severely demented cases. It has been demonstrated that since the pain thresholds in normal persons show such great variations it would be extremely difficult to decide where to set the limit between normal variations and pathological inhibition (918). In a sample of fifty subchronic schizophrenics who replied when they felt the electrical stimulation, the thresholds were practically the same as in the sample of normals.

The author has mainly been concerned with the question of exhaustion of unconditional responses to unconditional electrical stimulation. According to Protopopov, Kaufman, Traugott, and Chistovich (161, 409, 729, 977) a marked tendency to exhaustion of the unconditional responses indicates a weakness of the excitatory processes of subcortex with easily developing passive inhibition. In order to measure such aspects of the unconditional response, the author gradually increased the strength of the electrical stimulation with the Du Bois-Reymond inductor. The maximum tolerance was defined as the maximum electrical stimulation the patient was willing to endure. As several of our patients were not able to tell when they wanted the experiment to be stopped, the motor and respiratory responses served as independent measures of the response. The motor responses were classified as increasing with the strength of the stimulation, as independent of the strength or decreasing with the strength of the stimulation. It has been established by several authors, that normally there is an increase of motor responses parallel with the increase of electrical stimulation (409, 729). Similar motor responses indicate inhibition of the subcortical centres with equivalent phases, whereas decreasing responses indicate a deeper step of inhibition with phasic paradoxic reactions (729). In the same way equivalent or decreasing respiratory reactions to increasing electrical stimulation can give indices of inhibitory states of the autonomic component of the unconditional pain reaction.

B. Defensive Reflexes in a Sample of Forty Normal Persons

It is assumed that the normals would react to electrical stimulation with a withdrawal response and easily be able to avoid the current through an instruction. In the present investigation the before mentioned sample of forty normals was studied. The threshold varied between 15 and 18 cm with an average of 17 cm on the Du Bois-Reymond inductor. On an average the maximum tolerance was 11.2 ± 2.7 cm. With increasing strength of the electrical current, all reacted with increasing motor and respiratory responses in accordance with previous studies (729). The maximum tolerance showed great variations. Among the females the mean maximum was thirteen and in males nine.

One man even endured a strength of 3 cm before he wanted to stop. This shows clearly the semi-voluntary aspect of the method. The females probably have equal tolerance to pain, but find less interest than the men in showing their ability to endure a strong current. As for the motor reflexes with verbal reinforcement, we are faced with the problem that one can decide only with great difficulty what is an impairment of ability to react, and what is due to conscious decision. But it is also assumed here that one must take the total functioning into account. A combination of great pain endurance and decreasing or equivalent motor and respiratory reactions definitely indicates an inhibition of the unconditional responses, which is not found in normals. In the individual case, the inhibition may be due to voluntary attempts to endure the current. For comparisons of pathological and normal groups, the voluntary factor cannot be estimated. Even if differences are due to voluntary factors, the changes of will and attitudes may be related to changes of nervous processes and may not be entirely subjective phenomena.

All normals avoided the current by instruction in five subsequent trials. For comparison with pathological materials the reactions not found in the normal sample were considered as inadequate. These were a maximum tolerance of less than 3 cm, lack of increase of motor and respiratory responses to the increase of the stimulating current, and failures to avoid the current after instruction (sign of dissociation).

5. VASCULAR AND RESPIRATORY REACTIONS TO UNCONDITIONAL AND VERBAL STIMULI

A.   Theoretical Background and Methodological Problems

There is vast literature upon measures of respiratory and vascular reactions in mental disorders. Clausen has given detailed description of methods of studying respiration and has summarized data available for normals, neurotics and psychotics (169). In our study we have used the Lehmann pneumograph, which Clausen also found most suitable for the study of respiration in psychiatric patients. From the literature it seems that studies upon respiration have not given any types of respiratory reactions related to types of psychiatric diseases, and especially not to schizophrenia (17, 173, 231, 232, 302). The author has made no attempt to correlate in detail the respiratory curves with clinical symptomatology. As discussed later in this chapter, arrhythmic respiratory oscillations and dissociations between respiratory and vascular curves have been registered. The respiratory responses to pathodynamic structures have been used as a control for the evaluation of the vascular responses to such structures. In brief the respiratory curve has mainly been considered in connection with the vascular reactions.

In the present investigation the vascular responses were measured with the plethysmographic method. Abramson, Altschule, Ackner, Stürup, Pshonik, and Rogov have given extensive bibliographic references with regard to the plethysmographic method (4, 5, 17, 734, 764, 936). From animal studies and studies of humans with neurological diseases it is believed that vasoconstriction and vasodilatation depend upon autonomic centers situated in the hypothalamus (5). Vasoconstrictions usually follow an adequate stimulus, such as noise, light, pain, cold, etc. For light and noise the reactions represent orienting reflexes (762) which are extinguished by repetition. The reactions to pain and cold are considered by Traugott to be components of the unconditional defensive reflexes, and are not extinguished by repetition. She also stresses that the unconditional as well as the conditional vascular reflexes are fragile and may be disturbed by overstrain of the nervous system (985). In psychopathological conditions there are often, according to Rogov, primitive vascular responses. These responses are weak, develop slowly and last for a long time (764).

A systematic study of conditional vasomotor reflexes was initiated by Zitovich in 1918 (1095). Since then Russian authors have studied large series of normals, patients with bodily, psychosomatic, and psychiatric diseases with conditional vasomotor reflexes. For discussion of methodological problems reference will be made to the literature (9, 734, 756, 764, 797, 851).

In the majority of such studies the forearm plethysmograph has been used.

The author employed the Lehmann plethysmograph, the use of which is described in detail by Lehmann, and had the opportunity to compare his results with studies of Schunk and Schnabl with the Lehmann plethysmograph in normal persons (524, 801, 810).

Pshonik recommends the technique of a zero plethysmogram before starting to elaborate conditional vasomotor reflexes (734). A zero plethysmogram is a curve of pulse waves, almost horizontal. In normal persons there are considerable variations in the plethysmograms, which are due to orienting reflexes (762). Pshonik finds that a zero plethysmogram in normal persons will not usually be obtained until the 20th or 40th session (734). For our purposes such a time consuming method could not be used. According to Bykov a stable conditional vasomotor reflex will regularly need from seventy to ninety trials in order to be formed (146). After ten trials the first signs of a conditional reflex usually are observed (146). In a pilot study of neurotics, only in a few patients with general tendencies of predominance of the excitatory processes the author was able to obtain signs of conditional responses in the course of one or two sessions (52). As a test in a battery used for mass investigations it was not practical to have more than one session for each patient for the study of autonomic responses. For this reason the author in later studies has not elaborated conditional vasomotor responses.

A variety of psychiatric disorders and somatic diseases both show that conditional vasomotor responses are formed with difficulty. This would mean that even a time-consuming elaboration of conditional reflexes would not give very much information of the differences with regard to responses in schizophrenic and other mental disorders.

In the present study the reaction apparatus described in part 3 of this chapter was used to mark the stimuli, which together with the respiratory and vascular responses were recorded on a Zuntz kymograph (type 20840, Zimmermann). The patients were informed beforehand that their respiratory and vascular responses to various stimuli would be investigated, and that the only inconvenience would be cold stimulation on the free forearm. The first stimulus was a buzzer sound in order to give an orienting reflex. When the eventual vascular effects of the response had subsided, the free forearm was touched by a metal container filled with ice during 30 seconds, as a comparatively uniform cold stimulation for all patients. To cold stimulation the unconditional response is a vasoconstriction, which gives a drop in the plethysmographic curve. Each person was given from one to three stimulations with cold. In order to counteract the vasoconstriction the same areas were stimulated by metal containers with warm water (40°-50° C). The heat stimulation gives vasodilatation as the unconditional response. According to the literature heat in the beginning usually also gives vasoconstriction, and only after some sessions is a stable dilatation to heat obtained (648).

Strong and rapid reactions to the unconditional cold stimulation are due to a simultaneous activity of a great number of neurones under the influence of the stimulation. The weak and slow reactions are formed when a small number of neurones successively come into action. According to Kreindler the successive more or less slow reaction of a greater or smaller number of neurones is especially characteristic of the subcortical formations (492). A weak unconditional reaction indicates a weakness of the subcortical excitatory process, with predominance of the passive inhibitory processes (492). Kononjachenko states strong inhibition of the cortical processes will also reduce the unconditional vasomotor responses (454). It seems that slight or no reactions to orienting stimuli and cold stimulation not only indicate inhibition of subcortical centres, but also inhibition of the cerebral cortex. If the unconditional reflexes set in slowly and last very long, this indicates an inertia of the vegetative responses.

To study the influences of the second signaling system upon the vasomotor activity, the patients were first told to solve simple arithmetical tasks (100-17), and those who were able to do this correctly, then were asked to multiply 16 by 25. It was assumed that the calculations should be affectively rather neutral stimuli, although in several cases failure to solve the problems was embarassing for the patients. To compare the influence of affectively neutral versus charged ideas upon the autonomic reactions, associative experiments were used, in some cases in the beginning. Neutral stimulus-words were chosen, words which regularly do not give complex responses in association experiments. Affectively charged words were chosen stimulus-words, which, according to the case histories should be related to delusions, hallucinations and other pathodynamic structures. It was rather difficult to select effective words as one cannot know beforehand if the stimulus-words actually are affectively charged. In studies of neurotics similar experiences were seen with the association test, and it was replaced with discussions about affectively charged themes (380).

In the present study it was most practical to give questions related to the psychopathological experiences known from the case histories. Whether or not the patients were able to answer the direct question seemed to have its effects on some types of patients. It was observed that dissimulating patients regularly betrayed their denials with severe autonomic responses. Besides the more specifically individual questions upon special concrete psychopathological experiences, some standard questions were given to all patients. Affectively neutral questions were difficult to find, because paranoid patients often in an experimental setting have a tendency to take most remarks in a personal way, as pointedly referring to their abnormal experiences. The psychopathological symptoms are often common to many patients. It was regularly asked if the patients were worried by voices, if somebody was slandering them, and if they felt somebody wanted to do them harm, or more crudely expressed, if they felt persecuted. Questions concerning megalomanic ideas, somatic influences and hypochondriacal delusions were also regularly asked. The aim was to try as far as possible to see if autonomic reactions to pathodynamic structures might be provoked. Since the examiner, before the examination, had psychiatric interviews with all patients, with special regard to studying the pathodynamic structures, it was always possible for verbally communicating patients to have an impression of which ideas could probably be affectively charged.

More than 50 years ago, Vogt pointed out that psychotic patients often reacted with extreme vasomotor responses, and rapid pulse movements, when their psychotic ideas were discussed (1043). In experiences of the author there are some differences with regard to the psychopathological symptoms. Symptoms expressing schizophrenic projection symptoms do not usually give any autonomic reactions when they are asked for, which might mean that such symptoms are not so affectively charged and express rather some general disturbances of the nervous functions, possibly of an automatic character, as expressed in the term *"automatisme mental"* of Clérambault (170, 758). (See Fig. 2.) Balonov, Lichko, and Rajeva had similar experiences (82, 745). Affectively charged systematized delusions tended to give "stormy" autonomic reactions and consequently to be of a different pathophysiological nature. Those experiences will be considered in Chapter VIII (see Fig. 3). When the forearm plethysmograph is used, large movements are always recognized as rapid changes in

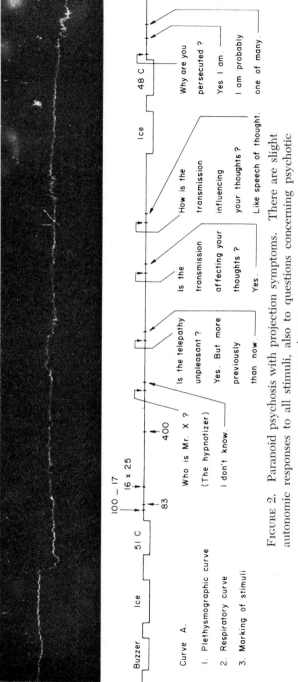

FIGURE 2.   Paranoid psychosis with projection symptoms.   There are slight autonomic responses to all stimuli, also to questions concerning psychotic experiences.

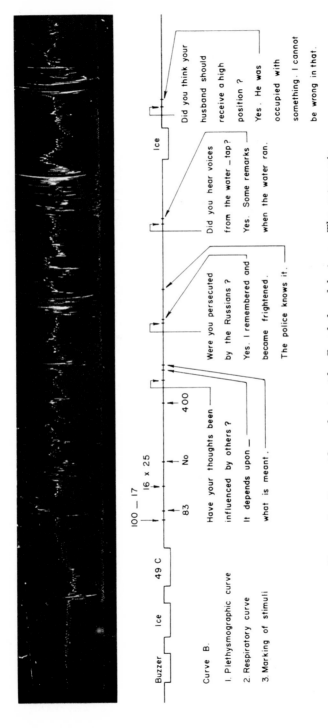

FIGURE 3. Paranoid psychosis with affect-laden delusions. The autonomic reactions to buzzer, ice and heat are weak. Calculation, however, gives strong responses. Questions concerning psychotic experiences give violent respiratory and vascular responses and a rather chaotic autonomic activity.

the plethysmogram in contrast to the smooth vascular changes. Smaller movements of the fingers may be difficult to detect.

It was of interest to decide if the "stormy" autonomic reaction actually might be more motor than autonomic. (It could be clearly observed that for the respiratory curve, the responses were due to respiratory movements.) The respiratory movements may cause some movements of the fingers in the plethysmograph, and with some patients the reaction to the affectively charged stimulus-words apparently gave a response from the whole body. Special studies of the influences of finger movements do not give curves resembling the "stormy" autonomic responses to pathodynamic structures. Those responses actually would mean pathological vascular activity related to pathodynamic structures. The irregular character of the responses, completely dissociated from the usual vasomotor curve, suggests that the aforementioned type of pathological activity means a pathological and inert excitation of subcortical structures freeing themselves from the regulating cortical control. In studies of other authors similar phenomena have been observed in psychotics with delusions (47, 82, 443, 1028), and they have interpreted the phenomena in the above way. As this seems to be the natural explanation of the phenomena observed, the "stormy" autonomic responses to pathodynamic structures will hereafter be regarded as representing pathological excited and inert subcortical structures.

It is noted that several authors claim that the types of vascular and respiratory curves give information about the higher nervous activity. The respiratory curve in normal persons is usually even and regular. Chistovich has pointed out that schizophrenics often have arrhythmic respiratory rhythms, which may be related to inhibition of the cortical regulation and disinhibition of subcortical mechanisms (152). Segal and Stanishevskaya hold similar opinions. They observed that in schizophrenics the vascular curve often is chaotic; they also related this to deficient cortical regulation. The respiratory oscillations of the plethysmogram in many schizophrenics are not parallel with the respiratory curve. The above types of respiratory and vascular curves could be regarded as signs of dissociation in the autonomic regulation, and, as seen from the next part of this chapter, were not observed in a sample of normals (816, 907, 912, 913).

B. Vascular and Respiratory Reactions in a Sample of Forty Normal Persons

For the normals as well as for the patient groups, no attempts have been made to obtain zero plethysmograms. Nevertheless in our normal sample thirty-five actually showed zero plethysmograms without oscillations of the third order. It is concluded that absence of oscillations of the third order does not mean any decreased excitability of the cortical vascular regulation. The respiratory oscillations of the second order are missing in two cases. In the others they are present and well coordinated with the respiratory movements, without any signs of dissociation.

Although only one session has been used, and the vessels, because of the new experimental situation, might be contracted, all but two show clear unconditional reactions to cold stimulation. Only eleven reacted to heat. This is in accordance with the experience of Novikov, namely, that heat dilatation generally needs some time to be developed (648). In 19 persons reactions to a buzzer sound were observed. Absence of reaction to this sound is not pathological, and can be regarded as related to the adaptation to the experimental situation, as shown by the absence of oscillations of the third order. To the calculation all but three had clear-cut vascular reactions, in some accompanied by movements. In the normal sample, no reactions to delusions or known complexes could be studied. They were asked to think of pleasant experiences and unpleasant personal conflict situations. They were then asked to tell what they thought about. To the pleasant experiences there were no consistently defined vascular reactions. Twenty-six had vascular and respiratory reactions to the revival of unpleasant conflict situations. In some of the normals the reactions were quite strong, but had not the uncoordinated "stormy" character which was found in patients with paranoid ideas. The complex reactions of the normal persons corresponded to the complex reactions observed in neurotics (51, 52, 372, 373). This indicated that complex reactions in neurotics are rather unspecific, or that within a normal population, some have reactions similar to those of neurotics and actually might be neurotic. Complex reactions can be regarded as indices of excited psychodynamic structures. In the chapter on neuroses, the complex structures are not the only changes found in the clinically ascertained neuroses, which need special treatment.

For comparisons with psychotic patients several factors were used. Adequate reactions were recorded with + and 0, and inadequate reactions with − . There are the following reaction types.

1. Oscillations of third order in the plethysmogram +.
2. No oscillations in the plethysmogram 0.
3. Chaotic plethysmographic curves—(sign of dissociation).
4. Regular respiratory curves +.
5. Arrhythmic respiratory curves − (sign of dissociation).
6. Parallel plethysmographic and respiratory rhythms +.
7. Dissociation of plethysmographic and respiratory rhythms—(sign of dissociation).
8. Reactions to unconditional cold stimulation +.
9. No reactions to unconditional cold stimulation—(sign of inhibition).
10. Reactions to calculation +.
11. No reactions to calculation − (sign of inhibition).
12. No reactions to pathodynamic structures 0.
13. Moderate reactions to pathodynamic structures +.
14. Violent reactions to pathodynamic structures—(signs of localized inertia).

A few normal persons showed no reactions to cold nor to calculation. This lack of reaction is not a pathological one, and is probably due to orienting vasoconstriction, because a zero plethysmogram was not elaborated. No reactions to heat and buzzer were so frequent in the normal sample, that such reactions could not be considered pathological. These reactions could not be used in the comparisons of normals and psychotics, but they were applied in the analysis of changes of reactivity in patients studied repeatedly.

Chapter III

THE DISTURBANCES OF THE HIGHER NERVOUS ACTIVITY PRODUCED BY DRUGS AND VARIOUS SOMATIC TREATMENTS

THE INFLUENCES of several drugs upon the higher nervous activity were studied in detail by Pavlov and his pupils (371, 674, 786). In later years there have been several different trends in the conditional reflex studies of drugs in animals, as well as in men. One aim has been to elucidate the dynamics of the neurophysiological changes in psychopathological conditions. Another task has been to postulate dynamic theories of the mechanisms of model psychoses. The most important trend has been the study of the actions of drugs used in the treatment of mental disorders (14, 15, 135, 136, 219, 220, 221, 240, 263, 276, 277, 281, 298, 304, 335, 377, 697, 742, 763, 945).

Several authors have studied the effects of chlorpromazine (aminazine*) on the higher nervous activity, mainly in animals but also in schizophrenics (6, 41, 44, 73, 75, 92, 96, 189, 195, 200, 201, 297, 403, 427, 475, 484, 502, 587, 661, 722, 763, 779, 780, 865, 868, 934, 970, 986, 989, 1042, 1103). Kaminsky and Savchuk, working on dogs, found weakening of the excitatory cortical processes, and, dependent upon the doses of the drugs, strengthening of cortical inhibition. They assumed that the actions of chlorpromazine were greater upon cortical than subcortical structures, as in some experiments a complete inhibition of conditional reflexes was associated with full strength of unconditional responses (403). Shumilina, again from studies of dogs, held the opinion that actions on the cortical processes were secondary to actions on the subcortical structures, lowering the tonus of the cerebral cortex. Evidence of this was the fact that the conditional responses, although weaker, became more adequate to the

---

* In the Russian literature chlorpromazine is called aminazine.

stimuli (865). Bambas and co-workers also studied dogs. With large doses of *chlorpromazine*, the unconditional defensive reflexes were more inhibited than the conditional ones. The opinion of these authors was that chlorpromazine acted mainly upon subcortical structures (92). Of particular interest for the evaluation of the clinical effects of chlorpromazine are the studies of Traugott and Balonov on psychiatric patients.

With the same methods as in the present investigation, they studied the higher nervous activity before, during, and after the administration of a single dose of chlorpromazine. The drugs inhibited considerably the unconditional responses to electrical stimulation, whereas performances with conditional motor reflexes and association experiments were less inhibited. In patients with paranoid schizophrenia, the improvement of associations and conditional motor reflexes was related to decreased negative induction from pathodynamic structures. The stimulation of such structures by questions concerning hallucinations and delusions, after chlorpromazine, disturbed the higher nervous activity less. The autonomic components of the pathodynamic structures persisted, but were less violent. The clinical improvement of paranoid schizophrenias was considered to be related to weakened influences of pathodynamic structures, and especially the unconditional defensive components of these structures. Traugott and Balonov stress that chlorpromazine does not inhibit all unconditional reflexes, and that the orienting (762) and alimentary reflexes may not be inhibited (989).

Although the effects of chlorpromazine upon the higher nervous activity are complex, observations from several studies show that this drug, compared with alcohol and barbiturates, has a considerably greater effect upon unconditional reflexes, and an especially inhibiting influence. This is in accordance with studies showing great effects on the reticular system and other subcortical structures (265, 371, 763, 786).

Other ataraxic drugs and new stimulating drugs, though less investigated, also seem to have great effects on unconditional reflexes (34, 43, 133, 224, 297, 336, 381, 502, 605, 696, 963). As several of our experimentally studied patients have received ataraxic drugs, the treatment must be taken into consideration by evaluating the experimental findings. One must be aware of the effects upon unconditional reflex activity. In pathological material it is extremely difficult to decide in the individual case which disturbances might be due to drugs, and which might be due to changes in the clinical condition. By comparing clinically matched groups of patients treated or not treated with ataraxic drugs, an attempt can be made to analyze the eventual effects of the drugs.

The influences of insulin coma and shock-treatment upon higher nervous activity have been studied in men as well as in animals (20, 22, 23, 84, 118, 156, 158, 159, 178, 179, 237, 288, 314, 440, 494, 517, 543, 544, 545, 546, 547, 548, 549, 772, 783, 807, 984, 1089, 1090).

Works of several authors state a series of shocks weaken the excitatory processes and the active cortical inhibition. Villars Lunn studied the influences of electric shock upon the conditional withdrawal reflex. The most characteristic finding was a complete disappearance of previously elaborated reflexes during the first 20 minutes after the shock (565). The restoration of nervous functions after convulsive treatment and insulin coma has been studied in detail by Traugott and others (984). Immediately after the treatment the unconditional as well as the conditional activity was severely inhibited. The unconditional reflexes were restored, then conditional connections related to the unconditional reflex systems. The reactions of the second signaling system are restored later than the reactions of the first signaling system. As a general rule, the ontogenetically early-developed connections are restored before the ones acquired later. This is also reflected in the restoration of the second signaling system. The first step patients are able to respond with movements to word-stimuli. Next, they can react with words to stimuli in the first signaling system. Then comes the ability to react with words to words. The association experiment usually cannot be carried out during the first 25-30 minutes after a convulsion. Comparisons of the associative reactions before and after shock show prolonged reaction times and an increased proportion of primitive associations.

In patients under insulin treatment, it could be observed how the associative reactions gradually changed with increasing effects of the drugs. Prolonged reaction times were observed. The adequate higher reactions were replaced by primitive reactions. There were tendencies to perseveration, the reproduction became impossible, and after a few reactions the patients were exhausted and could not answer (984). In the author's experience patients treated with electrical shock regularly improve in their associative reactions parallel with clinical improvement, if they are not re-examined during the same day as they receive the convulsive treatment (51). In a study of Villars Lunn conditional withdrawal responses on the day following convulsive treatment are to a great extent restored (565). In order to avoid gross impairment of nervous activity due to shock treatment, the patients in this material have not been examined experimentally the same day as they received convulsive treatment. Neither were patients investigated during a series of ECT. In several studies schizophrenics improved their conditional and unconditional reflex activity, with corresponding clinical improvement during convulsive and insulin treatment (82, 314, 543, 781, 907, 976, 984, 1070, 1089, 1090).

This demonstrates that the effect of the psychotic state upon higher nervous activity predominates over that of convulsions and coma, when the patients are not studied immediately after the treatments. Considering the comparatively rapid restoration of most conditional reflex activity after convulsive treatment in psychiatric patients, it was deemed unnecessary to exclude from the study patients previously treated with ECT. Comparing clinically matched groups of such cases with cases without somatic treatment, there were no statistical significant differences in the impairment of the higher nervous activity ($X^2 = 0.827$).

In animal experiments, leucotomy led to considerable changes of the higher nervous activity. The excitatory as well as the inhibitory processes were weakened. The ability to train cortical functions decreased greatly. Noted was a pronounced inertia of the nervous processes (857). As it would be difficult to decide which disturbances of the nervous processes are due to the operation, leucotomized patients were excluded from the study, except for four who showed comparatively greater impairment of nervous activity than clinically comparable non-leucotomized patients. With the chi-square method the leucotomized patients had a minor proportion of adequate responses, statistically significant at the 0.001 level.

Chapter IV

THE DISTURBANCES OF THE HIGHER NERVOUS ACTIVITY IN NON-SCHIZOPHRENIC CONDITIONS

1. DISTURBANCES OF THE HIGHER NERVOUS ACTIVITY IN NEUROSES

Pavlov was of the opinion that the neurasthenic types of neuroses in man very much resembled the experimental animal neuroses, with weakening of excitatory and inhibitory processes (673, 674). For other types of neuroses, Pavlov assumed that disturbances in the interactions of the two signaling systems were of great importance. In hysterics he assumed that there was a predominance of the first signaling system, whereas in psychasthenic or anancastic conditions there was a predominance of the second signaling system. For the anancastic neuroses, pathological inertness of "sore points" was also assumed to be of great importance (673). Since the classical studies of Jung and his pupils, several authors have studied complex reactions in neuroses (35, 94, 113, 168, 174, 391, 566, 760, 887, 930, 958, 959).

Some of the principal difficulties in evaluating the significance of complex factors have been pointed out in the previous chapter. Independent of the interpretation of the psychological and physiological nature of the complex reactions, there is a general agreement that complex reactions are often pronounced in neuroses (372, 373). As there are several principles of clinical classification of various forms of neuroses, the studies of disturbances of the higher mental functions in neuroses cannot always be directly compared.

Ivanov-Smolensky found that neurasthenic neuroses could be divided into three forms according to the degree of severity. In the cases of brief duration clinically characterized by great irritability and lack of capacity to inhibit actions and emotions, the main experimental finding was a weakness of internal inhibition. Next was a lability of the excitatory processes, which were rapidly exhausted. In cases of long duration with great fatigue and severely impaired capacity to work, there was a weakness of the excitatory processes and predominance of the inhibitory processes in the cerebral cortex (354, 357, 371). These stages in the development of the disturbances of the higher nervous processes have also been found by other authors in several psychosomatic and even somatic diseases (10, 87, 93, 127, 129, 196, 211, 249, 250, 272, 296, 307, 310, 341, 342, 402, 405, 438, 454, 455, 456, 457, 539, 568, 572, 604, 659, 680, 735, 775, 846, 890, 900, 901, 929, 1085, 1098). It is very probable that, independent of clinical type, the brief nervous disorders primarily show an impairment of the phylogenetically and ontogenetically latest developed internal inhibition, which is especially vulnerable. In chronic conditions a passive inhibition of more or less protective character tends to develop. Astrup had similar findings in a study of fifty-five patients with various types of neuroses (52, 53). Some authors have reported deficient internal inhibition in explosive psychopaths (244, 707, 1073). Most authors state the interactions of the signaling systems are balanced in neurasthenia and depressive neuroses (11, 24, 25, 115, 119, 192, 284, 424, 588, 704, 768, 796, 891, 892, 1015, 1074).

Several authors have studied hysterical patients with conditional reflex methods (11, 70, 115, 150, 284, 581, 647, 676, 689, 690, 691, 692, 701, 702, 703, 705, 719, 724, 725, 737, 738, 739, 740, 744, 829, 892, 1074). From such studies it seems that the disturbances of the second signaling system tend to be great in hysterias. Faddeyeva and Povorinsky found that even in severe forms of hysteria, new cortical connections are formed, but passive inhibition tended to develop very soon (719). Seredina and Rajeva pointed out that hysterics had difficulty in explaining adequately their motor reactions to various stimuli. This was mainly found in the more complex conditional connections (738, 829).

From studies of anancastic neuroses and psychasthenia, the first signaling system tends to be more impaired than the second signaling system. There are also strong influences of localized pathologically excited complex structures (11, 19, 32, 33, 107, 252, 253, 257, 258, 323, 350, 422, 467, 627, 628, 629, 676, 726, 827, 831, 835, 839, 863, 892, 896, 897, 950, 1003, 1004, 1006, 1009, 1019, 1067, 1068, 1074). Seredina, in experimental studies, has stressed the significance of complexes in association experiments combined with respiratory and vascular responses. A tendency to weakness of the internal inhibition could also be established (835). Belousova says a predominance of passive inhibition is found in phobias, but in the compulsive states there is an inertia of the nervous processes (107.) For neuroses at the involutional age Elizarova found a tendency to inertia of the nervous processes (208).

Sleep treatment has been greatly advocated for neuroses in order to overcome the general disturbances of the higher nervous activity through protective inhibition (101, 293, 371, 1059). Also the psychotherapeutic factors are analyzed physiologically. The physiological nature of the special conditioning procedure is sharply seen. In Pavlovian theories also words are principally considered as acting through a physiological stimulation of the second signaling system. On the interpretations of neurotic mechanisms and therapeutic procedures based upon Pavlovian theories, there is an abundant literature (11, 35, 62, 66, 67, 278, 303, 323, 384, 419, 481, 522, 590, 633, 699, 700, 749, 785, 789, 920, 927, 930, 1045, 1046, 1054, 1055). Conditional reflex studies of hypnosis have been carried out by many authors (71, 162, 180, 181, 460, 461, 462, 463, 464, 465, 466, 569, 570, 571, 647, 670, 671, 677, 700, 718, 720, 923, 924, 941, 1104, 1105). These studies support Pavlov's conception of hypnosis as a state of inhibition intermediate between wakefulness and sleep. The strong influences of suggestions are also physiologically elucidated. Systematic experimental studies of the influences of other psychotherapeutic procedures upon the higher nervous activity have been carried out by a few authors (35, 141, 323, 930). Studies of neurotics show that improvement of the clinical conditions runs fairly parallel with the improvement in the experimental tests (35, 323, 739, 839, 930). This applies not only to the general disturbances of the excitatory and inhibitory processes, but also to the complex structures. The autonomic components of the complexes are modified with difficulty (322, 372). This corresponds to the *schizokinesis* of visceral and motor reactions in animals found by Gantt (275, 280).

Astrup found that the general disturbances of nervous processes in neurotics are often small and within the range of the normal variation (51, 52, 53). In neurasthenic, and especially in hysteric neuroses, the verbal reactions tend to be severely inhibited. The associative reactions of anancastic neuroses are mostly normal. Anancastic neuroses tend to show greater disturbances in the first signaling system than hysterics. As described by Ivanov-Smolensky, disturbances of the higher nervous functions in neuroses seem to be centered about the strong psychodynamic complex influences. Complex reactions are even found in our sample of normal persons, so that these structures cannot necessarily be regarded as indicators of clinically manifest neuroses. The more pronounced the general disturbances of excitatory and inhibitory processes, the more socially disabling are the neuroses in most cases. To what extent a strong predominance of one of the signaling systems is actually caused by a general disturbance of nervous activity or related to premorbid typological reaction types is still unsettled (193). There is a general agreement that in neuroses mainly the cortical functions are disturbed, and to a small degree the subcortical functions (372, 373). Chapman and others found that neurotics often have an increased reactivity to pain (149, 326, 576, 577, 578, 918).

In the author's experience, neurotics reacted as normals to electrical stimulation (53). The autonomic reactivity is considerably increased to complex factors, but not in the stormy way found in some schizophrenics (55, 56, 372, 373). In a study of seventy plethysmographic curves of neurotics, the author noticed that in the majority oscillations of the third order was observed. This illustrates that the autonomic reactivity of neurotics not only with respect to complex factors, but in general tends to be increased compared with normals. This is in contrast to the schizophrenics, who have a decreased autonomic reactivity. In the associative experiments neurotics predominantly react like normals with higher verbal reactions. In psychoses primitive reactions are frequent. With motor reactions the disturbances also tend to be smaller than in psychoses. Except for some inexactness of the description of the performance in hysterics, neurotics mostly explain their reactions adequately, like normals. In psychotics and especially schizophrenics adequate explanations are rather rare (52, 55, 56).

It can be presumed that the higher nervous activity of neurotics is not much different from normals, and that pathogenetically the psychodynamic complex structures play a dominant role, although basic impairment of nervous activity is also found. This impairment mainly affects the cortical processes, whereas unconditional reflex activity is not essentially interfered with. As to the experimental differences between various types of neuroses, most studies indicate that in neurasthenia, the interaction of the signaling systems is balanced. In hysterics the second signaling system, and in anancastic neuroses the first signaling system, is mainly affected.

For all types of neuroses, the disturbances of the higher nervous activity tend to be greater, the longer the condition has lasted.

2. DISTURBANCES OF THE HIGHER NERVOUS ACTIVITY IN REACTIVE (PSYCHOGENIC) PSYCHOSES

In 1928 Ivanov-Smolensky tried to explain the psychogenic depression by analogy with animal neuroses (358). Later Ivanov-Smolensky demonstrated the significance of combinations of psychogenic and somatic factors in reactive psychoses. The animal experiments had shown that neurotic dogs developed intoxications more rapidly than non-neurotic dogs. Correspondingly dogs weakened by somatic disorders, intoxication and operations became neurotic sooner than bodily healthy dogs (371, 376). In follow-up studies of reactive psychoses, Astrup, Fossum, and Holmboe found that psychogenic psychoses mainly occur in neurotic and psychopathic personalities and are often precipitated by combinations of psychodynamic and somatic factors (64). The obviously reactive psychoses are mainly characterized by depressions and disturbances of consciousness of hysteriform types. In such cases paranoid traits are often found, but do not dominate the clinical picture (64). Few authors have studied hysteriform psychoses experimentally (58, 199, 200, 201, 226, 309, 426, 557, 1014). Turova has studied the pathodynamics of 12 patients reacting with hysterical puerilism and stupor in connection with imprisonment. In the puerile state the conditional connections developed very slowly, with strongly prolonged reaction times. In the association experiment reaction times were also long with mainly primitive reactions. For complex words the prolongations were especially strong. With clinical improvement the higher nervous activity was normalized (1014).

Astrup found that patients with confusional hysteriform psychoses mainly react with primitive associative reactions. With clinical improvement their reactions resemble those of neurotics (58). Harzstein, in several papers, has described the disturbances of the higher nervous activity in reactive depressions. Her cases were typically psychogenic reactions, often developing after the death of close relatives (315, 316, 318, 319, 320, 322, 323, 324, 325, 987). In such cases the complex influences were especially strong in the associative experiment. Motor conditional reflexes were not so much affected prior to associative experiments or discussions of the depressive content. After reactivation of the complex structures, the reaction times were strongly prolonged with equivalent, paradoxical and ultraparadoxical phases. The autonomic component of the complex structure either had the character of inhibited reactivity or of excitation (318). Astrup had similar findings in reactive depressions. It was noticed that in some reactive depressions in old age, the associative disturbances more resembled the organic than the neurotic reaction types (58). Gantt and co-workers claimed that psychogenic reactions could be distinguished from organic psychoses by his conditional reflex test.

Whereas psychogenic cases easily develop integrated conditional reflexes, this was not possible in the organic cases (267, 268, 269, 752). According to Astrup, the general disturbances of nervous processes were considerably greater in patients with organic psychoses and organic dementia than in reactive psychoses

(60). Ivanov-Smolensky maintains that during confusional states the cortical activity may be severely inhibited in reactive states (372, 373). In Astrup's experience paranoid psychoses precipitated by external factors usually have some schizophrenic symptoms and resemble schizophrenic cases in their disturbances of the higher nervous activity (58). In the typical reactive depressive and hysteriform psychoses, the disturbances of the higher nervous activity mainly affect the predominantly cortical functions and resemble those of the neuroses with strong influences of complexes.

3. DISTURBANCES OF THE HIGHER NERVOUS ACTIVITY IN OLIGOPHRENICS

The associative reactions of oligophrenics have been studied by a number of authors (51, 59, 148, 204, 383, 642, 662, 898, 899, 1050, 1057, 1060). Sommer says that oligophrenics are often unable to find an answer, and their reactions reveal a poverty of ideas (899). Wehrlin studied the associations in three groups of oligophrenics, namely torpid imbeciles, erethic imbeciles and those with slight mental deficiency. The torpid imbeciles were in most cases not capable of following the instruction and to answer with one word, but reacted with several words or a whole sentence. The answer often had the character of a definition (1050). This is analogous to the experiences of Jung and Riklin with uneducated persons, who gave more inner associations than the educated (389). Nathan discussed the diagnostic application of the association test for oligophrenics and mentioned some characteristics. The reaction times are prolonged. Stereotypes or meaningless reactions are often found. The linguistic form of the answers is rather inadequate (642). Wreschner states idiots often answer with adjectives (1060). Wimmer found tendencies to egocentric reactions, definitions and very prolonged reaction times in oligophrenics (1057). Jolly compared the association test with an intelligence test, and concluded that the lower the intelligence, the greater the disturbances of the associative functions (383).

Astrup studied all degrees of oligophrenics, from severe idiocy to slight debility, with the association test. Idiots and the severely afflicted imbeciles were either unable to answer, or answered only with primitive reactions. The imbeciles reacted predominantly with echolalia, rejecting words, tautologies, word connections, questions, egocentric reactions or meaningless words. In the feeble-minded, reactions were mostly of the middle type, beginning with echolalia or "yes." The reaction consisted generally of several words, and represented usually attempts at definition, as pointed out by Jung. These changes are interpreted as indicating strong inhibition and severe inertia of the second signaling system. In a few erethic oligophrenics the reaction times were short, and the main associative disturbance was a poor ability to reproduce the associations combined with lowered quality of the associations (51, 59). Incoherent reactions of the types found in many schizophrenics were not found in oligophrenics. The associative reactions of dull normals did not differ essentially from our sample of normals.

Several authors have studied the higher nervous activity of oligophrenics with conditional reflex methods (59, 241, 242, 243, 247, 255, 260, 264, 561, 562, 586, 621, 622, 623, 624, 625, 717, 723, 823, 997, 998, 999, 1000, 1002, 1034). There seems to be general agreement that in oligophrenics the functions of the second signaling system are especially severely interfered with, as is revealed by the studies with the association test cited above. Also in the first signaling system considerable changes are found. Idiots are often unable to develop stable motor conditional reflexes. Imbeciles and debiles are able to give conditional reflexes. For stable motor reflexes the reaction times are usually short and regular, which indicates that the first signaling system is not so much disturbed as the second signaling system. But oligophrenics regularly have a defective internal inhibition and inertia of the reactions in the first signaling system. Oligophrenics can usually describe their simple reactions adequately, and fail only in the description of more complex reactions. The autonomic reactivity is usually greater than in organics, and does not essentially differ from our sample of normals. Only in idiots and severe imbeciles were arrhythmic respiratory and chaotic vascular reactions found.

Oligophrenics generally react like the sample of normals to electrical stimulation, which indicates that the subcortical activity is not essentially interfered with. Astrup found only two cases suspect of being schizophrenic in high grade oligophrenics, showing inhibition of the motor and autonomic reactions to electrical current (59). Popper states some oligophrenics show great endurance of pain (716). Taking into consideration that no large-scale studies of the unconditional reflex activity of oligophrenics have been carried out, one cannot exclude the possibility of disturbances of unconditional reflexes in some types of oligophrenics. Compared with schizophrenics the general rule is that, while in oligophrenics predominantly the cortical activity and the functions of the second signaling system are disturbed, schizophrenics tend to show more disturbances of the unconditional reflex activity and less disturbances in the second signaling system. It is felt that the higher nervous activity of oligophrenics is mainly characterized by a deficient development of the second signaling system.

4. DISTURBANCES OF THE HIGHER NERVOUS ACTIVITY IN NERVOUS DISORDERS RELATED TO ORGANIC BRAIN LESIONS

In this part of the chapter reflexological studies in nervous disorders associated with organic lesions of the brain will be discussed. Several authors have studied the disturbances of the higher nervous activity in patients with head injury, aphasia and various forms of brain lesions (38, 39, 40, 42, 45, 46, 209, 229, 251, 306, 348, 398, 401, 425, 447, 448, 449, 487, 493, 495, 496, 497, 498, 503, 505, 582, 583, 592, 594, 597, 615, 616, 648, 649, 650, 658, 726, 755, 825, 861, 940, 971, 1097).

From these studies it seems that, in the acute stage, the conditional reflex activity is disturbed and tends to be strongly inhibited. Brain traumata evoke protective inhibition, weakness of internal inhibition and inertia of the nervous processes.

In epileptics the associative functions have been studied by Holzinger, Rittershaus, Jung, Roth, Klepper, and others (332, 390, 437, 761, 773). Shortly after epileptic seizures, Seredina and Vinogradov have found changes of the higher nervous activity similar to those in patients treated with shock and insulin coma (828, 832, 1039). In the intervals between the seizures several investigators have found considerable changes in the conditional reflex activity of epileptics (21, 60, 301, 365, 563, 652, 832, 847, 856, 877, 888, 889, 893, 928, 1036, 1039, 1096). Apter has given a survey of such disturbances in epileptics. Motor conditional reflexes were rapidly formed in most patients. They were unstable, however, and the internal inhibition was severely impaired. A considerable inertia of the nervous processes, notably in the second signaling system was noticed (21).

In general paresis and other syphilitic psychoses associations have been studied by Feilbach, Brunnschweiler and Rohde, and plethysmographic reactions by de Jong (142, 225, 386, 766). Conditional reflex activity was investigated by Lenz, Klukan, Seredina, Yapontsev and others (404, 441, 525, 574, 830, 836, 1008, 1069). Seredina found that motor conditional reflexes developed slowly and were often unstable. Differentiation was impaired with strong tendencies to after-inhibition. The irradiation between the two signaling systems was often inadequate (836).

In animals as well as in men it has been found that with increasing age the internal inhibition is weakened, and nervous processes become more inert (259, 626, 674, 1023, 1024, 1029, 1030, 1031). In studies of human neuroses in the involutional age Elizarova noticed that the vascular reactions become more inert (208). Golovina, Shkurko and others also found increased inertia of nervous processes in involutional psychoses (227, 228, 300, 471, 474, 475, 476, 521, 859, 860, 864, 884, 886, 1093, 1094). In Astrup's experience, neuroses and affective psychoses in the elderly also had associative reactions resembling those of patients with organic disorders (51). Paramonova writes there is at advanced ages a tendency to stronger predominance of the second signaling system over the first signaling system (667). Gakkel thinks that the associations of old persons revealed several signs of inertia and especially echolalic and multiword responses (256).

The disturbances of the higher nervous activity in senile dementia, senile and arteriosclerotic psychoses have been studied by Batsha, Molakhaltsev, Tatarenko, Usov, and others (100, 125, 255, 619, 620, 663, 664, 947, 1017, 1025, 1026, 1027, 1028). Molakhaltsev and Rappeport found that in presenile psychoses the unconditional plethysmographic responses were weak with long latency. There were considerable after-effects of the stimuli, indicating a considerable inertia of the vasomotor reactions (619). Usov compared the nervous activity of healthy old persons and patients with old age psychoses by a complex investigation method. In healthy persons, there was a strong inductive interaction of the signaling systems. In psychotics with delusions the nervous processes showed a considerable inertia. Usov regarded the delusions as dependent upon pathologically inert pathodynamic structures particularly defined in the second signaling system. Stimulation of these structures by conversation about the delusions strongly inhibited the first signaling system as well as the general autonomic reactivity (1027, 1028).

Brunnschweiler claimed the associative reactions of patients with senile dementia were not different from those of general paresis and epileptic dementia. The reaction times were prolonged, and the reproduction severely impaired. There was a tendency to give multiword responses in spite of the instruction to react with one word. Affectively colored word stimuli improved the reactions in contrast to the neurotics (142). Bleuler states that patients with organic psychoses find it difficult to get rid of an idea; they repeat over and over again the same word in the association experiment (perseveration). The prolongations of reaction times and the difficulties of apperception are of significance. The associations have an emotional character, and show frequent repetitions, partly as perseveration, partly as lack of ideas. As in oligophrenics a great proporation of the reactions are tautologies and definitions. The complexes reveal themselves directly without suppression. As soon as the disease has reached a marked degree, the organics are not capable of answering with one word.

They cannot isolate the ideas, but must express the whole complex of thought which occupies them (122). Astrup has had experiences similar to those of Brunnschweiler and Bleuler. The
organic demented patients predominantly react with multiword
and echolalic responses of the middletype. Severely demented
patients are not capable of answering to the stimulus-words. Some
can only give such primitive reactions as echolalia or "yes." It
has been found that non-demented epileptics give normal associative reactions.

The associative reactions of patients with organic psychoses
and organic dementia very much resemble those of oligophrenics.
Besides the primitive reactions they often give more complex
responses, which are beyond the capacity of oligophrenics (60).

Rohde compared the associative disturbances of general paresis
and epileptics with those of schizophrenics; the schizophrenics
differed by greater variations (765, 766). In Astrup's experience
this is often the case. The associations of many demented schizophrenics cannot actually be distinguished from the organics (60).
Astrup has the impression that the organic demented cases like
the oligophrenics reveal the greatest impairment of nervous functions in the second signaling system. Simple motor reflexes are
developed in most of them. But with the more complex tasks
of internal inhibition and reversal of reflexes they usually fail
(60). Gantt and co-workers pointed out that even the inability
to form integrated conditional reflexes may be used for the differentiation of organic cases from psychogenic cases (267, 268,
269, 752). But he states that the conditional reflex is often absent
in the schizophrenic because of inhibition, while the severe organic may have a complete loss of the ability to form conditional
reflexes.

In Kaufman's work it is found organic and schizophrenic demented cases in many ways show opposite types of disturbances
of the higher nervous activity. With demented epileptics conditional responses to unconditional electrical stimulations were
rapidly formed, but slowly in the schizophrenics. In the description of the experiment the epileptics always stressed the unconditional stimulation, yet schizophrenics were less concerned with

this. Conditional motor reflexes to verbal stimuli were more easily developed in schizophrenics than in epileptics (409). In a later study Kaufman has stressed the importance of disturbances of unconditional reflex activity and dissociative phenomena in chronic schizophrenics when compared with epileptics (414). In Astrup's experiments conditional reflexes to verbal stimuli in normals as well as in all kinds of nervous disorders are for the most part more rapidly developed to verbal stimuli than to stimuli in the first signaling system. In the literature there is a general agreement that the functions of the first as well as the second signaling system and the autonomic functions show considerable inertia in organic cases. Dissociative phenomena play a smaller role than in the schizophrenics. In three epileptics Astrup found such inhibitions of unconditional reflexes as usually are found in schizophrenics (60). The observations about pain-asymbolia in some organics may indicate that unconditional responses can be altered in organic cases (800). Usually unconditional responses are not inhibited in organic cases. It is assumed that the neurophysiological mechanisms of organic dementia are predominantly impairment of cortical functions, especially the ontogenetically latest developed second signaling system.

5. DISTURBANCES OF THE HIGHER NERVOUS ACTIVITY IN CHRONIC ALCOHOLISM, ALCOHOLIC PSYCHOSES AND DRUG ADDICTION

In animal experiments acute as well as chronic intoxications tend to affect first the recent phylogenetically developed internal inhibition. There follows a weakening of the excitatory processes with predominance of passive protective inhibition and phasic states (371, 376). Strelchuk has found phasic conditional reflex activity in morphine addicts (922, 926). The higher nervous activity of chronic alcoholics has been studied by many investigators (50, 51, 151, 439, 595, 870, 873, 874, 875, 876, 921, 925, 926, 943, 994, 995, 996, 1088). Strelchuk and Sinkevich found the conditional reflex activity of chronic alcoholics is considerably impaired. Passive inhibitions develop soon and there are phasic states. The interactions of the first and second signaling systems may be impaired, when compared with normals. The conditional responses to verbal stimuli often developed slowly. With clinical improvement the conditional reflex activity was also normalized (870).

Gantt found that patients with Korsakoff's psychosis were deficient in the ability to form conditional responses. Similar results were obtained by others (185, 269, 285, 479, 480, 520, 552, 553, 641). Seredina *et al.* studied the disturbances of the nervous processes of patients with delirium tremens. In the association experiments they predominantly reacted with echolalia and other primitive responses, indicating a severe inhibition of the second signaling system. The first signaling system was also inhibited with phasic conditions. The motor analyzer was not inhibited, which was also clinically apparent from the behavior of the patients. With clinical improvement, the conditional reflex activity was also improved (347, 833, 841, 844, 1013). Seredina has carried out conditional reflex investigations of patients with alcoholic hallucinosis (834, 837, 838, 842, 845). In hallucinated patients the first signaling system was severely inhibited, but the patients in non-hallucinated periods easily formed conditional reflexes. With experimental increase of the external inhibition, the verbal hallucinations were more pronounced, which was interpreted as an effect of positive induction from the first to the second signaling system. The association test in some cases increased and in other cases decreased the hallucinations. These influences were interpreted either as the effect of stimulation of inert pathodynamic structures, or as repression through stimulation of non-pathological dominant structures of the second signaling system (834).

In another study Seredina found that the verbal hallucination was dependent upon inert pathological structures, although the non-verbal hallucinations of delirious alcoholics were more related to inhibitory states in the first signaling system. In the acute alcoholic psychoses severe inhibition of cortical functions were dominant, while in chronic verbal alcoholic hallucinoses, pathological inertia of the excitatory processes was the neurodynamically most important disturbance of the nervous activity (837).

In patients with alcoholic hallucinosis of recurring course therapeutic doses of caffein made the hallucinations disappear for some hours.   In these cases the association experiment gave shorter reaction times and better quality of the associative responses.   For motor conditional reflexes the reaction times became shorter, and the phasic conditions disappeared.   Seredina thought that the caffein represented supramaximal stimulation of the pathodynamic hallucinatory structures, which by positive induction increased the cortical tonus.

In patients with a non-recurring course, caffein gave increased reaction times and lowered the quality of the associative responses, which indicated an increased inhibition of the second signaling system.   In the first signaling system the phasic state decreased, with paradoxic reactions being replaced by equivalent reactions.   The verbal hallucinations became weaker, and in some cases were transformed from external hallucinosis to pseudohallucinations.   These changes were interpreted as due to inhibition of the pathodynamic structures.   These changes, however, were not sufficiently strong to make the hallucinations disappear (838).

The author has studied a few alcoholics with conditional reflexes, and found in these cases equivalent and paradoxical phasic conditions (50).   One hundred and twenty-four alcoholics, drug addicts, and other intoxication psychoses have been studied with the association test (51).   If the alcoholism had not been of long duration, the associative responses resembled those of neurotics with strong complex influences.   In persons with several years of alcoholic abuse, some clinical signs of personality reduction were always present.   Such cases showed several types of associative disturbances.   Some of them were able to react according to the instruction with one word.   They tended to give prolonged reaction times with many echolalic responses.   In others the ability to reproduce the associations was severely impaired.   Most alcoholics, like organic demented, reacted predominantly with multiword responses, mainly associations of the middle type, and few responses of the higher type.   Severely demented alcoholics predominantly gave primitive associative responses.

In chronic alcoholism long reaction times were mostly related to the difficulty of the stimulus-words. To affectively colored stimulus-words, the reactions usually came rapidly. In simple stimulus-words, such as concrete substantives, the reaction times could be practically normal. For more complicated stimuli such as verbs, abstract substantives or adjectives, the reaction times increased considerably. This would indicate that the ontogenetically youngest structures of the second signaling system were most inhibited (50, 1101). Word reactions to direct stimuli came rapidly, and for motor conditional reflexes the reaction times were not essentially prolonged. There is less inhibition of the first than of the second signaling system. In patients with drug addiction the associative reactions according to the degree of clinical demential resembled those of the alcoholics. All associations of patients with delirium tremens at the height of the delirium were primitive. With clinical improvement, the associations corresponded to those of more or less reduced alcoholics (51).

It seems that the higher nervous activity of *chronic alcoholics* and alcoholic psychoses are mainly characterized by cortical inhibition, particularly of the second signaling system. Cases of long duration tend, as in organic dementia, to develop considerable inertia of the nervous processes.

6. DISTURBANCES OF THE HIGHER NERVOUS ACTIVITY IN INFECTIOUS PSYCHOSES

Conditional reflex studies of *infectious psychoses* have mainly been carried out by Chistovich, Traugott and their co-workers (80, 81, 161, 343, 421, 500, 541, 542, 544, 788, 880, 881, 882, 883, 975, 978, 979, 980, 981, 983, 984, 1011). In several articles Chistovich has expressed the opinion that what are called cases of schizophrenia are mostly infectious psychoses with unfavorable courses (161, 163, 164). In a personal communication to the author, Chistovich writes that endogenous psychoses, and, especially, schizophrenia, are more and more considered to be infectious psychoses. Traugott, Balonov and Lichko feel that delimitation of infectious psychoses from schizophrenia is only formal. Schizophrenia can be considered as an unfavorable variety of the infectious psychoses (983). From these quotations it is obvious that several of the cases classified as infectious psychoses would have been classified by other authors as schizophrenias or other forms of functional psychoses.

Traugott has undertaken a detailed clinical and experimental study of the infectious psychoses in her monograph about the disturbances of the interactions of the signaling systems (984). In infectious psychoses, with confusion and disorientation, the cortical functions were severely inhibited. The experimental disturbances of the higher nervous activity resemble those of patients awakening from insulin coma or convulsive treatment. The restoration of nervous activity also went along similar lines, but needed a considerably longer time, weeks and even months. Amentia patients predominantly reacted with primitive responses in the association test. The interactions of the first and second signaling systems were severely disturbed. The disorientated patients could not describe their performances adequately. In patients with effector stupor, it was possible to obtain information through movements and gesticulations. In these cases the ability to evaluate the circumstances did not run parallel with the severe motor inhibition characteristic of the effector stupor. In cases with severely disturbed interactions of the signaling systems, the forming and stabilization of conditional reactions in the first signaling system was impaired, and the unconditional reflexes were easily exhausted. All the three levels of the higher nervous activity were severely impaired. During the recovery the unconditional reflexes were restored first, then the conditional reflex activity and lastly the interactions of the three levels of the higher nervous activity.

Traugott found two main types of disturbances of the nervous processes. In the effector stupor (with impaired mobility) especially the expressive speech was impaired due to predominant inhibition of the motor speech analyzer. Simultaneously there was a selective disturbance of the evaluation of the motor reactions and the conditions evoking those reactions. In conditions of cortical excitation the evaluation of personal conditions, unconditional stimuli and of reactions to such stimuli were disturbed. This was interpreted as weakening of the unconditional activity and disturbances of the interactions of cortex and subcortex. Such disturbances were observed in cases showing schizophrenic deterioration.

In receptor stupor (stupor with impaired perception) together with inhibition of the unconditional reflexes and the first signaling system, there was some excitation of the second signaling system. In other cases during the recovery a predominance of the first signaling system was observed. Traugott mentioned several factors which she thought were related neurodynamically to impairment of orientation: 1) Conditions with subcortical excitation; 2) Conditions with cortical excitation or inert excitation of isolated structures in an inhibited cortex; 3) Receptor stupor; 4) Conditions characterized by increased activity of the first signaling system; 5) Some variations of the effector stupor.

During her experimental studies it was found that the characteristics of the higher nervous activity of the acute stage to a great extent decided the favorable or unfavorable course of the disease. One of the prognostically favorable factors was a strong and diffuse inhibition of the cortical activity. Among forty cases with infectious psychoses, sixteen had an unfavorable course and developed schizophrenic deterioration. In seven cases with paranoid-hallucinatory syndromes influences of pathologically inert pathodynamic structures dominated the nervous activity, as in paranoid schizophrenias in the studies of Traugott and others (155, 976, 979). In cases with catatonic or hebephrenic deterioration the unconditional reflex activity was severely inhibited, and the disturbances of the higher nervous activity resembled those of defect schizophrenias studied by Kaufman (409, 410).

It appears that the prognostically favorable cases of infectious psychoses experimentally resemble the confusional reactive psychoses, where there was a diffuse inhibition of the cortical activity. The cases taking a schizophrenic course resemble the reactive psychoses studied by Astrup, which were suspect of developing schizophrenic deterioration (58).

7. DISTURBANCES OF THE HIGHER NERVOUS ACTIVITY IN MANIC-DEPRESSIVE PSYCHOSES

Because of different principles of delimitation of manic-depressive psychoses, it is probable that the reflexological studies in manic-depressive psychoses have been carried out on samples with different clinical characteristics. Within the group of typical manic-depressive psychoses there seem to be great variations in clinical symptomatologies (64). For the above reasons one would expect that the findings of various authors are not directly comparable.

Numerous studies have been carried out in manic-depressive patients with the association test (37, 51, 57, 116, 203, 345, 352, 428, 585, 630, 634, 635, 685, 806, 935, 967, 968, 1048, 1051, 1091). Most authors find that the reaction times are prolonged in melancholia. Moravcsik divided a sample of various psychiatric diseases into groups with depression, elation and indifferent mood. In the depressive group the longest, and in the elated group the shortest reaction times were found. There were manics with considerable prolongations, as well as melancholias with practically normal reaction times (630). Birnbaum stated hysterics as well as melancholic depressed patients gave prolonged reaction times with accompanying affective reactions, such as sighing and crying on hearing unpleasant stimulus words. In hysterics several ideas were produced, where in comparison the melancholias were more restricted in their reactions. The reactions of the hysterics also reflected more of the personal interests (116). Aschaffenburg studied the associations of manics with flight of ideas. In hypomanic conditions were reactions, which expressed old and stable elaborated verbal connections. With increasing excitation came sound reactions. In no case were the reaction times shorter than in normals (37). Isserlin had similar findings (345). Scholl mentions that manics do not show complex reactions (806). Kilian held the opinion that manics often show tendencies to answer with many words, echolalia, perseveration, sound reactions and meaningless sentences (428). Walitzky found in manics shorter reaction times than in normals (1048). According to Ivanov-

Smolensky hypomanic patients often have shortened reaction times without lowering of the quality of the answers (352).

In the author's experience patients with typical melancholias or atypical melancholias in the young react with rather regular prolongations of the reaction times and small complex influences. Reactions with associations of the higher type were predominant. In melancholics in the involutional age multiword and echolalic responses were frequent. The ability to reproduce the associations was also impaired. The anxious and agitated depressions had marked difficulties with the reproduction.

Hypomanic patients had practically normal reaction times. The reactions were of the higher type, but with more simple external associations. The reactions came rapidly, but represented more speech-motor than conceptual verbal connections. In fully developed mania, the reaction times were prolonged. Echolalia, sound reactions, rhymes and multiword responses appeared, and the percentage of higher associations was reduced. The ability to reproduce the associations was impaired. As in melancholias the complex influences were small. This stands in contrast to the reactive depressions, where Harzstein especially has shown the great influences of complex structures (57, 318). In the individual case this difference between manic-depressive and reactive psychoses cannot always be clearly and convincingly demonstrated (57, 58). In manic-depressive cases Astrup did not find incoherent associations, which are so frequent in schizophrenias (55).

Conditional reflex studies of manic-depressive patients have been carried out by a considerable number of authors (57, 88, 154, 216, 217, 218, 287, 683, 684, 685, 730, 732, 843, 884, 885, 906, 931, 965, 966, 967, 968, 969, 972). Ivanov-Smolensky and Faddeyeva hold that new cortical connections are slowly elaborated in depressives, but that the internal inhibition is not impaired. In hypomania new cortical connections and associations are rapidly formed, but the internal inhibition is considerably impaired. In high grade manic states the second signaling system undergoes a passive inhibition (371).

Protopopov is of the opinion that in manic-depressive psychoses there is a somatic symptomatology indicating disturbances of the equilibrium of the autonomic nervous system (730, 732). His clinical description of vegetative instability corresponds well to the findings in our catamnestically verified manic-depressive psychoses (64, 732). Protopopov assumes the somatic symptomatology of the manic-depressive psychoses could be interpreted as due to a pathological predominance of the sympathetic nervous system. He thought that studies with motor defensive reflexes, motor reflexes with verbal instruction and vascular reflexes supported this view. In manic patients strong reactions were observed to minimal unconditional electrical stimulation. Unconditional cold stimulation also gave very unpleasant feelings. In depressives such hypersensitivity was not observed. The motor reactions were not so strong, and the latency periods prolonged. Voluntary inhibition of the motor defensive reactions was not possible, either in manics or in depressives. This was interpreted as due to impairment of the cortical control and a predominance of the subcortical centers of the thalamic regions. The diffuse character of emotional changes, with lack of cognition in manic-depressive psychoses, was related to increased excitation of the thalamic regions.

Studies of conditional reflexes, which reflect the cortical activity, showed that in manic patients the tonus of the excitatory processes was increased, and the tonus of the inhibitory processes decreased. Conditional reflexes were developed rapidly and inhibitory reflexes slowly. This was especially so for conditional and delayed inhibition, which needs strong inhibitory processes. In depressive patients the positive conditional reflexes were slowly elaborated, the latency periods longer and the responses weaker than in the manics. The weakening of the excitatory processes was not accompanied by any strengthening of the inhibitory processes. The inhibitory reactions were even more difficult to elaborate than in the manics, and especially the delayed inhibition. It was assumed that in depressives also the excitatory processes were predominant over the inhibitory processes. Protopopov found that in manic states there was an irradiation of excitation and in depressive states a negative induction from excited thalamic regions. When manic-depressive patients were studied during remissions, the relations between excitatory and inhibitory processes were more normalized. There were still signs of insufficient strength of the inhibitory processes. Differentiation and delayed inhibition could with some difficulties be carried out, but after stabilization disinhibition was easily demonstrated by experimental passive inhibition with extrastimuli (732).

Astrup has studied motor conditional reflexes with verbal reinforcement in manic-depressive psychoses. No essential differences could be established for the excitatory and inhibitory processes of the manic and depressive cases. Most cases showed a considerable inertia of the conditional responses. In the manics there was mainly an inertia of the excitatory processes, and in the depressives mainly an inertia of the inhibitory processes. All had short regular reaction times, and the irregular prolongations of reaction times, observed in many schizophrenics, were not found in manic-depressive cases. Unless the manic-depressives were severely anxious and agitated, they could adequately describe their motor performances. In schizophrenics a deficient ability to verbalization was even frequent in calm and well controlled persons who took part in group treatment (57, 62). Dissociations between the respiratory curve and the respiratory oscillations in the plethysmogram were not found in manic-depressive patients. In several cases there was an inhibition of the unconditional vascular responses to cold stimulation. In some cases vascular and respiratory responses to pathodynamic structures were observed, but never in a "stormy" manner similar to those in some paranoid schizophrenias. If manic-depressive patients were not too disturbed in their behavior they usually succeeded in avoiding electrical stimulation after instruction.

In several manic and depressive cases there was a strong tendency to exhaustion of the unconditional defensive reflexes, indicating inhibition of subcortical centers. This stands somewhat in contrast to the findings of Protopopov. It was observed that the unconditional responses had a stronger tendency to inhibition in manics than in depressives. Astrup states that there is more an inhibition of subcortical activity than excitation as assumed by Protopopov. There is an agreement that disturbances of the unconditional reflex activity may play an important role in the neurophysiological mechanisms of manic-depressive psychoses. This is a common trait in the schizophrenic psychoses, which was not found in the typical reactive psychoses. In Astrup's investigations, the variations of the thresholds for motor and respiratory reactions to electrical stimulation have not been specially studied as by Protopopov. There is a possibility that low pain thresholds may be combined with a tendency to exhaustion of the unconditional responses (57).

In the findings for manic-depressive psychoses, as in schizophrenics, disturbances of the unconditional reflex activity play an important role. Disturbances of the higher nervous activity resemble those of paranoid psychoses with projection symptoms, which often have a schizo-affective symptomatology (Chapter VIII). In schizo-affective cases developing a schizophrenic deterioration our studies reveal severe dissociations of the higher nervous activity or inert pathodynamic structures, which were not seen in typical manic-depressive psychoses.

Chapter V

PREVIOUS STUDIES OF THE HIGHER NERVOUS ACTIVITY IN SCHIZOPHRENIA

1. GENERAL THEORETICAL CONCEPTIONS OF NEURO-DYNAMIC MECHANISMS IN SCHIZOPHRENIA

In several papers Pavlov discussed the possible neurophysiological basis of different types of schizophrenic symptoms. Although he did not carry out research with schizophrenics personally, he made his assumptions from his experiences about disturbances of the higher nervous activity in animals. As characteristic of schizophrenia Pavlov regarded an increasing tendency to inhibition of the cerebral cortex, which in shifting intensities spread to other parts of the brain. By disinhibition and positive induction, older, more primitive and rudimentary functions could be liberated. In connection with the inhibition, intermediate conditions between wakefulness and sleep, so-called phasic conditions, were believed to be present.

Pavlov thought that besides the general disturbances, isolated pathodynamic structures were of importance. For paranoid and paranoia-like conditions he stressed the significance of relatively isolated inert pathological structures. Catalepsy was regarded as a disinhibition of statotonic reflexes positively induced from cortical inhibition. The catatonic excitation he explained as due to inhibition of cortical areas and disinhibition of subcortical centers. He also considered hebephrenic silliness to be related to disinhibition of ontogenetically older functional areas with inhibition of the younger functional areas. Pavlov found that the cortical inhibition of schizophrenics had the character of protective inhibition in several cases, preventing the destruction of the cortical cells through overstrain. Protective inhibition was regarded as a phylogenetically developed nervous defense mechanism. From such considerations Pavlov and several of his pupils considered it rational to support the physiological defense mechanisms by increasing protective inhibition. These findings have especially been the theoretical background for sleep treatment in schizophrenia and other conditions, where protective inhibition was regarded as an important factor in the neurodynamics. Ivanov-Smolensky, Popov, Chistovich and other authors have in numerous studies stressed viewpoints similar to those of Pavlov (143, 155, 157, 163, 238, 246, 359, 367, 371, 378, 420, 673, 674, 708, 710, 711, 712, 713, 714, 728, 729, 855, 946, 948, 949, 951, 953, 961, 1016, 1099, 1100, 1103).

Gantt and Bridger found that mescaline produced an inhibitory state accompanied by a *schizokinesis* or dissociation of systems. A dissociation of the second and first signaling systems and the unconditional reflexes occurs, in which each signaling system acts as if it were the same as the more primitive system on which it is based. Such factors were assumed to explain the mechanisms of several psychopathological phenomena (135, 136).

Gantt has described how the phenomena designated as *schizokinesis* and *autokinesis* are involved in the susceptibility to nervous breakdown. Schizokinesis is the inherent conflict between the general emotional responses and the more perfectly adaptive responses. Autokinesis is the ability of the organism to form new patterns of behavior (both destructive and constructive), without external stimulation, through an inner development on the basis of individual past experiences and the inner constitution of the organism (274, 275, 282, 283). It seems that the phenomena of protective inhibition can be regarded as related to the principle of autokinesis. For obvious reasons the splitting met with in the mental functions of schizophrenics might be set in relation to the general principle of schizokinesis. Recently Zurabashvili and co-workers, in their experimental studies, stressed the importance of dissociative phenomena in schizophrenia (1103).

2. THEORETICAL INTERPRETATIONS OF THE NEURODY-NAMIC BACKGROUND OF INDIVIDUAL SYMPTOMS IN SCHIZOPHRENIA

As mentioned in the previous chapter it was stated that the verbal hallucinosis in chronic alcoholic psychoses was related to pathodynamic inert structures of the second signaling system. In delirium tremens, where the hallucinations have a more vivid character of direct sensations, Seredina found that the basis was severe inhibition with phasic states in the first signaling system (837, 838). Popov demonstrated experimentally that by decreasing the cortical inhibition with caffein, hallucinations might disappear (709). Ivanov-Smolensky held the opinion that hallucinations in schizophrenia were partly related to general phasic states and partly to inert excitation of pathodynamic structures. In cases with clear picture-like delusions and optic hallucinations he felt that the disturbances were mainly in the first signaling system, but in cases with verbal hallucinations the disturbances were mainly in the second signaling system. The sleep resembling, dreamlike hallucinations, which are mostly found in the optic sphere and more seldom in the acoustic sphere were considered as dependent upon phasic conditions. If local pathological inertia of the excitatory processes was present, mainly in the optic and acoustic regions of the cerebral cortex, the hallucinations usually have the character of pseudohallucinations. If the inert excitation was extended to the cortical projection of the optic or acoustic accommodation of the corresponding sensory organ, the hallucinations were projected outward and had the character of real hallucinations (363, 371).

Giliarovsky thought that the vivacity of the hallucinatory experiences was related to changes in subcortical as well as in cortical systems. He believed that delusions were mainly dependent upon changes in the second signaling system, whereas by hallucinations the functions of the first signaling system were impaired (292, 294). Many other studies of hallucinations can be referred to (98, 606, 640, 682, 774, 817, 818, 821, 938, 944).

According to some workers inert pathologically excited structures are of great significance for schizophrenic delusions (47, 155, 371, 372, 373, 400, 443, 745, 795, 815, 816, 973, 984). Tatarenko thought that in paranoia the pathodynamic structures predominantly affected the second signaling system. In hypochondriacal delusions the cortical analyzer of interoceptors, and in anancastic neuroses both signaling systems as well as adjoining subcortical structures take part in the formation of the pathological structures (950, 955).

Balonov found experimentally that the mental automatisms of Clérambault and Kandinsky were not related to pathologically excited inert structures. Strongly affect-laden paranoid ideas could be interpreted as related to such structures (82). Ultraparadoxical phases are assumed to be related to mental automatisms (420, 644, 666, 819).

Aslanov and others claimed that in paranoid schizophrenia pathodynamic structures of hallucinations and delusions negatively induced an inhibition of the cortical activity (47, 371, 741, 745). Baskina with audiometric and Miljutin with psychogalvanic studies came to the conclusion that hallucinations in schizophrenia were related to pathological inertia of excitatory processes as well as to phasic conditions (97, 607).

Many have tried to study the neurodynamics of hypochondriacal delusions experimentally and clinically (43, 120, 245, 406, 407, 443, 444, 445, 482, 483, 499, 668, 669, 784, 792, 793, 794, 795, 814, 956, 1021). In some cases violent vascular changes could be related to hypochondriacal experiences, although in other cases complete vascular non-reactivity was observed. There is an assumption that hypochondriacal sensations may result from pathological stimulation from interoceptors. Savaneli stated that while neurotics with hypochondriacal sensations had a strong lability of the autonomic reactions, schizophrenics with hypochondriacal delusions had an extreme stability of the autonomic functions (795).

Schizophasia, according to Ivanov-Smolensky, was related to disturbances of the interactions of the two signaling systems, with the strongest impairment of the second signaling system. In the second signaling system there should be phasic conditions, sometimes combined with pathological inertia (364). Other studies of incoherence in schizophrenia can also be referred to (30, 31, 399, 409, 468, 598, 599, 600, 601, 610, 611, 612, 613, 643, 977, 1047, 1077, 1078).

The neurodynamics of depersonalization have mainly been analyzed from theoretical considerations—the possibilities of splitting in the interactions of the nervous processes, and weakness of the first signaling system and subcortex (408, 420, 538, 1010).

From the above cited studies it is obvious that experimental findings, as well as theoretical interpretations, have given no uniformly accepted explanations of the neurodynamics of individual schizophrenic symptoms. Probably the same individual clinical symptoms are related to several forms of disturbances of the higher nervous activity.

3. THE NEURODYNAMICS OF SCHIZOPHRENIC SYMPTOM COMPLEXES

It has been found that positive conditional reflexes as well as inhibitory reactions may be easily formed in paranoid schizophrenia (47, 321, 458, 469, 470, 472, 715, 741, 742, 743, 745, 907, 909, 912, 913, 1007, 1094). Most of these authors stress the significance of pathodynamic structures in paranoid schizophrenia. Kostandov finds that paranoiacs can only with difficulty verbalize their performances, which indicates some dissociation in the interaction of the signaling systems (469, 470). Traugott and Chistovich studied the higher nervous activity in paraphrenia. They found delayed formation of positive conditional and inhibitory reflexes for complex stimuli more than for simple stimuli, which indicates an impairment of the highest cortical functions. There was also a considerable inertia of the nervous processes. They found that the paraphrenic cases do not entirely show the isolated changes due to pathodynamic structures, but also general impairment of the higher nervous activity (155, 973).

Few systematic investigations of hebephrenic patients have been carried out (12, 197, 653). Dobrzhanskaya stresses that in hebephrenia the conditional reflex activity is chaotic (197).

A great number have studied the higher nervous activity of catatonic patients (152, 153, 160, 186, 187, 188, 189, 190, 191, 290, 299, 305, 361, 362, 371, 382, 394, 396, 397, 450, 472, 473, 477, 491, 523, 580, 637, 639, 698, 708, 710, 769, 908, 910, 916, 1037, 1038, 1062, 1063, 1064, 1079, 1080).

Studies of stuporous catatonics with catalepsy showed that these patients slept superficially with no clear distinction between sleep and wakefulness. If the sleep during short periods was deep, the cataleptic phenomena disappeared (1038). Golovina, Stchastny and others found a lowered vegetative reactivity with a predominance of the parasympathetic system in inhibited catatonics, and they had the impression that the phasic conditions were extended to the vegetative subcortical centers (299, 916). In most catatonics the ability to form conditional reflexes was considerably impaired. In several cases where it was impossible to form conditional motor reflexes, conditional respiratory or vascular responses could be evoked, showing that the ability to condition is very different for various types of reflexes (371).

Several studies show that the unconditional defensive and orienting reflexes are inhibited in catatonics. Sometimes the motor components were present, but the usual changes of respiration and pulse were lacking (371, 637, 729, 916). Narbutovich pointed out that the inhibition of the higher unconditional reflexes of catatonics led to disinhibition of primitive rudimentary reflexes, such as the grasping and sucking reflexes (371, 637, 638). Arieti discussed similar primitive behavior of chronic schizophrenics, which he considered as due to psychological regression mechanisms (26). Yakovleva concluded from chronaximetric studies that the higher nervous activity of catatonias had a chaotic character (1063, 1064).

Ivanov-Smolensky thought that the disturbances of the higher nervous activity could be very different in catatonics. The inhibition could extend to different depths of the basal ganglia and lower cerebral centers and be differently localized in the cerebral cortex. Different disturbances of somatic and vegetative functions were discovered to be of significance, e.g., inhibition, excitation or dissociation. The extension of the inhibition of the cerebral cortex in stupor was considered to be of two main types. In receptor stupor there is a widely extended negative induction (induced inhibition), which surrounds a complicated dynamic structure with intensive inert excitation. This excitation usually reflects strong affective impressions, connected with the past life experiences of the patient. The extraordinary strong negative induction excludes the patient from the surrounding reality and makes him to some degree blind and deaf to the real events. In the effector stupor the inhibition of the cerebral cortex is mainly concentrated in the motor-kinesthetic regions and prevents the patients from moving, but does not impair their ability to observe external events (371). Ivanov-Smolensky considered catatonic mutism as related to inhibition of the second signaling system, in some cases, predominantly in the sensory, and, in others, in the motor analyzers (361, 1075).

Some workers have specialized in the studies of the disturbances of the higher nervous activity in acute schizophrenia (110, 111, 197, 198, 413, 1040, 1041). Dobrzhanskaya found great changes in the conditional reflex activity from day to day. As several cases showed good remissions, they were probably more schizophreniform states than nuclear schizophrenias (513, 514).

Conditional reflex activity of chronic schizophrenics has been intensively studied (130, 131, 409, 410, 411, 412, 414, 415, 416, 456, 504, 646, 977, 1012, 1044, 1047, 1079). Kaufman found that in chronic schizophrenias several previously acquired conditional connections are intact, and conditional reflexes may be developed. Some unconditional reflexes may be strong. There is a clear tendency to inhibition of unconditional responses. This inhibition is mainly characterized by rapidly developing exhaustion, which indicates a lowered working capacity of the subcortical regions. The interrelations of cortex and subcortex are disturbed. The application of stimuli, which increase the tonus of the subcortex, impairs the cortical activity and the ability to form conditional reactions. In the cerebral cortex there are from minute-to-minute changes of phasic conditions with periodic changes of the working capacity of the cerebral cortex. There are great disturbances of the interactions of the two signaling systems, with inadequate elective irradiation. The dynamics of the inhibitory and excitatory processes of the two signaling systems showed great differences (409). Kutin divided a group of chronic schizophrenics into cases with clearly psychotic symptoms and cases with slighter schizophrenic residuals. In the first group there was pronounced weakness and inertia of the excitatory as well as the inhibitory processes. The interactions of cortex and subcortex and the signaling systems were severely disturbed. In the second group there were only slight neurodynamic changes when compared with normals (504).

Stjerbina and others found that in recurrent schizophrenics with clearly psychotic residuals the neurodynamics resembled those of malignant process schizophrenias. In recovered cases the higher nervous activity did not differ much from normals (79, 177, 446, 550, 665, 919, 1020, 1035). A few of the followed-up patients from Gaustad hospital, who clinically were characterized as improved and later admitted to Gaustad hospital with relapses, had similar disturbances of nervous processes. In several of the improved cases in the sample of acute and subchronic functional psychoses the disturbances of the higher nervous activity resembled those of process cases. This might indicate that the symptoms which are described as characteristic of improved schizophrenics can be objectively related to impairment of the higher nervous activity. To the present time the number of such clinically and experimentally investigated improved schizophrenics is too small to give any definite conclusions. Some studies especially deal with schizophreniform psychoses and pseudoneurotic schizophrenia (1, 2, 99, 722, 970).

A series of studies has not been so much occupied with finding characteristics of schizophrenic subgroups as possible common disturbances for all types of schizophrenia (78, 308, 453, 469, 519, 551, 556, 614, 654, 655, 686, 694, 757, 777, 782, 903, 982, 1081, 1082, 1083, 1084).

Kostandov, Vinogradov and Reiser stressed that schizophrenics usually showed severe dissociations in the interactions of the signaling systems (469, 470, 1040). Rushkevich and others thought that inertia and severe impairment of the internal inhibition was characteristic of schizophrenias (74, 194, 195, 777, 862). Studies of Sinkevich, Chuchmareva and Vinogradov were also concerned with studies of the internal inhibition, which consistently was severely impaired (165, 871, 872, 1041). Several studies have been contradictory in regard to the ability of schizophrenics to condition. This is probably due to differences in the clinical samples and the techniques of conditioning (654).

Many investigators have been concerned with the effects of treatment upon the higher nervous activity of schizophrenias (73,

75, 82, 84, 118, 176, 177, 178, 179, 194, 312, 313, 430, 543, 693, 729, 781, 822, 907, 911, 912, 957, 970, 976, 989, 1005, 1022, 1063, 1070, 1089, 1090).

There is a general agreement that with improvement of the clinical condition, the conditional and unconditional reflex activity is also improved.

In preliminary studies Astrup has made attempts to correlate the disturbances of the higher nervous activity with types of clinical symptom complexes (55, 56, 61, 62, 63, 65, 66).

From these studies it appeared that similiar symptom complexes tended to have similiar impairment of the higher nervous activity. Individual symptoms did not reveal any characteristic experimental disturbances. The two next chapters have been built upon the experiences of the preliminary studies. With further experiences there have been modifications for the clinical subgrouping, as well as for the interpretation of the experimental data.

4. DISTURBANCES OF THE ASSOCIATIVE FUNCTIONS IN SCHIZOPHRENIA

A considerable number of studies have been carried out in schizophrenics with the association test either isolated or in combination with other tests (30, 31, 47, 51, 55, 56, 82, 117, 121, 132, 191, 202, 363, 364, 387, 418, 437, 450, 469, 477, 478, 584, 585, 607, 609, 634, 635, 678, 736, 748, 765, 766, 795, 798, 799, 849, 898, 899, 964, 973, 976, 1040, 1052, 1078, 1101, 1102).

Sommer mentions in 1899 that a great proportion of the responses of catatonics are normal. Yet in the midst of the series comes an unrelated response or no answer at all. A rapid break of the normal associations, extreme variations, a preponderance of the internal factors as against the external stimuli, and excessive variations of the reaction times suggest catatonia (898).

Bleuler finds that the experimental associations do not reveal any disturbances in the chronic stages of the slighter forms of schizophrenia. Peculiarities are found, which alone do not give a secure diagnosis, but with a great probability point to the nature of the disease. Bleuler then summarizes the following ten factors: 1) Great variability of the reaction times, which cannot be explained exclusively from dominant emotional complexes. The time variations are also significantly larger than otherwise for complex reactions, and often there is a peculiar shifting. Periodically the associations come slowly and then patients, even in the same experiment, can react very rapidly. In acute cases during the same trial the reactions often come more and more slowly. 2) Connections with earlier stimulus-words or previous responses. 3) After-effects of former thinking are also shown in tendencies to stereotypy in form and content of the responses. Some patients, namely acute cases, answer at the end of the experiment quite meaninglessly with a few expressions which formerly had been correctly used. 4) Often the patients catch the stimulus-word and repeat it, without adding a new idea. This form of echolalia is more frequently found in acute than in chronic cases. 5) Even if repetitions of the same words do not occur frequently, one sees in many patients a poverty of ideas. They do not respond with the same words, but with similar and very adjacent ideas. 6) The schizophrenics have more individual reactions, which do not appear in others. If the same stimulus-words are given after longer intervals, the response words vary more than in normals. 7) Most remarkable are the bizarre reactions, where the stimulus-words only represent signals for reactions with fortuitous words. 8) Frequently there are no connections to be found between stimulus and response words even by inquiring of the patient. 9) A pronounced tendency to mediate associations is not uncommon. 10) The characteristics of emotional complexes often appear in a very exaggerated way. The reaction times of complex producing stimulus-words are often so long that they cannot be measured, or the reaction completely fails. All other complex signs described by Jung, are in many cases exaggerated, the superficiality with long reaction times, quotations from foreign languages, rapid forgetting, intellectual and affective after-effects to the following (succeeding) associations. The tendency to definitions often reveals a bizarre form (121).

The experience of Bleuler is quoted in some detail because it probably has given important evidence for his theory of dissolution of the associative connections as a primary symptom of schizophrenia. Later studies with the association experiment have not added much to the description given by Bleuler of pathological association reactions of schizophrenics.

Kent and Rosanoff concluded that by the application of the association test according to their method, no sharp distinction can be drawn between mental health and disease. A large collection of material shows a gradual and not an abrupt transition from the normal state to the pathological states. Yet in dementia praecox some tendencies, when appearing, are so highly characteristic as to be almost pathognomonic. Among these may be mentioned: 1) The tendency to neologisms, particular those of the senseless type. 2) The tendency to unclassified reactions largely of the incoherent type. 3) The tendency toward stereotypy, manifested chiefly by abnormal frequent repetitions of the same reaction. Fairly characteristic also is the occasional tendency to give sound reactions. Again, occasionally one encounters pronounced perseveration, and at least two of their subjects gave a good many unclassified reactions obviously due to distraction (418). The findings of Kent and Rosanoff have been corroborated by the later studies of Murphy, Martin and Shakow (585, 634, 635, 849).

In the studies of Schafer, Rapaport and Gill several measures seem to correlate well with the clinical diagnoses of schizophrenia. The distant reactions, where the relationship between the two words is scarcely comprehensible, are found especially often in schizophrenia (748). Schafer thinks that the distant reactions imply some disorganization of the associative processes. They also represent an extreme complexity and quantity of pre-response ideas; consequently they are in all groups—psychotic to normal— the most difficult to reproduce when this is required. He stresses that normal subjects and, to a lesser extent, neurotic subjects adhere to conventional conceptual relationship in their reactions (798, 799). There is a fair agreement between Schafer and De (182) that distant or vague reactions and failures of reproduction are measures of psychoticism.

Those working with Pavlovian concepts of the higher nervous functions have applied the association experiment in connection with other methods to study the disturbances of the higher nervous system, and their works will be considered. It is noted that Ivanov-Smolensky utilized the association experiment in his analysis of delusions, structural dementia in schizophrenia and the language disturbances of schizophasia (363, 364). Zurabashvili studied schizophrenics with an association experiment based upon different word groups demonstrating disturbances at different levels of the second signaling system. The patients generally showed greatest disturbances at the highest and ontogenetically latest developed levels, but no controls with other patient groups were used. There were severe inhibitions with strong variations in the verbal reactions, which he felt to be caused by increased unconditional inhibition (1101).

From the available data with the association experiment, it appears despite the various theoretical interpretations, the observed data indicate that most authors have obtained similiar results for the various psychiatric disorders. There are apparently some connections between the types of associative disturbances found, and the clinical syndromes. It apparently is not possible to find any pathognomonic associative pathology for the psychiatric disorders. In schizophrenia the differences between the various types of associative performances in various groups of patients, are probably greater than the resemblances. As mentioned by Bell in 1948 (105) the weak point in the numerous studies of associative disturbances has been the lack of an underlying basic hypothesis to evaluate the data obtained. The present author feels that the Pavlovian physiological terms may give such a basic theory, making it possible to relate the associative disturbances to other levels of the higher nervous functions.

5. DISTURBANCES OF MOTOR CONDITIONAL REFLEXES IN SCHIZOPHRENIA

A considerable number of workers have studied schizophrenic patients with motor conditional reflexes (47, 55, 56, 165, 191, 197, 198, 409, 410, 414, 469, 470, 477, 504, 607, 610, 617, 654, 655, 679, 729, 745, 777, 795, 853, 854, 872, 907, 973, 977, 989, 1040, 1041, 1078, 1081, 1082, 1087). In catatonic patients the forming and stabilization of conditional reflexes was either completely or almost impossible. Many samples of schizophrenics could rapidly give conditional responses.

Protopopov found extreme weakness of the inhibitory as well as the excitatory processes and assumed that the cortical functions were severely inhibited in schizophrenia. He demonstrated the existence of equivalent, paradoxical and ultraparadoxical phases in the motor reactions, which he regarded as characteristic of a hypnoid state (729). According to Rushkevich the motor reflexes show a pronounced disturbance of the active internal inhibition and severe inertia of the nervous processes (777). Traugott and Chistovich studied chronic schizophrenics with incoherent speech. They learned that the disturbances of speech were connected with a pronounced tendency to exhaustion of the cerebral cortex. The irradiation from the first to the second signaling system was diffuse and inadequate. Because of the disturbances of the interactions between the signaling systems, it was believed that the speech lost its significance for regulating behavior and became floating along "empty" pathways (977).

Vinogradov and Reiser, in acute schizophrenia, find no irradiation between the signaling systems. In schizophrenics with remissions the elective irradiation is partly or completely restored (1040).

In preliminary studies by the author of motor conditional reflexes in schizophrenia, the changes observed by other authors were found. Strong variations of the reaction times and severe dissociations in the interactions of the signaling system were highly suggestive of a schizophrenic disease, but scarcely pathognomonic, and in several schizophrenic patients such disturbances were not observed (55, 56). Many of the disturbances found in schizophrenia are often observed in non-schizophrenic patients, so that they probably have small differential diagnostical values. This is notably so in the phasic conditions of the cerebral cortex, which have been reported in many forms of psychiatric and psychosomatic disease, and even in normal persons in the course of the working day (184, 349, 675). In Astrup's experience, phasic conditions were frequent in neuroses, and taking into consideration the experiences of other authors with respect to the unspecificity, the rather time-consuming study of phasic states was not carried out for the schizophrenic group.

The survey of studies with motor conditional reflexes does not give great hope of finding any pathognomonic disturbances of the higher nervous system in schizophrenia. It seems that the disturbances for all kinds of mental disorders can be correlated fairly well with patterns of behavior, as the most severely deteriorated cases tend to have the greatest impairment of reflex activity.

6. REACTIONS TO PAIN STIMULI IN SCHIZOPHRENICS

Studies of unconditional defensive reactions to electrical stimulation or other pain stimuli in schizophrenics have been carried out by several authors (55, 56, 108, 190, 262, 268, 305, 311, 338, 409, 410, 414, 450, 554, 555, 556, 576, 577, 578, 637, 729, 733, 933, 946, 977, 989). According to Protopopov, schizophrenics often show severe inhibitions of the unconditional responses to electrical stimulation with extreme tendencies to exhaustion. Conditional reflexes to electrical stimulation are formed very slowly, if at all (729). Kaufman, Traugott and Chistovich had similar results for deteriorated schizophrenias. They also emphasize the failures of schizophrenics to avoid electrical stimulation after instruction (409, 410, 977). Protopopov stresses that the thresholds for pain are not significantly lowered in schizophrenia, which is in accordance with other authors. Igersheimer used the cold pressor test for various psychiatric syndromes, and found lower cold pressor responses in schizophrenias and manic-depressive psychoses. This he related to Gellhorn's theory of deficient reactivity of the sympathetic division of the hypothalamus in the functional psychoses, particularly in schizophrenia. In five schizophrenic cases there were paradoxical reactions (289, 339).

Malmo, Shagass *et al.* compared the reactions to pain in normals, neurotics, acute and chronic schizophrenics. The level of muscle tension was as high in schizophrenics under stress as in other psychiatric patients, but the schizophrenics were tensionally hyporeactive to pain stimuli of brief duration. Since their tensional responses in other situations (particularly those calling for active participation) was not diminished, it was concluded that there was no general reduction in capacity for physiological reactivity (577). In another paper Malmo and Shagass compared the reactions to pain in anxiety and in early schizophrenia. In terms of general levels of responsiveness, the early schizophrenic group resembled the most anxious groups more than any other. In two different types of reaction, the schizophrenic group showed a relative lack of discrimination among the various intensities. Their poor discrimination appeared to reflect (at a simple level) the inappropriateness of response, which is generally typical of schizophrenia (576).

Hall and Stride carried out an experimental investigation of the response to pain in 400 psychiatric patients of different diagnostical categories. Depressive and schizophrenic patients tended to report pain at uniformly high level, irrespective of age. The anxiety neurotics tend both to perceive and to react early to pain, although this tendency is reduced with age. Fourteen schizophrenias tended to vary considerably both intra-individually and in the group, and the overall results for the group show a very high verbal report of pain and pain reaction point (311).

Bender and Schilder studied unconditional and conditional reactions to pain in schizophrenia. They attempted to establish in sixteen stuporous, catatonic schizophrenics a conditional response to a light or touch when the unconditional stimulus was a strong faradic shock. Some evidence for conditioning appeared. But five refused to cooperate after one or two shocks. There was removal of the hand from the electrode (natural reaction) in two patients. Ambivalent reactions consisting of small athetoid movements and slow crawling away from the electrode were observed, interpreted as resulting from simultaneous impulses to follow the experimenter's instructions and to respond to the light or touch. Some patients gave partial responses consisting of lifting one or two fingers. Similiar responses were obtained by touching different points of the patient's body, indicating to Bender and Schilder that the psychological changes of a stuporous condition result in an "incomplete analysis of the situation" (108). Malmo, Shagass and Smith studied responsiveness in chronic schizophrenia. In the pain-stress the act of pressing the button to signal pain was relatively infrequent, even though the level of tension in the signaling arm was high. They would not have obtained evidence which might have been interpreted as supporting the "hyporeactivity" theory, had not the simultaneous presence of contradictory data forced a more detailed analysis and a different interpretation. It was noted that all curves, except the one for the chronic schizophrenics, show a correlation of the amplitude of response with intensity of stimulation. The schizophrenic curve is flat. In comparison with other groups the schizophrenics were relatively unresponsive in terms of the measure of respiratory irregularity. This was particularly evident at the higher intensities (578).

Huston studied the sensory threshold to direct current stimulation in schizophrenic and in normal subjects. As a check on the statement that high faradic current threshold are found in about 50 per cent of patients with dementia praecox, a technique of direct current stimulation was employed. This revealed no significant differences between a schizophrenic group and a comparable normal one (338).

To judge from the available data, dissociations between cortical functions and subcortical functions and inhibitions of unconditional reflexes are found in some types of schizophrenia, but not in all cases and are not pathognomonic for schizophrenic disorders.

7. VASOMOTOR AND RESPIRATORY REACTIONS IN SCHIZOPHRENIA

To some extent in the discussion of methodological problems the respiratory and vascular reactions of schizophrenics have been considered. Bumke and Kehrer first pointed out that in schizophrenia the plethysmographic curve often showed an inactivity similar to that observed in pupillary reactions (145). Later this observation was confirmed by Küppers, de Jong and others (134, 385, 501). In the detailed study of Jung and Carmichael, eight stuporous catatonics reacted to all external and internal stimuli with contraction after their vessels had been dilated by putting the feet for a period in water at 44-45° C. They concluded that the previously found non-reactivity was due to an extreme vasoconstriction. It was found that vasodilatation with heating was normal, though sometimes delayed. It was assumed that the vasoconstriction was a consequence of the lack of movements in the patients, and was an appropriate way of regulating the body temperature (393). Minski found a vasomotor instability in schizophrenics with cyanosis. Since massage and passive movements did not reveal cyanosis, this observer does not believe it to result from a lack of exercise (608).

Studies of Abramson, Schkloven and Katzenstein (3), Abramson (4), Henschel, Brozek and Keys (327) and others agree that there is a strong tendency to vasoconstriction in schizophrenia. Abramson was able to demonstrate a tendency to diminished blood flow in the hands of psychotic patients, due to a neurogenic reduction of the calibre of the vessels. Excessive vasoconstriction was abolished after local or reflex warming which resulted in full vasodilatation, providing the absence of organic lesions of the vasomotor tree (3).

Henschel *et al* found that the schizophrenic patient, compared with the normal subjects, exhibited a significantly prolonged latent period before vasodilatation began, but once dilatation started, the time course and magnitude of the response were clearly similiar in the two groups. Conclusively there is no evidence for abnormality of the peripheral vessels in schizophrenics, but in such patients there tends to be either an exceptionally high and persistent state of tonus in the skin vessels or an abnormally high temperature threshold in the hypothalamus (327). Shattock found that the average blood pressure of refractory (mainly catatonic) schizophrenics was lower than that of paranoid and socialized patients. With improvement in the systemic circulation coinciding with the onset of a remission, it is possible that some of the abnormalities of behavior in refractory patients may be related to a relatively inadequate cerebral circulation. He concluded that prolonged vasoconstriction is necessary to conserve body heat. This is owing to the failure to respond to increasing bodily requirements during chilling and muscular exercise by adequate rises in metabolic level. Disturbances of the hypothalamic centers play an important part in the somatic disturbances of schizophrenia (852). Baruk and others have pointed out that the oscillometric oscillations are especially small in schizophrenia (95, 137, 138, 210).

A great many authors have carried out studies of unconditional and conditional vascular reflexes in schizophrenia (plethysmography and pulse) (47, 55, 56, 76, 82, 190, 191, 482, 499, 509, 510, 523, 698, 729, 756, 795, 814, 815, 816, 817, 820, 907, 908, 909, 910, 911, 912, 913, 914, 1033, 1079).

Protopopov found that the unconditional vasomotor responses of schizophrenics are small or lacking with regard to *orienting reflexes,* cold and pain stimulation. This is describing in other terms the observations about lowered reactivity referred to above. In patients with vasomotor responses it has been shown that the conditional responses were formed with great difficulty. The unconditional responses tended to show phasic states with equivalent and paradoxical reactions to varying strength of the unconditional stimulation, thus revealing severe inhibitions of the unconditional responses of a qualitative different form from normals (729). Other investigators have found that the schizophrenics tend to show phasic unconditional responses (756, 815). Such reactions were not pathognomonic for schizophrenia. Segal and others have shown that dissociations between respiratory and plethysmographic reactions were characteristic of schizophrenics (417, 816, 820, 907, 912, 913). In preliminary studies of Astrup, the schizophrenics tended to show severe inhibitions of the unconditional responses. There are also often dissociations between respiratory reactions and the respiratory oscillations of the plethysmogram. In some types of schizophrenia "stormy" autonomic reactions to questions concerning delusions were observed. The reactions mentioned are not disturbances common to all forms of schizophrenia, and although generally found in schizophrenia are probably not pathognomonic (55, 56). The inhibition of unconditional responses seems to be rather unspecific. A more intensive vasodilatation by heat, as proposed by Jung and Carmichael, might possibly have decreased the number of patients with inactive curves. The aim of this study was to compare normals and different mental disorders in order to analyze the differences with regard to reactivity to the same stimuli. In this connection the factors of vasodilatation mainly express different influences of the central regulation of vasomotor tonus.

8. COMPARISONS WITH OTHER REFLEXOGICAL,
PSYCHOLOGICAL AND SOMATIC
STUDIES IN SCHIZOPHRENIA

From the review of the methods applied in this investigation
and from previous studies with these methods, it is found that disturbances of the higher nervous activity are practically always
found in schizophrenics. At all levels of nervous functions there
are strong tendencies to inhibition.

It is seen that dissociations of verbal reactions, dissociations between the first and second signaling system, dissociations between
unconditional motor reactions to electrical stimulation and verbal
stimulation, between unconditional motor and autonomic reactions to electrical stimulation and between the plethysmographic
and respiratory curves are often observed in schizophrenia. For
associative, motor and autonomic reactions, inertia of nervous
processes and deficient internal inhibition are frequent. Characteristic of schizophrenic patients were inhibitions of unconditional
motor reactions to electrical stimulation, and unconditional plethysmographic reactions to all forms of stimulation. These findings point definitely to the importance of subcortical disturbances,
probably in the hypothalamus and adjoining areas of the brain.
It should be stressed that none of the findings mentioned seem to
be pathognomonic for schizophrenia. A single test would often
give practically normal reactions in several schizophrenics.

The methods chosen for the present study give only short "snap-
shots" of very limited aspects of mental functioning at different
integrative levels. It is possible that differentiated psychological
tests at the higher verbal level and somatic studies of various somatic functions depending upon different centers of subcortical
regulation might give more adequate description of the disturbances of the higher nervous functions in schizophrenia. We find
it useful to compare our results with those obtained by other
investigation methods. The results of projective tests and other
psychological tests building upon introspective psychodynamic
theories will not be considered, as the present state of knowledge
makes it difficult to interpret the results in simple physiological
terms. The vast body of metabolic and biochemical investigations
falls outside the framework of the present study.

It will only be mentioned briefly that several reviews of somatic studies in schizophrenia have assumed that the hypothalamus and other deep-lying subcortical centers play an important role in the causation of the observed variations of endocrine and biochemical functions. In several studies results have been obtained that indicate the conceptual functions as measured by psychological tests suffer in schizophrenia (106). To what extent these phenomena, in analogy with the results obtained with the association test, may signify dissociations within the second signaling system or possibly between the signaling systems has not been closely studied (73, 410, 451, 731). Several authors have shown that the cognitive functions of schizophrenia as measures of intelligence tests are often not essentially interfered with (106, 337). Also many authors have pointed to the slowness of motor functions in schizophrenia (337, 429, 849, 850). The wide studies of King have made this aspect of schizophrenia evident, and the findings are in agreement with the results obtained with motor conditional reflexes (429).

In the early 1920's Langfeldt carried out a detailed investigation of the influences of the sympathetic and parasympathetic nervous systems in schizophrenia (512). Gellhorn has later in several studies discussed the significance of diminished central sympathetico-adrenal reactivity in schizophrenia. He concludes that the complex action of central autonomic excitation cannot be arbitrarily identified with only one of the factors involved, and that studies of the influences of adrenalin cannot disprove the disturbances of the system. In addition he states that the spinal autonomic reflexes are not essentially altered in schizophrenia (289). The claims of the value of the *Funkenstein* test with ephinephrine and mecholyl for prognostic predictions have not been confirmed by Silverstein, Kline and others. Gantt and co-workers, however, suggest results with conditional reflex methodology (140, 248, 869). Angyal, Blackman, Hoskins and others have revealed that the schizophrenic in vestibular investigations is less reactive than the normal in regard to his equilibrium response (18, 333, 651, 917).

With chronaximetric studies Last and Ström-Olsen and several other authors have shown that the chronaxie is abnormal, especially prolonged with marked changes (17, 518). These findings are suggestive of a central disorder. The difficulties in the measurement of *chronaxie* in man are such that these observations cannot be accepted unreservedly, according to Altschule (17). In several studies the chronaximetric method has been modified to serve as a link of conditional reflex studies. Such studies suggest that there is impairment of the cortical-subcortical interactions in schizophrenia (558, 787, 1062, 1063). The well known pupillary phenomenon of Bumke has been confirmed by Löwenstein, Westphal and others (144, 560). Tatarenko has modified the method of pupillary reflexes in order to study interactions of cortical and subcortical processes, and feels that this method indicates the presence of inhibition of unconditional responses in schizophrenia (554, 555, 556, 932, 933, 952, 954, 957).

With EEG Sem-Jacobsen and his collaborators found high voltage paroxysmal rhythms in depth recordings of some forms of schizophrenia, suggesting that the subcortical centres have a special pathological role in schizophrenia (826). Hill considered evidence related to thalamo-cortical integrations in schizophrenia with EEG. These investigations illustrated a defective or delayed autonomic response to stress in schizophrenics—a finding in agreement with Gellhorn who studied these responses in schizophrenics using other stresses. However, he found no phenomena specific for schizophrenia (329, 759). Several authors have tried to evaluate EEG findings in schizophrenics based on Pavlovian concepts (118, 166, 167, 245, 286, 394, 395, 396, 397, 1103).

Jus has presented a summarized classification of the modern heuristic bioelectrical theories in schizophrenia and critically assesses them. He illustrates that a synchronous electroencephalo-electromyo- and mechanographic study in a conditional setting has shown the different pathophysiological mechanisms of effector and receptor stupor (397). Zurabashvili and co-workers think that EEG shows great dissociative disturbances in schizophrenia (1103). Several authors have studied the psychogalvanic responses in schizophrenia. Ödegård found that in schizophrenia the reactivity is most atypical in cases where a marked disturbance of the emotional sphere is present—and also in catatonic and deteriorated patients. In cases with a more sudden, attack-like onset, the reactivity is most atypical in the beginning; among the more chronic and insidious cases, those with a long duration are most atypical. Organic and schizophrenic psychoses show the greatest decrease in reactivity (656). In another study Ödegård showed that in restless and agitated cases the reactivity is very atypical, mainly in the form of a greatly decreased positive component of the psychogalvanic curve, and in schizophrenia decrease of the positive component was the most important pathological factor. Ödegård observed that the positive component (relatively increased potential on palm of hand) represents the higher and controlling "cortical" mechanisms, and that the opposite negative component represents the more primitive, instinctive, "subcortical" levels of anxiety (657). Studies of unconditional and conditional psychogalvanic reactions indicate that the responses are often severely inhibited (334, 506, 607, 937, 938, 939, 1102).

Many studies carried out on conditional and unconditional responses to other biological functions have also indicated frequent inhibitions of unconditional responses in schizophrenia (340, 575, 729, 867, 915, 957, 960, 1086, 1099, 1103).

In the evidence present from experimental studies the factors of dissociations of nervous functions and disturbances of subcortical functions, especially in the sense of reduced reactivity, are most commonly mentioned in schizophrenia. None of the mentioned types of disturbances is present in all cases of schizophrenia and none has been proved to be pathognomonic for schizophrenia. There is a possibility that there are no disturbances pathognomonic for all cases of schizophrenia. These cases show very obviously different types of clinical pictures. In the following we analyze the extent to which detailed clinical subdivisions show correlations between disturbances of the higher mental functions and the clinical pictures.

Chapter VI

GENERAL CHARACTERISTICS OF THE CLINICAL MATERIAL

1. PRINCIPLES OF CLINICAL ANALYSIS AND CLASSIFICATION IN ACUTE AND SUBACUTE FUNCTIONAL PSYCHOSES

WHEN THE AUTHOR started his studies of disturbances of the higher nervous activity in schizophrenia, it soon became apparent that patients diagnosed as schizophrenics were very different clinically as well as in their experimental reactions. In the acute psychoses the classification of a schizophrenic disorder varies a great deal. As demonstrated clearly in the literature survey of Bellak, there is also extensive disagreement on which psychiatric conditions should be labeled schizophrenia (106). Holmboe, Fossum and Astrup, in follow-up studies of acute functional psychoses, related the clinical symptoms in the acute stages in great detail to the outcome of the disease, judged by personal re-examinations six to nineteen years after the first admission (64, 331). They sorted out a group of pure manic-depressive psychoses, and a group of reactive (psychogenic) psychoses without typical schizophrenic symptoms, with a very small risk of schizophrenic deterioration. The presence of typical schizophrenic symptoms would always indicate a definite possibility of schizophrenic deterioration. Cases with such symptoms were considered to belong to the group of schizophrenias, although a considerable chance of recovery exists, especially for the schizo-affective states.

The following symptoms were defined as typical schizophrenic: 1) Hebephrenic traits. 2) Catatonic traits. 3) Depersonalization. 4) Passivity. 5) Disturbance of symbolization. 6) Haptic hallucinations. 7) Special forms of auditory hallucinations. 8) Religious megalomania. 9) Corresponding nonreligious megalomania. 10) Fantastic ideas of jealousy. 11) Fantasy lover. 12) Delusions of noble origin. (8-12 are defined as typical schizophrenic delusions.) These symptoms are more extensively defined in the paper (331). The clinical analysis revealed that several of the typical schizophrenic symptoms had the character of mental automatisms, in the sense of Clérambault and Kandinsky (170, 206, 207, 681, 758, 866). It was of particular interest to see whether such symptoms might be related to fundamental impairment of nervous activity, rather than to psychodynamic mechanisms.

In order to study the influence of schizophrenic symptom complexes, the patients were divided into subgroups, according to the principles of Langfeldt and Carl Schneider (205, 513, 514, 515, 516, 803).

The viewpoints of Langfeldt are especially stressed because of his fundamental separation of prognostically favorable schizophreniform psychoses and the malignant process schizophrenias. Carl Schneider, and later Arnold in their clinical studies have shown how schizophrenic symptom complexes might be considered as analogous to mental processes in the states of falling asleep and awakening (27, 802, 803). In Chapter V, several authors assume that schizophrenic symptoms may be interpreted as due to states of the higher nervous activity resembling sleep. Because of this it was felt that the classification principles of Carl Schneider would be suitable for testing these hypotheses. He writes that three different symptom complexes occur in schizophrenia. These symptom complexes can occur in pure form, be mixed together or follow on one another. They are:

1. The syndrome of *"Gedankenentzug"* (thought withdrawal). Cosmic, universal and religious experiences—breaking up of thoughts, thought withdrawal—perplexity—inspiration—made experiences which are forced on the patient or in which the will is paralyzed—verbal derailments—blocking.

2. The syndrome of *"Sprunghaftigkeit"* (desultoriness). Desultory thinking—paucity of affect and poverty of inner drive, defect in vital dynamism, elasticity and reactivity—extinction of joy and sadness—states of anxiety, anger, whining, desperation—changes of bodily feelings, of bodily perception of oneself, physical hallucinations.

3. Syndrome of *"Faseln"* (drivelling). Delusions of significa-
tion, primary delusional experiences—vague drivelling thinking—lack of interest in actual things and values—incoherence
—inadequate affects—paraboulic impulses.

The acute and subacute schizophrenics were divided into four
groups: 1) Hebephrenic and hebephrenic-paranoid cases. 2)
Catatonic and mixed catatonic cases. 3) Paranoid cases with projection symptoms. 4) Paranoid cases with systematized delusions.

After E. Bleuler, hebephrenia is the residual group in schizophrenia, when clearly catatonic, paranoid and simplex cases are
excluded (122). Kleist and Leonhard illustrated the necessity of
a more precise definition of hebephrenia, stressing that the central
symptoms are the affective changes. In catatonia, psychomotor
disturbances, and, in paranoid cases, the delusions dominate the
clinical picture (537). In the present study the affective blunting
has been the main criteria for the classification as hebephrenia.
It is emphasized that the hebephrenic cases should reveal the
symptom complex of *"Sprunghaftigkeit"* as defined by Carl Schneider (803).

All cases with catatonic symptoms have been included in the
catatonic group. These psychoses also show the symptom complex
of *"Sprunghaftigkeit."*

The clinical classification of paranoid schizophrenia is often extremely difficult. Carl Schneider states that the paranoid schizophrenias are characterized by the symptom complexes of *"Faseln"*
and *"Gedankenentzug"* (803). Similarly, Langfeldt has divided the
paranoid schizophrenias into psychoses with projection symptoms,
and dementia paranoides, which is mainly characterized by primary delusions (513).

Characteristic of all projection phenomena is their automatic
nature, the patients feeling that something is being imposed upon
them. There may be considerable general emotional changes in
the direction of perplexity, depression, elation or ecstasy. The
patients regularly show an affectively neutral coloring to the feelings of splitting and the corresponding delusions. The projection
symptoms very clearly satisfy the criteria of mental automatisms,
as established by Clérambault (170). In order precisely to define
this group, all cases must show the symptom complex of *"Gedan-*

kenentzug" and have feelings of passivity. Because of the great tendency to general emotional disturbances in these psychoses, several cases will not be classified as nuclear process schizophrenias, but as schizophreniform or schizo-affective states.

In the group of paranoid psychoses with systematized delusions the main clinical symptom is that the delusions are strongly affect-laden. It is characteristic of the delusions that real perceptions are given an abnormal significance, not rationally or emotionally understandable. This implies a peculiar disturbance of symbolization. The "primary" character of the delusions is realized when contrasted with the paranoid ideas in catamnestically verified non-schizophrenic psychoses, where the delusions clearly can be set in relation to personality structures and life experiences (64, 331). By scrutinizing the case histories, one can always find factors which at least pathoplastically can make the "primary" delusions psychologically comprehensible. The connections, however, are not so defined as in the non-schizophrenic paranoid states. This is demonstrated by Binswanger (114).

As schizophrenic autism and emotional blunting are regularly lacking in the paranoid cases with systematized delusions, doubts often arise whether they are not non-schizophrenic functional psychoses. There are also differential diagnostic problems towards involutional and arteriosclerotic psychoses, as these psychoses tend to start later than psychoses in the other schizophrenic subgroups. M. Bleuler recognizes that there is a great divergence of opinion in the literature concerning the diagnostic classification of schizophrenia in older age, especially as to the paranoid forms (124).

The psychoses with systematized delusions correspond to the paraphrenias of Kraepelin and the "chronic *delire*" with hallucinations of French authors, which were also separated from a more nuclear paranoid dementia praecox (213, 486, 866). One reason for considering such psychoses as schizophrenia is that all present the symptom complex of "*Faseln*" of Schneider, with the typical schizophrenic disturbances of symbolization (803). Our follow-up studies showed that most such psychoses developed schizophrenic deterioration (331).

All acute and subacute functional psychoses have been subdivided according to the clinical picture in the acute stage. A detailed analysis of clinical factors was carried out according to the same principles as in our follow-up studies (331). Comparisons of deteriorating and recurring cases will be made, in order to see if the experimental methods may contribute to the differential diagnosis between process schizophrenias and schizophreniform psychoses.

2. PRINCIPLES OF CLINICAL ANALYSIS AND CLASSIFICATION IN CHRONIC SCHIZOPHRENIA

Only chronic schizophrenia clearly shows the mental abnormalities, which led Kraepelin to formulate the concept of dementia praecox, and the present study will be especially concerned with the study of chronic schizophrenics. The more the acute cases resemble the chronic ones, the greater is the probability that they pathogenetically have something in common. The acute clinical symptoms of the present chronic cases have been analyzed in the same way as the acute and subacute material and the followed up cases (331). This may serve as a check on the prognostic studies based on catamnesis, where the starting point was the acute clinical symptomatologies.

Systematic attempts to establish well defined subtypes of chronic schizophrenia have been carried out by Leonhard and other pupils of Kleist (222, 223, 431, 432, 433, 434, 435, 436, 442, 526, 527, 528, 529, 530, 531, 532, 533, 534, 535, 536, 537, 603, 645, 804, 808, 809, 811, 812, 813).

In the present study the author has adopted the classification system proposed by Leonhard in his latest book. This classification does not differ essentially from that of Kleist. The main advantage is that the subtypes described do not imply so much the acceptance of the localization theory of Kleist, being mainly clinical descriptions which can be interpreted within any set of theoretical framework (537).

During a visit to the Charité clinic in Berlin the author had the opportunity to see how Leonhard classified the schizophrenias, using clinical cases from most of the described subtypes. The author found that his classification of the individual cases has been fairly close to the classification proposed by Leonhard. Outside Germany, Sarró Burbano and co-workers in Spain, Henry Ey in France and Fish in England have applied the Kleist-Leonhard system of classification. These investigators agree that the schemata give a good basis for classification (171, 213, 234, 235, 236, 790, 791).

The author has had the opportunity to see the cases classified by Fish and discuss the individual cases with him in some detail (236). In comparatively few cases was there uncertainty or disagreement about how to classify the patients. This would indicate that the classification is rather independent of subjective evaluation.

Leonhard asserts that the subforms of schizophrenia are distinctly circumscript and do not overlap. If overlapping is found, such overlapping is considered due to combinations of two subtypes. By operating with combined forms, the classification system becomes very complicated with nearly 100 subtypes, making it very difficult to apply the classification in clinical work. The combined forms are so rare that no one would have the opportunity to see many such cases. In the author's experience the combined forms must actually be regarded as representing gradual transitions between the typical pictures. For this reason the author classifies such cases within the subgroups they resemble most. Henri Ey and Fish hold the opinion that the subgroups are overlapping (213, 236). In a personal communication to the author Leonhard does not object to this consideration of the combined forms.

Using the nomenclature of Leonhard as translated by Fish, the present investigation will operate with the following paranoid subgroups: (236). 1) Affect-laden paraphrenia. 2) Schizophasia. 3) Hypochondriacal paraphrenia. 4) Phonemic paraphrenia. 5) Confabulatory paraphrenia. 6) Expansive paraphrenia. 7) Fantastic paraphrenia. 8) Incoherent paraphrenia. The hebephrenias are divided into the following forms: 1) Autistic hebephrenia. 2) Eccentric hebephrenia. 3) Shallow hebephrenia. 4) Silly hebephrenia.

The catatonic subtypes are: 1) Periodic catatonia. 2) Parakinetic catatonia. 3) Manneristic catatonia. 4) Proskinetic catatonia. 5) Negativistic catatonia. 6) Speech-prompt catatonia. 7) Speech-inactive catatonia.

Affect-laden paraphrenia, schizophasia and periodic catatonia are designated as non-systematic and the other defects as systematic schizophrenias.

Leonhard thinks that already at an early stage one can determine into which subtype a schizophrenic psychosis will develop. The classification is considerably easier in chronic cases with fairly stable clinical pictures. In the present investigation only cases which have been sick for at least 5 years since the last remission are considered chronic, with fairly stable clinical pictures, which can be divided into the mentioned subtypes. All other cases are regarded as acute or subacute.

Another important problem was to decide the degree of deterioration in schizophrenia in the clinical subgroups. Various scales have been proposed for evaluating the amount of deterioration. The author chose to measure it along several dimensions, namely:

1. *Working capacity.*
   a. Able to carry out independent responsible work.
   b. Able to carry out simple work under supervision.
   c. Unable to work or only in habit-training activities.
2. *Placement in the hospital during the last year.*
   a. Quiet and open wards.
   b. Half-disturbed and semi-open wards.
   c. Closed, disturbed and nursing wards.
3. *Ability to communicate.*
   a. Adequate verbal communication.
   b. Inadequate verbal communication.
   c. No verbal communication.
4. *Ability to care for own person.*
   a. Caring for themselves.
   b. Helpless nursing patients.

Slightly deteriorated cases were then defined as those having the *a* qualities, and the severely deteriorated mainly would have the qualities *b* and *c*. As analyzed in more specific detail in Chapter VII, schizophasia, affect-laden, phonemic and hypochondriacal paraphrenia, autistic and eccentric hebephrenia and some cases of periodic catatonia could be considered slightly deteriorated. All other subgroups of chronic schizophrenia by and large showed the characteristics of severe deterioration.

Clinically one has the impression that the differences between several of the subgroups are not very great. For reasons of comparison it might be practical to use the wider categories of slightly and severely deteriorated paraphrenia, hebephrenia, and periodic and systematic catatonia.

3. PRINCIPLES OF ANALYZING THE HEREDITARY LOADING

Leonhard thinks the diseased relatives tend to have similar defect forms, and it was studied in some detail how far the relatives of our probands might be classified in the same subgroups. Genetically it appears, as shown by M. Bleuler, that hereditary factors are of great importance also for the course of the disease (123).

The family study was limited to the closest groups of relatives, grandparents, uncles, aunts, parents and siblings. There were only a few psychotic children, and their observation periods were rather short for evaluating the course of the disease. Therefore, children were not included. Nephews, nieces and cousins are rather numerous, but mostly difficult to obtain information about, and they were also excluded. It was then enumerated for each clinical subgroup how many of the types of relatives mentioned probably had functional psychoses.

No attempt has been made to carry out a complete family investigation of our patients, but in every case information about relatives known to have been insane was collected, from the case history and from the central register of the insane. The clinical picture presented by the insane relatives was ascertained from their case histories and could be compared with the clinical condition of the patient himself. No doubt our knowledge of psychotic relatives is incomplete, and, as we have not gathered information about the total number of relatives, we cannot give any morbidity figures. We believe that our material of *insane relatives* is a representative sample with regard to clinical picture and outcome, and that a comparison between probands and relatives may be of some interest. We also believe that the sample is fairly complete. Compared with the careful proband investigation of Dahl and Ödegård we have probably missed only one per cent of the hospitalized relatives with functional psychoses (175).

For the acute and subacute psychoses of the probands, it was possible with a detailed symptom analysis to divide the cases into various schizophrenic symptom complexes and affective psychoses. The symptomatic descriptions of the psychoses of the relatives for the acute stages varied so much that this was not practical. One had to take into consideration the total clinical picture and especially the course.

Some relatives with clearly catatonic symptoms, who apparently had remissions, were included in the group of periodic catatonias, which regularly have a strong tendency to these remissions. The other relatives with remissions were classified as affective psychotics, even if clinically some schizophrenic symptoms were present during the acute stage. It was assumed that the familiar tendency to remissions might give important information about constitutional factors. There remain the deteriorated schizophrenics among the functional psychoses. These cases were classified according to Leonhard. Although all possible efforts have been made to analyze the case histories of the relatives, the data cannot be so detailed as for the probands studied personally. The classification of relatives into subgroups has only a limited validity. More substantial is the classification of the relatives into greater subgroups of slight and severe paranoid or hebephrenic defects, systematic and periodic catatonias and affective psychoses. These broader groups will also be used for the tabular survey of heredity in Chapter IX.

4. THE SELECTION OF MATERIAL

Altogether the author has studied a sample of 306 chronic schizophrenics from Gaustad hospital. The only limitation in the selection of the patients is that only a few leucotomized cases have been included. Leucotomy seems to change the clinical pictures of chronic schizophrenia. As discussed in Chapter III, it was assumed that it would be difficult to decide which changes were postoperative and organic and which changes were related to the schizophrenic defect state. The majority of the patients could be studied by all the investigative methods selected. Some of them, because of negativism, unwillingness or other reasons, could not be studied experimentally. These cases will also be included in the study of the clinical and hereditary factors. They belong mainly to the groups of affect-laden and fantastic paraphrenia, autistic hebephrenia and negativistic catatonia. An exclusion of these cases would distort the picture of the clinical and hereditary characteristics of various forms of chronic schizophrenia.

In the sample of acute and subacute functional psychoses there are 178 cases. These have all been studied by experimental methods, and only in a few cases was it impossible to apply the complex method of investigation. As much as possible the case material is unselected, with symptoms varying broadly. The one limitation is the severely excited or stuporous patients, who were not investigated experimentally before they could safely go with the investigator into the room where the experiments were carried out.

From the above it is seen that the present study represents an attempt to analyze how far combinations of clinical, hereditary and experimental data may give characteristic findings for the subgroups of functional psychoses. In the following two chapters these findings will be analyzed in detail.

Chapter VII

CLINICAL AND EXPERIMENTAL STUDIES OF CHRONIC SCHIZOPHRENIAS

A. THE PARANOID TYPES OF CHRONIC SCHIZOPHRENIA

1. Affect-laden Paraphrenia

ACCORDING to Leonhard this group is characterized by the strong affective anchoring of the delusions. To the present author it seems that other chronic paranoid schizophrenias may also react with strong affects to their delusions and hallucinations. It is extremely difficult to decide clinically the degree of affectivity in the attitude to the delusions.

The affect-laden paraphrenias are considered to be atypical forms of schizophrenia. This corresponds to our experiences in follow-up studies of patients originally diagnosed as manic-depressive psychoses, who in several cases turned out to be affect-laden paraphrenias (236, 535, 537, 645). In the author's experience paranoia-resembling paraphrenic cases most clearly satisfy the criteria of affect-laden paraphrenia. In the present material there are twenty-five such cases. When clinically there is a development into an expansive or fantastic deterioration, the affect is actually considerably impoverished, just as in the so-called typical or systematic schizophrenias. Such severely deteriorated cases are not included in this group.

In fourteen cases the schizophrenic clinical pictures were so uncharacteristic that originally non-schizophrenic disorders were diagnosed, and in a few of them there is still doubt if they actually are schizophrenics. It is evident that this group is rather different from the classical dementia praecox. The affect is usually well preserved, verbal communication good, and the patients mostly have a good working ability. Nearly all are in open wards and nine have been discharged from the hospital during the observation period.

Clinically the psychoses usually start with the symptom complex of *"Faseln"* with systematized delusions and disturbance of symbolization. The affect-laden paraphrenias tend to start in the older age group, the average age of onset being 42.8 years, and the average duration of the psychoses was 14.7 years. It is noted that several cases had had previous nervous illnesses earlier in life. Sixteen were self-assertive, two schizoid and only two were considered to have balanced premorbid personalities. It is very possible that what were assumed to be abnormal personality structures were actually changes due to a long standing and insidious psychotic development. The initial symptoms of the manifest psychosis were as a rule suspiciousness, jealousy or ideas of reference.

Nineteen relatives were probably psychotic. For twelve of them case histories were available. Three of them had typical affective psychoses. One had a mild systematic paranoid schizophrenia. Eight relatives had non-systematic schizophrenias, one a schizophasia, and seven had affect-laden paraphrenias. There is among the relatives a strong tendency to develop psychoses similar to those of the probands.

The results of the experimental investigations are given in Table 1.

Three cases refused the experimental investigation and one case could not be studied with the whole complex method. The reasons for the objections to the tests were mainly marked suspiciousness.

Most patients reacted with violent respiratory and plethymographic responses to questions concerning pathodynamic structures. These reactions seem to be an objective correlate with their affect-laden delusions. Most cases gave some autonomic responses to calculation, which indicates that the second signaling system generally has a marked influence upon the autonomic curves. A great proportion of cases had no vascular responses to unconditional cold stimulation. There is no increased autonomic reactivity, but on the contrary a tendency to inhibition of the unconditional vascular reflexes. Only a few cases showed dissociations between the respiratory and vascular curve.

With electrical stimulation eleven showed one or more signs of inhibition of the unconditional responses, and only three cases

TABLE 1
Affect-Laden Paraphrenia

	Adequate Responses	Inadequate Responses	Too Difficult Tasks	No Information	Total Patients
Associations					
Reproduction	15	5	1	1	22
Mean reaction times	7	14	0	1	22
Median reaction times	8	13	0	1	22
Echolalic responses	3	18	0	1	22
Multiword responses	8	13	0	1	22
Higher responses	5	16	0	1	22
Primitive responses	18	3	0	1	22
Incoherent responses	18	3	0	1	22
Motor Conditional Reflexes					
First reflex in first system	13	8	0	1	22
Second reflex in first system	20	1	0	1	22
Reflex in second system	21	0	0	1	22
Reaction times	16	5	0	1	22
After-inhibitions	10	11	0	1	22
Extinction	20	1	0	1	22
Restoration	15	6	0	1	22
Differentiation	9	12	0	1	22
Reversal of negative reflexes	15	6	0	1	22
Reversal of positive reflexes	10	11	0	1	22
Description of performances	12	9	0	1	22
Unstable reflexes	21	0	0	1	22
Extrasignaling reactions	21	0	0	1	22
Continuous pressing	21	0	0	1	22
Autonomic Reactions					
Vascular curve	22	0	0	0	22
Respiratory curve	22	0	0	0	22
Respiratory and vascular dissociation	16	6	0	0	22
Vascular responses to cold	6	16	0	0	22
Vascular responses to calculation	18	4	0	0	22
Effects of pathodynamic structures	6	16	0	0	22
Defensive Reflexes					
Current tolerance	14	7	0	1	22
Motor exhaustion	12	9	0	1	22
Autonomic exhaustion	16	5	0	1	22
Dissociations	11	10	0	1	22
Number of inadequate responses		228			
Number of adequate responses	449				
Number of too difficult tasks			1		

had no inhibition of either defensive unconditional reflexes or unconditional vascular responses to cold. There is a general tendency to inhibition of unconditional reflexes.

Ten cases had a few reactions, where they failed to avoid the electrical stimulation after instruction. With repeated instructions they were able to avoid the shock. There is only a slight tendency to dissociation between unconditional reactions and the second signaling system.

With motor conditional reflexes the affect-laden paraphrenias did not essentially differ from the sample of normals in the ability to form conditional reflexes in the first and second signaling systems. Most cases reacted like normals with short and regular reaction times, but approximately one-half had strong after-inhibitions. There is a slight predominance of the inhibitory processes in the first signaling system. As to the internal inhibition, extinction is regularly easily performed, whereas most cases fail with differentiation. Some cases had difficulties with restoration. Most cases failed either in the reversal of the negative reflexes or in the reversal of the positive reflexes. There is a great tendency to inertia of the nervous processes. But in no case was the task of reversing the reflexes too difficult. The most severe signs of inertia as extra-signaling reactions or continuous pressing were not observed. Most cases were able to describe adequately their motor performances, but 9 had signs of dissociations in the interactions of the signaling systems.

With the association test the ability to reproduce was only impaired in a few cases. There was an emphasized tendency to inhibition of the responses, and in two cases only were the mean and median reaction times as well as the number of echolalic responses within the limits of the normal sample. Most cases had a tendency to react with echolalic or multiword responses, which indicates an inertia of the functions of the second signaling system. The majority had fewer higher responses than found in the normal sample. But only 3 cases had a great number of primitive responses. Predominantly the affect-laden paraphrenias gave responses of the middle type, which could neither be classified as higher nor as primitive reactions. Only three cases had incoherent reactions, and not more than two such responses. This shows a slight tendency to dissociation in the second signaling system.

Reviewing the experimental data it is found that pathodynamic structures in the affect-laden paraphrenia have a marked effect. There is considerable inertia of the first and second signaling systems, some impairment of the internal inhibition and passive inhibition of all three levels of the higher nervous activity. The dissociative phenomena are slight. Compared with the other groups of chronic schizophrenias, the proportion of adequate responses is considerably greater in the affect-laden paraphrenia. This runs parallel with the finding that these cases are also only slightly deteriorated clinically.

Among the experimentally studied cases nine received ataraxic drugs during the time of the experimental investigation. Only six of them had violent autonomic reactions to questions concerning pathodynamic structures. It may be that the drugs decrease the autonomic components of these structures.

Altogether eighteen cases have been treated with ataraxic drugs. Fifteen had considerable improvement and paid much less attention to their delusions. It seems that the affect-laden paraphrenias are likely to improve from drug treatment.

In conclusion it is found that the group of affect-laden paraphrenias seems to show many similarities, indicating that the group is rather homogeneous. They tend to start with systematized delusions, most relatives have similiar psychoses, the effects of ataraxic drugs are good, the impairment of the higher nervous activity is slight, and influences of pathodynamic structures are strong.

2. Schizophasia

Kraepelin's concept of schizophasia was narrower than that of Leonhard (486, 537). The main characteristics are the severe paraphasic disturbances of speech combined with a well ordered behavior (813). Delusions and hallucinations are as a rule absent. But, shown by Sarró and co-workers, such symptoms may appear periodically (171, 790). As the mood is regularly euphoric, one may have difficulty in separating the schizophasias from expansive paranoids. In the tendency to fluctuations and the well-ordered behavior the schizophasias also resemble the affect-laden paraphrenias. Here the affect-laden delusions help to establish the differential diagnosis. Leonhard also considered the schizophasias to belong to the atypical or non-systematic schizophrenias (236, 537).

In our material there are fifteen schizophasias. They are all definite schizophrenias. Eight of them have had recurring courses, and in seven cases the diagnosis originally was an affective psychosis.

Leonhard points out that schizophasias often start with stupor or excitement (537). In four of our cases such symptoms were present at the acute stage. Precipitating factors could be established in nine cases. Where nearly all the affect-laden paraphrenias started as systematized paranoid psychoses with disturbance of symbolization, only seven schizophrenics started in this way. The remaining were originally mixed paranoid-catatonic states or paranoid states dominated by projection symptoms. Nine had typical schizophrenic delusions of an expansive coloring during the acute stage.

The average age of onset was at 32.4 years, which is considerably younger than in affect-laden paraphrenias. The average observation period was 18.3 years. Only three cases had self-assertive personalities, four schizoid personalities and four balanced premorbid personalities. The onset was acute in seven cases.

Most cases had comparatively good working capacity within the hospital. With one exception they were in open and half-open wards. They could care for themselves and in spite of paraphasic disturbances were able to communicate verbally.

Seventeen relatives were psychotic. For ten of them case histories were obtained. Four had affective psychoses and six were schizophrenics. There was one catatonic schizophrenic, one fantastic paraphrenic and four schizophasiacs. This shows that a great proportion of the relatives develop similiar defects. As several of our schizophasiacs had recurring courses and even originally were diagnosed as affective psychotics, it is not surprising that four of the relatives could be classified as affective psychotics.

The results of the experimental investigations are shown in Table 2.

TABLE 2
SCHIZOPHASIA

	Adequate Responses	Inadequate Responses	Too Difficult Tasks	No Information	Total Patients
Associations					
Reproduction	6	8	1	0	15
Mean reaction times	4	11	0	0	15
Median reaction times	3	12	0	0	15
Echolalic responses	3	12	0	0	15
Multiword responses	4	11	0	0	15
Higher responses	2	13	0	0	15
Primitive responses	9	6	0	0	15
Incoherent responses	4	11	0	0	15
Motor Conditional Reflexes					
First reflex in first system	8	7	0	0	15
Second reflex in first system	11	1	0	3	15
Reflex in second system	13	2	0	0	15
Reaction times	8	7	0	0	15
After-inhibitions	1	11	3	0	15
Extinction	13	2	0	0	15
Restoration	8	7	0	0	15
Differentiation	1	11	3	0	15
Reversal of negative reflexes	6	5	4	0	15
Reversal of positive reflexes	4	7	4	0	15
Description of performances	6	9	0	0	15
Unstable reflexes	10	5	0	0	15
Extrasignaling reactions	11	4	0	0	15
Continuous pressing	10	5	0	0	15
Autonomic Reactions					
Vascular curve	15	0	0	0	15
Respiratory curve	14	1	0	0	15
Respiratory and vascular dissociation	9	6	0	0	15
Vascular responses to cold	1	14	0	0	15
Vascular responses to calculation	10	5	0	0	15
Effects of pathodynamic structures	11	4	0	0	15
Defensive Reflexes					
Current tolerance	11	4	0	0	15
Motor exhaustion	9	6	0	0	15
Autonomic exhaustion	13	2	0	0	15
Dissociations	6	9	0	0	15
Number of inadequate responses		218			
Number of adequate responses	244				
Number of too difficult tasks			15		

All fifteen cases could be studied experimentally. There was considerably less influence of pathodynamic structures on the respiratory and vascular curves than in the affect-laden paraphrenia. There was more autonomic dissociation. Most cases showed vascular responses to calculation. In all but one case there was a strong inhibition of the unconditional vascular responses to cold.

With defensive reflexes seven cases had signs of inhibition of the unconditional responses. Nine cases failed in one or more trials to avoid the electrical stimulation after instruction. The whole group had more dissociative reactions than the affect-laden paraphrenias.

The ability to form conditional reflexes in the first signaling system was not essentially different from normals. In about one-half of the cases the reaction times showed irregular prolongations. Some cases were not able to form stable conditional reflexes, and most cases also had strong after-inhibition. The schizophasias have several signs of passive inhibition of the first signaling system. Extinction was easily performed in most cases. Only one case could differentiate adequately, which indicates a severe impairment of active inhibition. The majority of cases were unable to carry out adequately the reversal of negative and positive reflexes. Five cases had either extra-signaling reactions or continuous pressing as a response to the signals. This indicates that there tends to be considerable inertia of the nervous processes in schizophasia. Nine cases could not describe adequately their motor performances, which shows considerable dissociation in the interaction of the signaling systems.

With the association experiment reproduction was impaired in most cases. The mean as well as the median reaction times were usually prolonged. There was a strong tendency to react with echolalic and multiword responses. Only two had a number of higher responses within the limits of the normal controls and six had more primitive reactions than the normal sample. The majority had incoherent responses, and some cases even several such responses. There is a strong tendency to dissociative reactions in the second signaling system, which clinically runs parallel with the disturbances of the speech. There is inhibition and inertia of the second signaling system.

Summarizing the experimental data, the schizophasias are less influenced by pathodynamic structures ($P < 0.02$),[*] and there is more general impairment ($P < 0.001$) and more dissociative phenomena ($P < 0.01$) than in the affect-laden paraphrenias. There is considerable inertia of the nervous processes, weakness of active inhibition and predominance of passive inhibition at all levels of the higher nervous activity. It can be seen from the table that there are great individual differences in the impairment of the higher nervous activity. Clinically there are variations in the degree of deterioration. The majority can be considered as mild paranoid defects.

Four patients received ataraxic drugs during the experimental investigation. None of them showed strong influences of pathodynamic structures. Altogether six have been treated with ataraxic drugs. All showed considerable improvement, which consisted in reduction of speech disturbances and excitation.

In conclusion it was found experimentally that the speech disturbances of schizophasias ran parallel with several signs of dissociation of the higher nervous activity. The effects of ataraxic drugs are comparatively good, which may be related to the tendency to periodicity in this form of schizophrenia. The genetic loading was mainly with affective psychoses and schizophasias. As several cases from the sample originally had good remissions and were considered to be affective psychoses, the hereditary factor may reflect a constitutional tendency to remissions.

3. Phonemic Paraphrenia

The phonemic paraphrenia corresponds to a large extent to the chronic *délire* with hallucinations of French authors (213, 222, 526).

In the chronic stage the verbal hallucinosis is the main psychotic trait. Often the voices are heard within the head. They often make comments on the thoughts. Sarró and co-workers found that in some cases the hallucinations were strongly affectively col-

---

[*]The level of statistical significance is determined by the chi-square method. This method is used below, except for some comparisons of the repeatedly studied patients with the sign test.

ored. In other cases they had more the character of mental automatisms (171, 790). Expansive ideas are not found in such patients. In the present sample practically all cases were in open wards, had good working ability and could carry on an orderly conversation. It is justified to consider this form of schizophrenia as a slight defect.

The differential diagnosis is mainly from the hypochondriacal and the affect-laden paraphrenias. Leonhard says the hallucinations in hypochondriacal paraphrenia are usually more elementary, less bound up with personal feelings and experiences (234, 236, 537). Decisive for the diagnosis of a hypochondriacal paraphrenia is the presence of haptic hallucinations, which are absent in the phonemic paraphrenia. Patients with phonemic paraphrenia are regularly euphoric, but the hypochondriacal paraphrenias tend to be depressed. As patients with phonemic paraphrenia often believe that the voices come from persons around them, they may from time to time show hostile attitudes. Their well-ordered behavior may give some resemblance to the behavior of affect-laden paraphrenia. If the typical form of hallucinosis can be found, the diagnosis can be established. Here is a problem, since many patients with phonemic paraphrenia are so well aware of the way other persons regard their voices, that they will not talk about their inner experiences unless good contact is obtained through several interviews.

The present series consists of twenty-one cases with phonemic paraphrenia. The average age of onset was at 36 years—comparatively high. The average observation period was 17.9 years. All cases are definite schizophrenias. Eight had recurring courses and only a few had originally been considered to be non-schizophrenic conditions. The onset had been gradual. In ten cases precipitating factors were found in the case histories. The prepsychotic personalities were variable. Four had self-assertive, two schizoid and five balanced premorbid personalities. Twelve cases started as systematized paranoid psychoses with the symptom complex of "Faseln." In the remaining nine cases projection symptoms dominated the clinical picture during the initial stage. Only one had hebephrenic and two had catatonic traits during the acute stage.

Nearly all had ideas of reference or suspiciousness as the first signs of the illness. Typical schizophrenic delusions (331) were found during the acute stage in nine cases. Affective blunting was as a rule absent when the patients entered the hospital. From the beginning all had auditory hallucinations, which dominated the clinical picture. Eleven cases had haptic hallucinations, which disappeared during the further course of the disease.

Twelve relatives were probably psychotic. Seven case histories were available. Two had affective psychoses and five were schizophrenias with slight paranoid defect, but in only two of them the diagnosis of phonemic paraphrenia could be established. It may be concluded that the relatives of this group show a tendency to develop slight paranoid defects.

The results of the experimental investigations are presented in Table 3.

Nineteen cases could be studied experimentally. With the association experiment the findings are rather similiar to the affect-laden paraphrenias. Reproduction was clearly impaired in only five cases. Most cases had prolonged reaction times, echolalic responses and multiword responses. The majority had few higher responses. The majority of these patients did not show any greater primitive reactions than the normals. Incoherent responses were only found in two cases. The main disorders of the second signaling system are passive inhibition and inertia.

Conditional motor reflexes in the first and second signaling systems were formed practically as rapidly as in the normal sample. The reaction times were mostly short and regular. There was a considerable tendency to after-inhibitions, which indicates a predominance of the passive inhibition in the first signaling system. All cases were able to form stable motor reflexes. Extinction was mostly easily performed, but most cases failed with the differentiation. The internal inhibition tended to be impaired. Restoration could be performed adequately in one-half of the cases. Only eight cases could adequately manage the reversal of negative as well as of positive reflexes. There is an inertia of the nervous processes, but only in one case was there a major abnormality in the form of extra-signaling reactions or continuous pressing. Eight

TABLE 3
PHONEMIC PARAPHRENIA

	Adequate Responses	Inadequate Responses	Too Difficult Tasks	No Information	Total Patients
Associations					
Reproduction	12	5	0	2	19
Mean reaction times	6	11	0	2	19
Median reaction times	5	12	0	2	19
Echolalic responses	5	12	0	2	19
Multiword responses	4	13	0	2	19
Higher responses	2	15	0	2	19
Primitive responses	14	3	0	2	19
Incoherent responses	15	2	0	2	19
Motor Conditional Reflexes					
First reflex in first system	11	7	0	1	19
Second reflex in first system	16	2	0	1	19
Reflex in second system	17	1	0	1	19
Reaction times	12	6	0	1	19
After-inhibitions	4	14	0	1	19
Extinction	16	2	0	1	19
Restoration	9	9	0	1	19
Differentiation	5	13	0	1	19
Reversal of negative reflexes	11	6	1	1	19
Reversal of positive reflexes	11	6	1	1	19
Description of performances	8	10	0	1	19
Unstable reflexes	18	0	0	1	19
Extrasignaling reactions	17	1	0	1	19
Continuous pressing	17	1	0	1	19
Autonomic Reactions					
Vascular curve	19	0	0	0	19
Respiratory curve	17	2	0	0	19
Respiratory and vascular dissociation	11	8	0	0	19
Vascular responses to cold	8	11	0	0	19
Vascular responses to calculation	13	6	0	0	19
Effects of pathodynamic structures	10	9	0	0	19
Defensive Reflexes					
Current tolerance	9	8	0	2	19
Motor exhaustion	8	9	0	2	19
Autonomic exhaustion	14	3	0	2	19
Dissociations	10	7	0	2	19
Number of inadequate responses		214			
Number of adequate responses	354				
Number of too difficult tasks			2		

cases could adequately describe their motor performances, which shows some dissociation in the interaction of the signaling systems.

The unconditional responses to electrical stimulation showed signs of inhibition in nine cases. Seven cases failed in one or more trials to avoid the electrical stimulation after instruction.

The plethysmographic curve in the majority of cases showed a zero curve from the beginning, and in nine cases there were signs of autonomic dissociation. Eight cases gave vascular responses to unconditional cold stimulation and thirteen to calculation. Only two cases gave no responses to pathodynamic structures, and nine gave violent autonomic reactions similiar to those observed in the affect-laden paraphrenias.

The experimental findings show the phonemic paraphrenias have disturbances of the higher nervous activity similiar to those of the affect-laden paraphrenias, but a smaller proportion of adequate responses. There are strong influences of pathodynamic structures, slight dissociative phenomena, inertia of the nervous processes, weakness of internal inhibition and predominance of passive inhibition at all three levels of the higher nervous activity.

At the time of the experimental investigation five cases received ataraxic drugs. As two of them had violent autonomic reactions to pathodynamic structures, the drugs can not account for the slight effects of such structures in the seven untreated cases. Altogether eleven cases have received ataraxic drugs during the period of observation, and nine of them showed considerable improvement. In none of the cases did the typical hallucinations disappear, but the patients paid much less attention to them.

In conclusion it is assumed that the phonemic paraphrenias have a certain resemblance to the affect-laden paraphrenias both experimentally and clinically. In the same way as the delusions play a dominant role in the latter, the comparatively isolated symptoms in the form of a special type of hallucinations dominate the clinical picture of phonemic paraphrenia. Experimentally both types of schizophrenia also had slight general disturbances of the higher, nervous activity, with slight dissociative phenomena, but yet the pathodynamic structures had a considerable effect in the experimental situation. They are also favorably influenced by ataraxic drugs. Constitutional factors must be of importance for the course of the disease, as most relatives of the phonemic paraphrenias also develop slight paranoid defects.

4. Hypochondriacal Paraphrenia

The dominating symptoms of this group are the bodily sensations, which always are accompanied by auditory hallucinations (236, 537, 603).

The hypochondriacal paraphrenias usually have a depressive mood and seem to suffer severely from their symptoms. In part 3 of this chapter the main differentiation from phonemic paraphrenia is mentioned. The affect-laden paraphrenic may also have bodily sensations, but if these sensations are combined with auditory hallucinations, one probably has a hypochondriacal paraphrenic. In the fantastic paraphrenia bodily sensations are regularly present. If the sensations are combined with expansive ideas or other symptoms, which in part 6 of this chapter are considered as characteristic of fantastic paraphrenia, then the differential diagnosis can be established. In the fantastic cases the mood is regularly euphoric in contrast to the hypochondriacal paraphrenias.

In the present series there were eighteen patients with hypochondriacal paraphrenia. The majority were in open or half-open wards. They had a good working ability and could carry on an ordered conversation. In their total behavior they can be characterized as slight paranoid defects.

The average age of onset is 35.2 years, practically the same as in the phonemic paraphrenia. The average observation period was 14.6 years. All are definite schizophrenias, and only one case had a recurring course. Two cases were originally considered to be non-schizophrenic psychoses.

The onset had been insidious with ideas of reference and suspiciousness, as in the phonemic paraphrenia. The prepsychotic personalities were variable. Six had self-assertive, four schizoid and three balanced premorbid personalities. In seven cases precipitating factors were found in the case histories.

Six cases started as systematized paranoid psychoses with the symptom complex of *"Faseln."* In the remaining cases the mental automatisms had dominated the initial stage. Affective blunting was present in four cases from the beginning, and nine cases started with a depressive mood. Five cases had typical schizophrenic delusions, and in ten cases hypochondriacal ideas were already noticed at the onset. All cases had auditory hallucinations in the acute stage and in fourteen cases haptic hallucinations were also present.

Eighteen relatives were probably psychotic. For eight of them case histories were available. One had an affective psychosis and seven were schizophrenics with slight paranoid defects. As five of these had hypochondriacal paraphrenias, there appears to be a strong tendency among the relatives to develop similiar defects.

The results of the experimental investigations are shown in Table 4.

Sixteen cases were studied experimentally. Two refused investigation. With the association test the findings were rather similiar to those in phonemic paraphrenia. The majority could reproduce adequately. Most cases had prolonged reaction times, echolalic and multiword responses. Only two had as many higher responses as in the normal sample, but the majority had no more primitive reactions than in the normals. Only four had incoherent reactions. The functions of the second signaling systems are characterized by inhibition and inertia.

The ability to form motor conditional reflexes in the first and second signaling system was not essentially different from the sample of normals. Most patients showed tendencies to inhibition of the first signaling system in the form of after-inhibitions, and in seven patients the reaction times were definitely prolonged and irregular. All but one could form stable conditional reflexes. Extinction of the conditional reflex occurred rapidly in most cases, but the majority had severe impairment of differentiation. Restoration could be adequately performed in four cases, and only three cases could adequately bring about the reversal of negative as well as of positive reflexes. Two cases had major signs of inertia such as extra-signaling reactions or continuous pressing. One half of the patients were not able to describe adequately their motor performances. The unconditional responses to electrical stimulation show signs of inhibition in twelve cases. They were at most

TABLE 4
Hypochondriacal Paraphrenia

	Adequate Responses	Inadequate Responses	Too Difficult Tasks	No Information	Total Patients
Associations					
Reproduction	9	5	2	0	16
Mean reaction times	5	11	0	0	16
Median reaction times	4	12	0	0	16
Echolalic responses	3	13	0	0	16
Multiword responses	4	12	0	0	16
Higher responses	2	14	0	0	16
Primitive responses	10	6	0	0	16
Incoherent responses	12	4	0	0	16
Motor Conditional Reflexes					
First reflex in first system	9	7	0	0	16
Second reflex in first system	14	1	0	1	16
Reflex in second system	15	1	0	0	16
Reaction times	9	7	0	0	16
After-inhibitions	3	13	0	0	16
Extinction	11	4	1	0	16
Restoration	4	11	1	0	16
Differentiation	4	11	1	0	16
Reversal of negative reflexes	6	7	3	0	16
Reversal of positive reflexes	7	6	3	0	16
Description of performances	8	8	0	0	16
Unstable reflexes	15	1	0	0	16
Extrasignaling reactions	15	1	0	0	16
Continuous pressing	15	1	0	0	16
Autonomic Reactions					
Vascular curve	16	0	0	0	16
Respiratory curve	16	0	0	0	16
Respiratory and vascular dissociation	11	5	0	0	16
Vascular responses to cold	3	13	0	0	16
Vascular responses to calculation	10	6	0	0	16
Effects of pathodynamic structures	11	5	0	0	16
Defensive Reflexes					
Current tolerance	6	10	0	0	16
Motor exhaustion	6	10	0	0	16
Autonomic exhaustion	7	9	0	0	16
Dissociations	7	9	0	0	16
Number of inadequate responses		223			
Number of adequate responses	277				
Number of too difficult tasks			11		

attempts able to avoid the electrical stimulation after instruction, but nine of them have one or more reactions, when they fail.

In all cases the plethysmogram gave a zero curve from the beginning. Five cases had signs of autonomic dissociation. Although the majority showed no vascular reaction to unconditional cold stimulation, they tended to give some responses to calculation. There were clearly patterned responses to words stimulating the pathodynamic structures in all but one case, and in five cases violent autonomic responses were observed.

The experimental data show that the general impairment of the higher nervous activity is slight in the hypochondriacal paraphrenia, but greater than in the phonemic paraphrenia ($P < 0.02$). The influences of pathodynamic structures are not so strong as in the latter. The dissociative phenomena are slight. There is an inertia of the nervous processes, weakness of internal inhibition and predominance of passive inhibition in all three levels of the higher nervous activity.

During the period of the experimental investigation six patients received ataraxic drugs. As only two of these showed violent autonomic reactions to pathodynamic structures it may be that the drugs decrease the autonomic concomitants of the pathodynamic structures. During the observation period thirteen have been treated with ataraxic drugs, and ten improved considerably. As in phonemic paraphrenia the characteristic symptoms did not disappear, but the affective coloring was reduced. Case 14044 is leucotomized and has comparatively severe disturbances of the higher nervous activity.

The hypochondriacal paraphrenias resemble very much the phonemic paraphrenias with their comparatively isolated psychotic symptoms, the slight general impairment of the nervous activity and the influences of pathodynamic structures. Symptomatologically the mental automatisms (170, 331, 758) dominate the acute stage of the hypochondriacal paraphrenias more than in the phonemic paraphrenia. In the further course of the illness the mental automatisms tend to be transformed into affect-laden delusions and hallucinations. Phenomenologically one can regard the hallucinations as well as the hypochondriacal sensations as a continuation of symptoms already present in the beginning of the disease. Haptic hallucinations are also often present during the acute stages of the phonemic paraphrenia, and later disappear. Considering the genetic aspects, it is probable that hereditary factors play an important role in determining the differences in the later course of the illness.

5. Expansive and Confabulatory Paraphrenias

In expansive paraphrenia expansive behavior and expansive ideas dominate the clinical picture (236, 537, 603). Such ideas have a mild affective coloring, and the general mood is euphoric. Confabulatory paraphrenias are also euphoric. Their main characteristic is that they tell fantastic stories about personal experiences (537, 812). Mentioned in part two of this chapter, the schizophasias also have a euphoric mood, and occasionally during psychotic exacerbations may mention expansive ideas. In contrast to the schizophasias, the expansive and confabulatory cases have less disturbances of speech and more permanent tendency to expansive behavior and confabulations. Even more important is the differential diagnosis from fantastic paraphrenia. In the present material, all cases which not only have comparatively isolated expansive symptoms or confabulation, but also have symptoms characteristic of fantastic paraphrenia are classified in this group. One has the impression that there are no sharp boundaries between these forms, which all have some expansive traits.

In the present series there were ten expansive cases and four confabulatory cases. In the confabulatory cases there were some expansive traits present, and the author finds it practical to combine these cases in an expansive-confabulatory group. Kraepelin finds the expansive paraphrenia often shows confabulations. These two forms were so similiar that in his first study Leonhard included the confabulatory cases in his group of expansive paraphrenias (486, 526).

The working ability of the patients in this group was slight. Half of them were in closed wards. They had difficulties in carrying on an ordered conversation, and the total impression was one of a severe deterioration.

The average age of onset was 32.6 years and the average observation period 18.6 years. Three had self-assertive, four schizoid and three balanced prepsychotic personalities. Precipitating factors could be found in six cases. Only in four cases were the initial symptoms ideas of reference or suspiciousness. Two cases started as systematized paranoid psychoses with the symptom complex of "*Faseln.*" Six cases had hebephrenic or catatonic traits at onset, and mental automatisms played a dominating role in the clinical picture during the acute stage. Expansive ideas were present in eight cases at an early stage of the disease. All had auditory hallucinations and seven also haptic hallucinations.

Eleven relatives were probably psychotic. For eight of them case histories were available. One had an affective psychosis. The remaining seven cases were schizophrenias: One catatonic defect, three slight paranoid defects and three severe paranoid defects. There were no relatives with confabulatory paraphrenia, but one patient with a confabulatory paraphrenia had a relative with an expansive paraphrenia. It seems that the genetic factor in this group is rather unspecific, and shows itself as a stronger tendency to more severe paranoid defects than in the relatives of patients with slight paranoid defects.

The results of the experimental investigations are presented in Table 5.

Thirteen cases have been studied experimentally. With the association test only two cases were able to reproduce their responses adequately. Four patients found this task was too difficult even to try. Most cases had prolonged reaction times, echolalic and multiword responses. None were able to respond with a number of higher reactions within the limits of the normal sample. All but one had incoherent responses, and most had several such reactions. Ten had more primitive reactions than found in the normal sample. The associative functions were severely impaired with marked dissociations of the second signaling system.

The ability to form conditional reflexes in the first and second signaling systems was only slightly inferior to that of the normal sample. There were strong after-inhibitions. All but one case had long fluctuating reaction times, and seven were not even able to form stable conditional reflexes. There was a considerably stronger inhibition of the functions of the first signaling system than in the slighter paranoid defects. Only six could carry out extinction

TABLE 5
Expansive and Confabulatory Paraphrenia

	Adequate Responses	Inadequate Responses	Too Difficult Tasks	No Information	Total Patients
Associations					
Reproduction	2	7	4	0	13
Mean reaction times	8	5	0	0	13
Median reaction times	4	9	0	0	13
Echolalic responses	4	9	0	0	13
Multiword responses	6	7	0	0	13
Higher responses	0	13	0	0	13
Primitive responses	3	10	0	0	13
Incoherent responses	1	12	0	0	13
Motor Conditional Reflexes					
First reflex in first system	4	9	0	0	13
Second reflex in first system	8	2	0	3	13
Reflex in second system	12	1	0	0	13
Reaction times	1	12	0	0	13
After-inhibitions	1	12	0	0	13
Extinction	6	4	3	0	13
Restoration	3	7	3	0	13
Differentiation	0	9	4	0	13
Reversal of negative reflexes	1	7	5	0	13
Reversal of positive reflexes	1	5	7	0	13
Description of performances	1	12	0	0	13
Unstable reflexes	6	7	0	0	13
Extrasignaling reactions	11	2	0	0	13
Continuous pressing	9	4	0	0	13
Autonomic Reactions					
Vascular curve	10	3	0	0	13
Respiratory curve	10	3	0	0	13
Respiratory and vascular dissociation	5	8	0	0	13
Vascular responses to cold	3	10	0	0	13
Vascular responses to calculation	3	9	0	1	13
Effects of pathodynamic structures	10	3	0	0	13
Defensive Reflexes					
Current tolerance	5	8	0	0	13
Motor exhaustion	5	8	0	0	13
Autonomic exhaustion	7	6	0	0	13
Dissociations	5	8	0	0	13
Number of inadequate responses		231			
Number of adequate responses	155				
Number of too difficult tasks			26		

adequately, and all failed with the differentiation. The internal inhibition was more impaired than in the slight paranoid defects. In several cases the reversal of the reflexes was a too difficult a task. None could adequately reverse the negative as well as the positive reflexes. Major signs of inertia such as extra-signaling reactions or continuous pressing were present in five cases. There is also considerable inertia of the nervous processes in this group. Only one case could give fairly adequate description of the motor performances. The remainder failed in this task. This shows that there are severe dissociations between the signaling systems.

The unconditional reactions to electrical stimulation were severely exhausted in most cases, but five cases had no signs of unconditional inhibition. The ability to avoid electrical stimulation through instruction is considerably more impaired than in the slight paranoid defects, since several failures occurred in most cases, but five were able to perform this task adequately.

It was noticed that in four cases there were chaotic plethysmograms or arrhythmic respiratory curves. Eight cases had dissociations between the respiratory and vascular curves. There is more vegetative dissociation than in the slight paranoid defects. Most cases did not give responses to unconditional cold stimulation nor to calculation. The majority showed some responses to pathodynamic structures, but only three gave violent reactions.

The experimental data show there is much more impairment of the higher nervous activity in this group than in the slight paranoid defects ($P < 0.001$). The influences of pathodynamic structures are smaller, and the dissociative phenomena are stronger ($P < 0.001$). There is more inertia of the nervous processes ($P < 0.001$), greater impairment of internal inhibition ($P < 0.001$) and greater predominance of the passive inhibition in all three levels of the higher nervous activity ($P < 0.001$).

Only one case received ataraxic drugs during the time of the experimental investigation. Five were treated with ataraxic drugs at other times, three with moderate improvement and two with no effect. The ataraxic drugs have less effect in this group than in the slight paranoid defects (groups 1-4).

It is concluded that for the group of expansive and confabulatory paraphrenias the severe clinical deterioration is accompanied by greater impairment of the higher nervous activity as shown in the experimental investigation than in the slight paranoid defects. The next chapter illustrates that during the acute stage, the hebephrenic and catatonic cases have greater impairment of the higher nervous activity than the paranoid cases. In the present series 6 patients during the acute stage had hebephrenic or catatonic traits, whereas the slighter paranoid defects only exceptionally showed hebephrenic or catatonic traits during the acute stage. There is a possibility that one of the elements favoring an expansive development is a severe impairment of nervous functions already from the start. The expansive group does not have a genetic loading with affective psychoses and slight paranoid defects similiar to that in the groups in the previous parts of this chapter.

6. Fantastic Paraphrenia

The descriptions of fantastic paraphrenia given by Leonhard have been elaborated in further detail by Sarró (236, 526, 537, 790, 791). Sarró stresses that in fantastic paraphrenia there are a number of clinical phenomena which tend to be combined. Such factors are: 1) Expansive ideas. 2) Somatic sensations, often of a grotesque and fantastic character in contrast to all physical laws, such as animals passing through the body or the brain being torn out and put in again. The hypochondriacal paraphrenias usually have sufficient self-criticism not to express ideas which are obviously absurd. 3) Mass phenomena. Thousands of people may be heard crying or may be seen in visual hallucinations. Often this is described as mass murder. 4) Misidentification of persons. The patients often believe that they have met persons in their surroundings previously under other names. 5) The patients can talk about travels in other countries or even to the moon or stars, which is also possible in confabulatory paraphrenia. 6) The borders between life and death are vanished. The patients can say that they have been dead and buried, and have come back to life again. 7) Age and time lose their proportions. The patients can say that they are millions of years old and that they have lived in the Stone Age. 8) Nature may seem to be alive like human beings, so that birds and trees speak.

According to Sarró the fantastic paraphrenia has a rather coherent symptomatology, expressing some sort of cosmic-anthropomorphological form of existence. He mentions that the Spanish patients are less absurd in their behavior than the Germans described by Leonhard. In the author's experience Norwegian and English fantastic paraphrenias have the symptoms as described by Sarró. This symptomatology can also be interpreted as due to severe impairment of the ability to distinguish between the possible and impossible, which is completely independent of any special philosophical form of existence. In the present series the fantastic symptom complexes are usually incomplete. There is a transition to the more monosymptomatic expansive and confabulatory cases, where general behavior and the ability to carry on an ordered conversation are improved. This is in contrast to the incoherent paraphrenias, where no ordered speech is possible. From the distorted speech in the incoherent paraphrenia there is the impression that some of them actually have expansive ideas. As they are unable to carry on a conversation, one can not verify this. Leonhard says that the affect-laden paraphrenias often develop fantastic traits, but that the affective anchoring of the delusions helps to establish the differential diagnosis. In the author's experience it is very difficult to estimate the degree of the affect, and all cases with the fantastic symptom complexes were classified in the fantastic group. Sometimes even in the most affectively blunted cases of fantastic paraphrenia, elementary rage outbursts are frequent. In cases starting with strongly affectively laden systematic delusions with a fantastic development, there is always some affective blunting and euphoria in between the affective outbursts.

In the present sample there are twenty-three cases with fantastic paraphrenia. The majority lived in wards for disturbed cases and nursing cases. Only one was in an open ward. Most of them were able to take care of themselves. Twelve had comparatively good working abilities, especially to help with the work in their ward, where the demands as to a well-ordered general behavior are not great. They have difficulties in carrying on an ordered conversation, and in their general behavior they seem to be more deteriorated than the former types.

The average age of onset was 33.8 years, and the average observation period is 26.1 years. In the majority of the cases the onset had been insidious, and only three had had recurring courses. Precipitating factors were mentioned in the case histories of nine patients. Seven cases had self-assertive, seven schizoid and only one balanced prepsychotic personality. Nine cases started as systematized paranoid psychoses with the symptom complex of "*Faseln.*" Six had catatonic traits and three hebephrenic traits during the acute stage. In nearly one half of the cases affective blunting was present from the beginning. Twelve had expansive ideas during the acute stage. All had auditory hallucinations. The majority also had haptic hallucinations from the beginning of the disease. Hypochondriacal ideas were present in only a few of the cases during the acute stage. These psychoses had projection symptoms in the beginning of the psychosis.

Eleven relatives were probably psychotic. Five case histories were obtained, and all five cases had fantastic paraphrenias. This would indicate that the relatives have a strong tendency towards homologous inheritance.

The results of the experimental investigations are presented in Table 6.

Sixteen patients were studied experimentally. Seven cases were so irritable and uncooperative in other ways that it was impossible to carry out the experimental investigation. Apparently general irritability rather than motivated arguments caused a lack of cooperation.

With the association test the disturbances were even greater than in the expansive group. Only two could reproduce adequately, thirteen had prolongations of mean and median reaction times. Most cases had several echolalic and multiword responses. Three had a number of primitive reactions and there were no higher responses within the limits of the normal sample. All but one had incoherent responses. The incoherent responses of the expansive group were predominantly mediate associations. Five of the fantastic cases also responded with incoherent speech, which indicates a stronger dissociation in the second signaling system.

The ability to form conditional motor reflexes in the first and second signaling system is slightly inferior to that of the normals.

TABLE 6
Fantastic Paraphrenia

	Adequate Responses	Inadequate Responses	Too Difficult Tasks	No Information	Total Patients
Associations					
Reproduction	2	7	7	0	16
Mean reaction times	3	13	0	0	16
Median reaction times	3	13	0	0	16
Echolalic responses	2	14	0	0	16
Multiword responses	3	13	0	0	16
Higher responses	0	16	0	0	16
Primitive responses	3	13	0	0	16
Incoherent responses	1	15	0	0	16
Motor Conditional Reflexes					
First reflex in first system	5	11	0	0	16
Second reflex in first system	5	1	0	10	16
Reflex in second system	15	1	0	0	16
Reaction times	2	14	0	0	16
After-inhibitions	1	6	9	0	16
Extinction	5	5	6	0	16
Restoration	3	6	7	0	16
Differentiation	0	6	10	0	16
Reversal of negative reflexes	2	3	11	0	16
Reversal of positive reflexes	2	3	11	0	16
Description of performances	3	13	0	0	16
Unstable reflexes	8	8	0	0	16
Extrasignaling reactions	11	5	0	0	16
Continuous pressing	8	8	0	0	16
Autonomic Reactions					
Vascular curve	12	4	0	0	16
Respiratory curve	12	4	0	0	16
Respiratory and vascular dissociation	3	13	0	0	16
Vascular responses to cold	1	15	0	0	16
Vascular responses to calculation	8	7	0	1	16
Effects of pathodynamic structures	11	5	0	0	16
Defensive Reflexes					
Current tolerance	7	9	0	0	16
Motor exhaustion	6	10	0	0	16
Autonomic exhaustion	8	8	0	0	16
Dissociations	3	12	0	1	16
Number of inadequate responses		281			
Number of adequate responses	158				
Number of too difficult tasks			61		

Only two reacted with short and regular reaction times, and eight were not even able to form stable motor conditional reflexes. Because of the long and varying reaction times and instability of the reflexes, tests of after-inhibition were too difficult for most cases. In the first signaling system there was a considerably stronger predominance of passive inhibition than in the slight paranoid defects. Extinction could be adequately performed in only five cases. None succeeded in differentiation, and for the majority this task was too difficult even to try. There is a marked weakness of internal inhibition. Only three cases could adequately carry out restoration, and for the majority the task of reversal of the negative and positive reflexes was too difficult. Major signs of inertia of the nervous processes such as extra-signaling reactions and continuous pressing were observed in eight cases. This shows clearly the strong tendency to inertia of the nervous processes. Three were able to describe adequately their motor performances.

Several cases had massive inhibition of the unconditional responses to electrical stimulation, but five had no signs of such inhibition. Three cases only were able to avoid the electrical stimulation upon instruction, and the majority failed in several trials in this task. There is a considerable dissociation between the unconditional reflexes and the second signaling system.

The plethysmogram in twelve cases gave a zero curve at once, and in four cases was completely chaotic. In four cases there were irregular respiratory rhythms. Dissociations between the respiratory and vascular curves were observed in thirteen cases. There are signs of severe autonomic dissociation in the group of fantastic paraphrenia. The vascular responses to unconditional cold stimulation were strongly inhibited in all but one case. About one-half of the cases gave vascular responses to calculation. Twelve cases showed autonomic reactions to pathodynamic structures, which were violent reactions in five cases. Pathodynamic structures tend to be effective, but not as marked as in the slighter paranoid defects.

In the experimental data, there is considerably more impairment of the higher nervous activity in fantastic paraphrenia than in the slight paranoid defects ($P < 0.001$) and even more than in the expansive-confabulatory group. The influences of pathodynamic structures are less than in the slight paranoid defects, and there are more dissociative phenomena ($P < 0.001$). There is strong inertia of the nervous processes, weakness of internal inhibition and passive inhibition of all three levels of the higher nervous activity. In particular the reactions of the first signaling system show greater passive inhibition than in the slight paranoid defects ($P < 0.001$). The quality of the reactions in the second signaling system is much inferior to that of the slight paranoid defects (< 0.001).

Five patients received ataraxic drugs at the time of the experimental investigations. As none had violent responses to pathodynamic structures, it is possible that the drugs have reduced the autonomic component of these structures. Altogether eight cases have been treated with ataraxic drugs. Three showed moderate improvement and in five the treatment had no effect.

Perhaps the severe impairment of the second signaling system is the physiological basis for the lack of critical awareness of their psychotic ideas in the fantastic paraphrenia. Another factor is the extreme inhibition of the first signaling system, and the unconditional responses combined with strong dissociations, which also might contribute to the great incongruity between psychotic ideas and reality. In the schizophasias, who, clinically, as well as experimentally, also have a great dissociation of speech, the well-ordered behavior is correlated with better quality in the associative reactions. There is less impairment of the unconditional reflexes and the reflexes in the first and second signaling system.

As to the clinical development of fantastic ideas, it is noted that expansive ideas are not as frequent in the fantastic cases as in other paranoid cases during the acute stage. Compared with the slighter paranoid defects more cases have hebephrenic or catatonic traits, affective blunting or incoherence at the initial stage of the psychosis. The next chapter demonstrates that catatonic and hebephrenic traits in acute stages have more pronounced dissociative phenomena and inhibitions of the first signaling system than the purely paranoid cases. It is believed that dissociative disturbances from the beginning of the psychosis are of greater importance than in the slighter paranoid defects. Another factor contributing to the fantastic course is probably heredity, because relatives of the fantastic paraphrenics tend to develop similiar defects. The severe deterioration may be related to the comparatively long observation periods.

7. Incoherent Paraphrenia

Incoherent paraphrenia is characterized by the severe dissociation of speech, which makes an ordered conversation impossible (236, 526, 537). Kleist and Schwab call such cases thought-confused schizophrenias, whereas they design the schizophasics as speech-confused (433). In contrast to the schizophasias the incoherent paraphrenias are disordered in general behavior, as well as in speech. Another central symptom is a massive auditory hallucinosis. The patients are constantly absorbed by hallucinatory experiences, pay little attention to the surroundings, seldom answer questions, but talk and shout, looking at the walls or the ceiling, as if quarreling with invisible people. They can easily be separated from the slighter paranoid defects with auditory hallucinations because of the speech incoherence. They may resemble the shallow hebephrenias, who have their hallucinatory periods, but here verbal communication is possible. The speech-inactive catatonics like the incoherent paraphrenics are also absorbed by their hallucinatory experiences. Here the presence of catatonic symptoms will help to establish the differential diagnosis.

In the present series there are eighteen cases with incoherent paraphrenia. The average age of onset is 28.0 years and the average observation period 31.7 years. These cases started at an earlier age than the other paranoid defects and also had a longer observation period. Only two cases had recurring courses. Three had self-assertive, ten schizoid and three balanced prepsychotic personalities. Precipitating factors were found in five cases. In fifteen cases the initial stage showed the symptom complex of "*Sprunghaftigkeit*," eight cases had hebephrenic and seven catatonic traits. In ten cases an emotional blunting was present nearly from the start. Expansive ideas were found in five cases. In most cases incoherence was already found in the acute stage. Auditory hallucinations were consistently present, and visual hallucinations more frequent than haptic hallucinations. All patients were in disturbed wards. They had no working ability and needed help in all ways, with dressing, eating and cleanliness. The total impression is that the incoherent paraphrenics have the most severe defects of all paranoid subgroups.

Fourteen relatives were probably psychotic, and for nine of these case histories were available. One had an affective psychosis and the remaining eight were schizophrenics. One had a hebephrenic and one a catatonic defect and one a slight paranoid defect. Five had severe paranoid defects, and one of them was probably an incoherent paraphrenic.

The results of the experimental investigations are given on Table 7.

Fifteen cases were studied experimentally. Three cases were so disturbed in their behavior that an experimental study was not possible.

With the association test the results were rather poor. None had adequate responses. All responded with some incoherent speech, echolalic, multiword and primitive responses. Only in one patient were a few higher responses observed. The quality of the reactions in the second signaling system is much inferior to that of the other groups of paranoid defects.

With conditional motor reflexes there was also a severe impairment of the higher nervous activity. Two developed conditional reflexes rapidly in the first signaling system, and seven could form reflexes in the second signaling system within the limits of the normal sample. None had short and regular reaction times, or stable conditional reflexes. Eight were not even able to develop motor conditional responses, and the tests of after-inhibition were too difficult in all cases. From the experimental data one can assume that there is a severe passive inhibition of the first signaling system. The more complicated tasks, such as differentiation and reversal of reflexes, were too difficult to try. Of these, two could make trials of extinction and restoration. Several patients had major signs of inertia such as extra-signaling reactions and continuous pressing. None of these patients could adequately describe the motor performances.

There was a strong tendency to inhibition of the unconditional responses to electrical stimulation, but four cases showed no signs of unconditional inhibition. One case was able to avoid electrical

TABLE 7
INCOHERENT PARAPHRENIA

	Adequate Responses	Inadequate Responses	Too Difficult Tasks	No Information	Total Patients
Associations					
Reproduction	0	3	12	0	15
Mean reaction times	0	15	0	0	15
Median reaction times	0	15	0	0	15
Echolalic responses	0	15	0	0	15
Multiword responses	0	15	0	0	15
Higher responses	0	15	0	0	15
Primitive responses	0	15	0	0	15
Incoherent responses	0	15	0	0	15
Motor Conditional Reflexes					
First reflex in first system	2	10	3	0	15
Second reflex in first system	7	5	3	0	15
Reflex in second system	7	5	3	0	15
Reaction times	0	12	3	0	15
After-inhibitions	0	0	15	0	15
Extinction	1	1	13	0	15
Restoration	0	1	14	0	15
Differentiation	0	0	15	0	15
Reversal of negative reflexes	0	0	15	0	15
Reversal of positive reflexes	0	0	15	0	15
Description of performances	0	12	3	0	15
Unstable reflexes	0	12	3	0	15
Extrasignaling reactions	4	8	3	0	15
Continuous pressing	2	10	3	0	15
Autonomic Reactions					
Vascular curve	11	4	0	0	15
Respiratory curve	5	10	0	0	15
Respiratory and vascular dissociation	1	14	0	0	15
Vascular responses to cold	2	13	0	0	15
Vascular responses to calculation	3	9	0	3	15
Effects of pathodynamic structures	15	0	0	0	15
Defensive Reflexes					
Current tolerance	8	7	0	0	15
Motor exhaustion	7	8	0	0	15
Autonomic exhaustion	7	8	0	0	15
Dissociations	1	14	0	0	15
Number of inadequate responses		271			
Number of adequate responses	83				
Number of too difficult tasks			123		

stimulation after instruction, and the majority failed in all trials to perform this task. The dissociation between unconditional reflexes and the second signaling system are much more severe in this group than in the other paranoid defects.

The plethysmographic curve in eleven cases had a zero form from the beginning and in four cases was chaotic. Respiratory arrhythmias were found in ten cases, and all but one had dissociations between the respiratory curve and the respiratory oscillations of the plethysmogram. This shows that the autonomic dissociation is especially severe in the incoherent paraphrenias. Most cases gave no vascular responses to unconditional cold stimulation nor to calculation. Effects of pathodynamic structures were noticed only in five cases, and no case showed violent autonomic responses.

In the experimental data, the severe clinical defects of the incoherent paraphrenics are accompanied by considerably greater impairment of the higher nervous activity than in other paranoid groups. Even a comparison with the fantastic paraphrenics shows greater ($P < 0.001$) general impairment. The influences of pathodynamic structures are slight or lacking. The dissociative phenomena are pronounced. There is severe passive inhibition of all three levels of the higher nervous activity, and the associative performances are very poor.

Four cases received ataraxic drugs at the time of the experimental investigation. These cases did not show experimental differences as compared with the untreated cases. Ten had been treated during the observation period with ataraxic drugs. In six the treatment had no effect and in four there was moderate improvement, which consisted in less nursing difficulties, but no change of the typical defect. It seems that the incoherent paraphrenics benefit very little from ataraxic drugs.

In the incoherent paraphrenias the severe clinical dissociations are paralleled by severe dissociative phenomena in the experimental studies. Even the poor verbal performances are responsible for an inability to express such complex ideas as are found in fantastic paraphrenia.

Among clinical factors in the acute stage indicating an incoherent course are hebephrenic and catatonic traits. The comparatively long observation period for most cases has possibly contributed to the large defect. In the family histories there seems to be a general tendency to the development of severe paranoid defects, but no specific predisposition to incoherent paraphrenia.

B. THE HEBEPHRENIC TYPES OF CHRONIC SCHIZOPHRENIA

8. Autistic Hebephrenia

Leonhard asserts that emotional blunting combined with an extreme autism are the most characteristic symptoms of the autistic hebephrenia. These patients actively shut themselves up, avoid all contacts with others and tend to reject attempts of others to communicate with them (236, 434, 435, 537). In his first studies Leonhard considered the autistic form to be a paranoid defect with some catatonic traits. Even the active seclusion from the external world, which appears to be combined with mistrust and suspiciousness, might indicate that paranoid ideas are present. These cannot be verified because of the unwillingness of the patients to speak about their inner experiences. As there often is absence of facial expression and the movements are awkward, they may also resemble catatonics (526). Leonhard, in his later studies, stressing the considerable emotional blunting, has considered the autistic schizophrenics to belong to the hebephrenics, where the affective disturbances are the central symptoms. In the author's experience the autistic hebephrenias resemble the eccentric hebephrenias very much. Both forms are usually irritable and dysphoric, and also the eccentric cases may seclude themselves and object to questions and attempts to obtain contact. Some affect-laden paraphrenias may also have a tendency to isolate themselves. In these cases one will find the mistrust bound up with delusions with strong affective loading, whereas the autistic hebephrenias appear to be unaffected by the events in their environment as long as they are left in peace.

In the present series there were fifteen autistic hebephrenias. The average age of onset was 31.3 years and the average observation period 19.7 years. Two cases had a recurring course. Precipitating factors were found in five cases. Two cases had self-assertive, eight schizoid and one balanced premorbid personality. During the acute stage eight had paranoid pictures dominated by projection phenomena. Five had paranoid-hebephrenic states and two were definite hebephrenias during the acute stage. Most cases started with ideas of suspiciousness as paranoid cases usually do, and six had typical schizophrenic delusions. Only in seven cases was emotional blunting the dominating affective disturbance during the acute stage. The others were generally depressed or elated and hallucinations were regularly present.

Nearly all autistic hebephrenias had a good working ability. Several did quite responsible work on their own in the hospital. Some worked like robots, as if concentration on the work was a way of avoiding disturbing contacts with other people. Because of their unwillingness to talk, it was difficult to estimate their intellectual capacities, but their good working ability indicated that they were not severely deteriorated. The majority were in open wards. Five were in wards for disturbed patients, mainly because of their extreme irritability and periodic aggressive behavior, which occurred when others tried to intrude upon them.

Eight relatives were probably psychotic. For six of them case histories were available. Four had affective psychoses. Two had schizophrenics and one a slight and one a severe paranoid defect. It appears that the autistic cases lack a similiar genetic loading.

The results of the experimental investigations are shown in Table 8.

The experimental data about the autistic hebephrenics are rather meagre. Eight of them, in spite of several attempts, refused to go to the experimental room. Three could be incompletely studied, and among the four who were studied with all four test methods, two refused during the first attempts. Five patients were studied experimentally with the association test. Their associative disturbances, as in the slighter paranoid defects, were mainly characterized by impaired reproduction, prolonged reaction times, echolalic and multiword responses. Approximately one-half of the responses were of the higher type. Four had incoherent reactions, but only a few mediate responses. They did not respond with incoherent speech, as did several of the severe paranoid defects.

With motor conditional reflexes their disturbances were also similiar to the slighter paranoid defects. All could form stable re-

TABLE 8
AUTISTIC HEBEPHRENIA

	Adequate Responses	Inadequate Responses	Too Difficult Tasks	No Information	Total Patients
Associations					
Reproduction	0	5	0	2	7
Mean reaction times	0	5	0	2	7
Median reaction times	1	4	0	2	7
Echolalic responses	1	4	0	2	7
Multiword responses	2	3	0	2	7
Higher responses	1	4	0	2	7
Primitive responses	2	3	0	2	7
Incoherent responses	1	4	0	2	7
Motor Conditional Reflexes					
First reflex in first system	4	1	0	2	7
Second reflex in first system	5	0	0	2	7
Reflex in second system	5	0	0	2	7
Reaction times	3	2	0	2	7
After-inhibitions	2	3	0	2	7
Extinction	4	1	0	2	7
Restoration	3	2	0	2	7
Differentiation	0	5	0	2	7
Reversal of negative reflexes	3	2	0	2	7
Reversal of positive reflexes	0	5	0	2	7
Description of performances	1	4	0	2	7
Unstable reflexes	5	0	0	2	7
Extrasignaling reactions	5	0	0	2	7
Continuous pressing	5	0	0	2	7
Autonomic Reactions					
Vascular curve	6	0	0	1	7
Respiratory curve	6	0	0	1	7
Respiratory and vascular dissociation	4	2	0	1	7
Vascular responses to cold	1	5	0	1	7
Vascular responses to calculation	1	4	0	2	7
Effects of pathodynamic structures	6	0	0	1	7
Defensive Reflexes					
Current tolerance	2	2	0	3	7
Motor exhaustion	2	2	0	3	7
Autonomic exhaustion	2	2	0	3	7
Dissociations	0	4	0	3	7
Number of inadequate responses		78			
Number of adequate responses	83				
Number of too difficult tasks			0		

flexes, and extra-signaling reactions and continuous pressing were not observed.

The responses tended to be exhausted to electrical stimulation. They were able to avoid the electrical stimulation after instruction, but none succeeded in avoiding the shock in all trials.

The plethysmogram in five cases gave a zero curve at once. One had oscillations of the third order. Also, one showed vascular responses to unconditional cold stimulation and one responded to calculation. Three patients showed autonomic responses to pathodynamic structures, but none gave violent autonomic responses. Signs of autonomic dissociation were present in two cases.

In the experimental data, it seems that the general disturbances of the higher nervous activity in autistic hebephrenia are not severe, and correspond more to those of the slighter paranoid defects than those of the severe paranoid defects. The influences of the pathodynamic structures are slight. The proportion of adequate responses is smaller than in the slight paranoid defects, but uncooperativeness of the patients may reduce the quality of the performances. If the autistic hebephrenics are willing to do the tests, the tasks are apparently not too difficult for them.

One of the incompletely studied cases received ataraxic drugs during the experimental investigation. Five had been treated with ataraxic drugs during the period of observation. There was no effect in three and two were only moderately improved. Their unwillingness to cooperate is also reflected in a negative attitude towards the treatment, and as these patients are well adapted to hospital routine treatment could be eliminated.

From the analysis of the clinical symptomatologies it was found that the autistic hebephrenias in their acute stage had predominantly paranoid symptoms. This was also one of the factors which originally made Leonhard classify the autistics as a paranoid subgroup (526).

Clinically no paranoid symptoms can be found, so experimentally the pathodynamic structures have a slight effect or no effect at all. The clinical course seems to be that the original paranoid symptoms in some way become encapsulated, and replaced by the autism and emotional blunting. In followed up schizophrenics with social remissions, encapsulation of psychotic ideas is often observed (331). Perhaps the autistic hebephrenia actually represents a healing process with respect to the paranoid ideas, but is accompanied by stronger emotional blunting than in the slighter paranoid defects. The absence of a similiar course of illness in the relatives and, comparatively, the many relatives with recurring psychoses, may indicate that the autistic hebephrenia has a favorable hereditary background with respect to "healing" of paranoid symptoms.

9. Eccentric Hebephrenia

Leonhard claims that affective blunting is a central symptom in the eccentric hebephrenics, who also regularly have mannerisms and an eccentric behavior. There is a cheerlessness about their mood, and they tend to be depressed. They can also often be irritable and aggressive (236, 434, 435). The differential diagnosis is mainly from the other hebephrenic forms.

Sarró states the hebephrenics often have a mixture of two or more hebephrenic subgroups (790). Leonhard has described several cases of combined systematic hebephrenias (537). In the author's experience some eccentric hebephrenias may resemble the autistic cases. The main problem is the delimitation of eccentric hebephrenia from shallow hebephrenia. In the shallow hebephrenias there are disturbed episodes with hallucinations. The eccentric cases usually are not hallucinated, but have dysphoric periods, which may resemble the hallucinatory excitement of the shallow hebephrenia. The typical eccentric cases have a depressive and cheerless mood, the shallow hebephrenics are often euphoric, and their mood is mainly characterized by an indifferent satisfaction. Cases which had the affective characteristics of the shallow hebephrenia have been classified in that group, even if they had some mannerisms. The group of eccentric hebephrenics has been limited to typical cases, who, like the autistic hebephrenics, have affective changes in the direction of depression, dysphoria, discontent and cheerlessness. Clinically the eccentric cases like the autistic cases can be considered as slightly deteriorated. In the shallow and silly hebephrenias, where euphoria and indifferent satisfaction are dominating affective traits, there is generally a severe deterioration clinically.

In the present series there were eighteen cases with eccentric hebephrenia. The average age of onset is 24.8 years and the average observation period 21.6 years. Three had self-assertive, eleven schizoid and none balanced prepsychotic personality. In seven cases precipitating factors were found in the case histories. The onset was generally insidious and two had recurring courses. In all cases hebephrenic traits were present from the onset of the disease, but eleven had some paranoid symptoms and four had catatonic symptoms. The dominant emotional symptom of the acute stage was emotional blunting, but nine had depressive or elated mood. Only three cases had typical schizophrenic delusions and only one of them expansive ideas. Feelings of passivity, which are such characteristic process symptoms, were only observed in three cases. The symptom complex of *"Sprunghaftigkeit"* dominated the initial clinical picture and was rather pure in most cases.

The eccentric hebephrenics are rather well ordered in their general behavior. Most of them have good working ability. Unless a mannerism prevents them from speaking, as in one case of this sample, they can carry on an adequate conversation. Most of them were in open wards. Six were in wards for disturbed patients, because their mannerisms and dysphoric periods were a nuisance in the open wards. From the above characteristics the author considers that the eccentric hebephrenias have a slight deterioration.

Twenty-one relatives were probably psychotic. For eleven of them case histories were available. Four had affective psychoses and seven, schizophrenia. Two had slight paranoid defects, two periodic catatonias, one autistic hebephrenia, one eccentric and one shallow hebephrenia. The relatives seem to have a slight tendency to develop similiar defects. It is striking that the relatives predominantly have recurring psychoses or slight schizophrenic defects. This indicates that in the relatives also there is no strong tendency to develop severe schizophrenic defects.

The results of the experimental investigations are shown in Table 9.

Seventeen cases were studied experimentally, and one case refused.

With the association test, the disturbances were very similiar to those of the slighter paranoid defects. One had more primitive

TABLE 9
ECCENTRIC HEBEPHRENIA

	Adequate Responses	Inadequate Responses	Too Difficult Tasks	No Information	Total Patients
Associations					
Reproduction	10	7	0	0	17
Mean reaction times	7	10	0	0	17
Median reaction times	5	12	0	0	17
Echolalic responses	2	15	0	0	17
Multiword responses	11	6	0	0	17
Higher responses	7	10	0	0	17
Primitive responses	16	1	0	0	17
Incoherent responses	8	9	0	0	17
Motor Conditional Reflexes					
First reflex in first system	10	6	0	1	17
Second reflex in first system	15	0	0	2	17
Reflex in second system	16	0	0	1	17
Reaction times	7	9	0	1	17
After-inhibitions	2	14	0	1	17
Extinction	14	2	0	1	17
Restoration	8	8	0	1	17
Differentiation	2	13	1	1	17
Reversal of negative reflexes	9	6	1	1	17
Reversal of positive reflexes	9	6	1	1	17
Description of performances	7	9	0	1	17
Unstable reflexes	16	0	0	1	17
Extrasignaling reactions	15	1	0	1	17
Continuous pressing	14	2	0	1	17
Autonomic Reactions					
Vascular curve	13	2	0	2	17
Respiratory curve	11	4	0	2	17
Respiratory and vascular dissociation	6	9	0	2	17
Vascular responses to cold	4	11	0	2	17
Vascular responses to calculation	11	4	0	2	17
Effects of pathodynamic structures	15	0	0	2	17
Defensive Reflexes					
Current tolerance	6	10	0	1	17
Motor exhaustion	3	13	0	1	17
Autonomic exhaustion	9	7	0	1	17
Dissociations	8	8	0	1	17
Number of inadequate responses		214			
Number of adequate responses	296				
Number of too difficult tasks			3		

reactions than in the normal sample. There was a tendency to impaired reproduction, prolonged reaction times, and echolalic and multiword responses. Seven had a number of higher responses within the normals limits, nine cases had incoherent responses, but only one had several such reactions. The incoherent responses were always mediate reactions and in no case incoherent sentences.

The ability to form conditional reflexes in the first as well as the second signaling system was not essentially different from that of the normal sample. In one-half of the cases, the reaction times were irregularly prolonged, and there was a strong tendency to after-inhibition. There is some inhibition of the first signaling system, but all cases were able to form stable conditional reflexes. Extinction was easily carried out in most cases, but with differentiation the majority had inadequate reactions. About one-half solved the problem of restoration adequately. Only four cases were able to reverse the negative as well as the positive reflexes adequately. From the experimental data it can be assumed that there is a weakness of internal inhibition and inertia of the nervous processes. Major signs of inertia, such as extra-signaling reactions or continuous pressing, were only observed in two cases. Seven cases were able to describe their motor performances adequately.

The unconditional responses to electrical stimulation in thirteen cases showed signs of inhibition. Eight cases could avoid the electrical stimulation in all trials after instruction, and the remainder succeeded in most trials. No severe dissociations between the unconditional reflexes and the signaling systems occurred.

The plethysmogram in most cases had a zero curve from the beginning, but in 2 cases the curve was chaotic. Four had respiratory arrhythmias, and dissociation between the respiratory curve and the respiratory oscillations of the plethysmogram was present in nine cases. There were several signs of autonomic dissociation. Vascular responses to unconditional cold stimulation were only observed in four cases. The majority gave vascular responses to calculation. In several cases some reaction could be observed when themes which were apparently affectively colored themes were mentioned, but none of these cases showed such violent autonomic reactions as were found in several of the paranoid defects.

Summing up the experimental data, eccentric hebephrenia is mainly characterized by passive inhibition of all three levels of the higher nervous activity, impairment of internal inhibition, inertia and dissociation. The dissociative phenomena of the second signaling system are slight, and the associative disturbances are not great. The experimental findings resemble those of the mild paranoid defects, but the marked effect of pathodynamic structures is absent.

Three patients received ataraxic drugs during the period of the experimental investigations, but did not show any clearly defined differences in the disturbances of the higher nervous activity as compared with untreated cases. Nine cases had been treated with ataraxic drugs during the period observed. In two there was no effect, in four, moderate improvement and in three, considerable improvement. The eccentric behavior and the mannerisms were not essentially influenced. The dysphoria tended to be reduced, so that the patients were more cooperative.

Clinically the symptom complex of *"Sprunghaftigkeit"* with hebephrenic symptoms dominated the symptomatology from the acute stage. There is no familial tendency to similar defects, but also no familial predisposition to severe schizophrenic deterioration. Although the onset of the disease had been early in life, the average observation period was so long that the eccentric hebephrenics could be considered as slowly progressive, slight schizophrenic defects.

In the chronic paranoid schizophrenia slightly deteriorated groups tended to have comparatively short observation periods and high ages of onset. The slightly deteriorated, eccentric hebephrenics have longer observation periods than the severely deteriorated hebephrenics. They also start at the same age as the severely deteriorated, silly hebephrenics.

10. Shallow Hebephrenia

Shallow hebephrenia was not described in the first study by Leonhard (526). In his later descriptions this form is distinguished by an affective blunting. The affective flattening passes beyond a defect in interests and leads to a deficiency in initiative.

The mood is mainly characterized by euphoria or indifferent satisfaction. This permanent state, in which the defect in affect appears to be the only symptom, is interrupted from time to time by short periods when the patients are hallucinated and can become excited and aggressive (236, 434, 435, 537). In the preceding part of this chapter the main criteria for the differential diagnosis from the eccentric hebephrenia are mentioned. With respect to mood changes the shallow hebephrenics may resemble the silly hebephrenias, but in the latter the presence of the childish and silly behavior should make the differential diagnosis possible.

In the present sample there are twelve patients with shallow hebephrenia. The average age of onset is 21.5 years and the average observation period sixteen years. These cases tend to start at earlier ages than the eccentric hebephrenics, and in spite of the shorter periods of observation, the defects are more severe. One had self-assertive, eight schizoid and two balanced prepsychotic personalities. Precipitating factors could only be found in one case, and the onset tended to be insidious. All cases had hebephrenic traits from the beginning of the disease. In two cases there were catatonic and in seven, paranoid traits. In all cases with paranoid traits, these could be regarded as mental automatisms related to feelings of passivity. Two had expansive ideas. In all cases the affective blunting was already present in the acute stage as a dominating emotional symptom. Most cases had auditory hallucinations from the start.

The shallow hebephrenics were mostly able to carry on a simple conversation, but it was far less reasonable than in the eccentric hebephrenics. Their behavior is so well ordered that the majority can be in open wards. Five, because of aggressive behavior, were in disturbed wards. They could help themselves with eating and dressing and were not unclean, but because of their lack of initiative, their working ability was small. The total impression is one of a severe deterioration.

Thirteen relatives were probably psychotic, and case histories were available in nine of these. Two had affective psychoses and seven schizophrenics. All the schizophrenic relatives developed hebephrenic defects. But five had the slighter eccentric hebephrenic defect and only two a shallow hebephrenia.

The results of the experimental investigations are shown in Table 10.

All twelve cases were studied experimentally. The associative functions were considerably more impaired than in the eccentric hebephrenics. The ability to reproduce was poor, the reaction times tended to be prolonged, and most cases had several echolalic and multiword responses. One patient had a number of higher reactions and three, a number of primitive reactions within the limits of the normal series. Eleven cases had incoherent responses and seven of them had several incoherent responses. There is considerably more dissociation in the second signaling system than in the eccentric hebephrenic.

The ability to form conditional reflexes in the first and second signaling systems was not essentially impaired. All cases had strong after-inhibitions. Ten had irregular prolongations of the reaction times and five could not even form stable motor conditional reflexes. There was more inhibition of the first signaling system than in the eccentric hebephrenic. While only a few cases had generalized reactions in the first signaling system, most cases had generalized reactions in the second signaling system. Extinction was easily performed in most cases, but none succeeded with differentiation and this task was too difficult even to try in five cases. Eight cases carried out the restoration of extinguished reflexes adequately. Only two cases succeeded in the reversal of negative and positive reflexes, which was too difficult a task for most patients. Major signs of inertia, such as extra-signaling reactions or continuous pressing, were observed in five cases. Two cases were able to describe their motor performances adequately.

The unconditional responses to electrical stimulation showed no signs of inhibition in only two cases. Four cases were able to avoid the electrical stimulation after instruction in all trials, and most cases failed in several trials. There was a severe inhibition of unconditional responses and considerable dissociation between unconditional reflexes and the second signaling system.

The plethysmogram showed a zero curve in eleven cases and a chaotic curve in one case. One case had respiratory arrhythmias and six dissociations between the respiratory curve and the respiratory oscillations of the plethysmogram. Vascular responses

TABLE 10
SHALLOW HEBEPHRENIA

	Adequate Responses	Inadequate Responses	Too Difficult Tasks	No Information	Total Patients
Associations					
Reproduction	2	6	4	0	12
Mean reaction times	3	9	0	0	12
Median reaction times	0	12	0	0	12
Echolalic responses	4	8	0	0	12
Multiword responses	6	6	0	0	12
Higher responses	1	11	0	0	12
Primitive responses	3	9	0	0	12
Incoherent responses	1	11	0	0	12
Motor Conditional Reflexes					
First reflex in first system	4	8	0	0	12
Second reflex in first system	6	1	0	5	12
Reflex in second system	12	0	0	0	12
Reaction times	2	10	0	0	12
After-inhibitions	0	12	0	0	12
Extinction	10	2	0	0	12
Restoration	8	4	0	0	12
Differentiation	0	7	5	0	12
Reversal of negative reflexes	3	2	7	0	12
Reversal of positive reflexes	2	3	7	0	12
Description of performances	2	10	0	0	12
Unstable reflexes	7	5	0	0	12
Extrasignaling reactions	10	2	0	0	12
Continuous pressing	8	4	0	0	12
Autonomic Reactions					
Vascular curve	11	1	0	0	12
Respiratory curve	11	1	0	0	12
Respiratory and vascular dissociation	6	6	0	0	12
Vascular responses to cold	4	8	0	0	12
Vascular responses to calculation	6	6	0	0	12
Effects of pathodynamic structures	12	0	0	0	12
Defensive Reflexes					
Current tolerance	4	8	0	0	12
Motor exhaustion	3	9	0	0	12
Autonomic exhaustion	5	7	0	0	12
Dissociations	4	8	0	0	12
Number of inadequate responses		196			
Number of adequate responses	160				
Number of too difficult tasks			23		

to unconditional cold stimulation were found in four and to calculation in six cases. In one half of the cases some responses to the mentioning of presumably affectively colored themes could be observed, but violent autonomic reactions could not be found in any of these cases.

The experimental data show disturbances of the higher nervous functions are considerably greater in the group of shallow hebephrenias than in the group of eccentric hebephrenias (P < 0.001). There are more dissociative phenomena between the signaling systems (P < 0.02) and the verbal functions are more impaired (P < 0.001).

Four cases received ataraxic drugs during the time of the experimental investigation. There were no sharp differences in the disturbances of the higher nervous activity between treated and untreated cases. Altogether six had been treated with ataraxic drugs. All treated cases had a moderate improvement, which usually consisted in reduction of the excitements and the aggressive behavior, but did not change the marked affective flattening.

It is noted that the clinical symptomatology in the acute stage is dominated by hebephrenic traits and process symptoms. The next chapter reviews cases which have such symptoms in the acute stage, severe disturbances of the higher nervous activity, and many dissociative phenomena. The tendency of the relatives to develop hebephrenic defects may indicate that hereditary factors also play a role in the development of the shallow hebephrenic defect.

11. Silly Hebephrenia

The silly or *"läppische"* hebephrenics seem to be a well circumscribed defect state; the descriptions of this by Kraepelin and his predecessors have been taken over practically unchanged by Leonhard (234, 236, 434, 435, 486, 537). In silly hebephrenia an intense affective blunting is associated with a mood which varies from being contented to mildly cheerful. A smiling or a pronounced giggling is particularly characteristic, and this becomes prominent under the influence of every external stimulus. Discussed in the previous parts of this chapter, the differential diagnosis is mainly from the shallow hebephrenic, where the affect is also often mildly cheerful.

In the present series there were fourteen patients with silly hebephrenia. The average age of onset was 24.7 years and the average observation period was 16.7 years. Most cases had an insidious onset and one case had a recurring course. One case had a self-assertive personality, eight schizoid and one balanced prepsychotic personalities. Precipitating factors were found in five cases. The hebephrenic traits were definite from the start, and in all but two cases the dominant initial emotional symptom was affective blunting. Two cases had catatonic and eight paranoid traits. As in the shallow hebephrenics the paranoid traits had the character of mental automatisms in connection with process symptoms. None had expansive ideas, but hallucinations were always present in the acute stage.

The silly hebephrenics are so disorganized that they can not carry on any ordered conversation, but answer adequately to simple questions. They are not unclean and helpless like severe catatonic defects, but they have practically no working ability. Nine of them were in disturbed wards, because of uncontrolled behavior, two in wards with much nursing supervision and only three in best wards. The general impression is that the silly hebephrenics are even more deteriorated than the shallow hebephrenics.

Thirteen relatives were probably psychotic, and in seven of them case histories were available. Three cases were diagnosed as schizophrenics, but had apparently complete remissions, so that the author, in accordance with the principles for the classification of the relatives, considered them to have affective psychoses. Symptomatologically typical schizophrenic process symptoms were also lacking in these cases. The remaining four cases were definite schizophrenics, three eccentric hebephrenics and one silly hebephrenia. It seems that the schizophrenic relatives of the silly hebephrenics, like the relatives of the shallow hebephrenics, have a marked tendency to develop hebephrenic defects.

The results of the experimental investigations are shown in Table 11.

All fourteen cases could be studied experimentally. With the association test they had disturbances similiar to the shallow hebe-

TABLE 11
SILLY HEBEPHRENIA

	Adequate Responses	Inadequate Responses	Too Difficult Tasks	No Information	Total Patients
Associations					
Reproduction	1	11	2	0	14
Mean reaction times	5	9	0	0	14
Median reaction times	3	11	0	0	14
Echolalic responses	4	10	0	0	14
Multiword responses	6	8	0	0	14
Higher responses	1	13	0	0	14
Primitive responses	4	10	0	0	14
Incoherent responses	1	13	0	0	14
Motor Conditional Reflexes					
First reflex in first system	7	7	0	0	14
Second reflex in first system	4	2	0	8	14
Reflex in second system	12	2	0	0	14
Reaction times	1	13	0	0	14
After-inhibitions	2	9	3	0	14
Extinction	9	1	4	0	14
Restoration	4	5	5	0	14
Differentiation	0	6	8	0	14
Reversal of negative reflexes	1	1	12	0	14
Reversal of positive reflexes	1	1	12	0	14
Description of performances	0	14	0	0	14
Unstable reflexes	6	8	0	0	14
Extrasignaling reactions	7	7	0	0	14
Continuous pressing	7	7	0	0	14
Autonomic Reactions					
Vascular curve	7	7	0	0	14
Respiratory curve	1	13	0	0	14
Respiratory and vascular dissociation	1	13	0	0	14
Vascular responses to cold	1	13	0	0	14
Vascular responses to calculation	3	11	0	0	14
Effects of pathodynamic structures	14	0	0	0	14
Defensive Reflexes					
Current tolerance	7	7	0	0	14
Motor exhaustion	7	7	0	0	14
Autonomic exhaustion	11	3	0	0	14
Dissociations	2	12	0	0	14
Number of inadequate responses		254			
Number of adequate responses	140				
Number of too difficult tasks			46		

phrenics. Reproduction was severely impaired, reaction times were prolonged and most cases had several echolalic or multiword responses. One had a number of higher reactions and four a number of primitive reactions within the limits of the normal sample. All but one had incoherent responses; most had several.

The ability to form conditional reflexes in the first and second signaling systems was only slightly inferior to that of the sample of normals. But four were not able to form motor reflexes even after instruction. Most cases had strong after-inhibitions, irregular and prolonged reaction times, and eight could not even form stable motor reflexes. There was a severe passive inhibition of the functions of the first signaling system. Many cases could carry out extinction adequately, but all failed with differentiation, and for eight cases this task was too difficult even to try. Four managed the task of restoration, but only one could adequately reverse the negative, as well as the positive reflexes. For the majority this task was too difficult. Major signs of inertia, such as extra-signaling reactions or continuous pressing, were observed in ten cases. None was able to describe the motor performances adequately.

The unconditional reflexes to electrical stimulation showed signs of inhibition in eight cases. For all signs there was less inhibition than in the shallow hebephrenics ($P < 0.05$). Two were able to avoid the electrical stimulation after instruction, and most cases failed in several trials with the task.

In one-half of the cases the plethysmogram gave a zero curve from the beginning. In the other half the curve was chaotic. Respiratory arrhythmias were found in all but one case. Thirteen cases had dissociations between the respiratory rhythms and the respiratory oscillations of the plethysmogram. The autonomic dissociative phenomena seemed especially strong in the group of silly hebephrenics. Most cases gave no responses to unconditional cold stimulation and calculation. Three cases had some autonomic responses to the mention of presumably affectively charged themes, but none had violent autonomic reactions.

In the experimental data, there was a severe impairment of the higher nervous activity in the silly hebephrenics. The proportion of adequate responses was smaller than in the group of shallow hebephrenics (P < 0.01), who had rather similiar disturbances of the nervous processes. The greater emotional lability of the silly hebephrenics may be related to their more severe dissociations of the autonomic functions (P < 0.001).

In seven cases who received ataraxic drugs during the experimental studies, there were no experimental differences compared with the untreated cases. Eleven cases had been treated with ataraxic drugs during the observation period. In two the treatment had no effect, and in nine there was moderate effect. The affective blunting was apparently unchanged by the treatment. The silly hebephrenics often play tricks and through their disorganized behavior may often be a nuisance in the wards. The improvement consisted in reduction of such symptoms.

It is possible that the emotional indifference and euphoria of the severe hebephrenic defects can be related to the combinations of strong dissociative phenomena and severe inhibitions of the first signaling system. Similiar general disturbances are also found in the expansive and fantastic paraphrenics, who also tend to have a euphoric mood. Their main experimental differences are the stronger influences of pathodynamic structures in the paranoid defects.

As to the clinical development of symptoms, it is noticeable that silly hebephrenics, like shallow hebephrenics and quite a number of expansive and fantastic paraphrenics, have a tendency to show the symptom complex of *"Sprunghaftigkeit"* during the acute stages. The next chapter shows that hebephrenics and progressive catatonics during the acute stage tend to have considerable inhibition of the first signaling system and dissociative phenomena also during the acute stage.

With regard to the hereditary factors, the silly hebephrenics, like the shallow hebephrenics, have relatives with a tendency to develop hebephrenic defects, but also relatives with affective psychoses.

C. THE CATATONIC TYPES OF CHRONIC SCHIZOPHRENIA

12. Periodic Catatonia

Leonhard is of the opinion that the periodic catatonia with respect to symptomatology, prognosis and heredity is very different from the typical or systematic catatonics (236, 527, 528, 529, 537, 809). Clinically periodic catatonia has hyperkinetic and akinetic stages. Remissions occur regularly after the acute catatonic shifts, and the defects may vary much in degree. If the defects are only of a mild kind, then they show themselves in a general psychic lameness, which predominantly affects the psychomotor activity, but also affects thinking and affectivity. A further degree of defect can be designated as dullness. In the most severe defects the patients have a stupidity in addition to the dullness which is reminiscent of an organic deterioration (236, 537).

In the author's experience the slighter defects were especially characteristic in the followed up acute catatonics which were classified as improved (331). Such cases only occasionally need to be hospitalized. The periodic catatonics in the present series mostly showed dullness without the characteristic symptoms of the systematic catatonia forms. If symptoms characteristic of systematic catatonias were found, the author classified them as such cases, even if remissions were recorded from the case histories. Yet a few cases with no complete remissions, but periodic shifts of hyperkinetic and akinetic stages developing the general dullness found in periodic catatonia were classified in this group.

In the present series there were nineteen cases with periodic catatonia. Because those with slighter defects are discharged from the hospital to a much greater extent than the more severe systematic catatonias, the number of periodic catatonias compared with the systematic cases is much smaller than the actual frequency of such states. The average age of onset was 28.5 years, and the average observation period 18.7 years. After the first catatonic shift fourteen had good social remissions and five considerable improvements, which were broken by new catatonic episodes. In five cases there was an insidious onset. The others had acute onsets, mostly with some prodromal symptoms before outbreak of the catatonic symptoms. For nine cases precipitating factors could be found in the case histories. One had self-assertive, seven schizoid and four balanced prepsychotic personalities.

An affective blunting was from the start present in nine cases, whereas depression, elation or perplexity were the dominating emotional disturbances of the remaining cases during the acute stage. One had hebephrenic and eleven paranoid traits. Pronounced projection symptoms with feelings of passivity could only be found in two cases. All but one case had hallucinations during the acute stage, sixteen had psychomotor excitation, and seven had marked stupors, two negativism and three mannerisms.

Thirty-one relatives had probably been psychotic, and twenty case histories were available. From the case histories of relatives it is difficult to decide whether recurring cases were periodic catatonics or affective psychotics, as hysteriform excitements may resemble catatonic excitations. Two relatives had definitely affective psychoses. One patient had developed a severe paranoid defect, one a systematic catatonia, and the remaining sixteen cases were probably periodic catatonics. Nine of them had good social remissions, and seven had progressive deterioration. This agrees very well with the experience of Leonhard, that periodic catatonics have a strong hereditary taint of similar psychoses (537).

In the present sample twelve cases had some working ability and only three were in need of nursing and attention to the same degree as most systematic catatonic defects. The majority were in open wards, a few in wards with nursing supervision and four in wards for disturbed patients.

The results of the experimental investigations are shown in Table 12.

Sixteen patients were studied experimentally. Just as the clinical degree of deterioration varied, so did the experimental findings show great variations. In cases with well-ordered behavior the associative disturbances corresponded to those of the slighter hebephrenic defects. The most deteriorated cases only responded with primitive reactions or gave no reactions at all. For the whole group reproduction was severely impaired, and reaction times prolonged. Most cases had several echolalic and multiword responses, and none had any number of higher responses within the limits of the normal sample. The majority had incoherent responses.

Five cases were not able to form motor reflexes in the first signaling system, even with the help of instruction, nine had unstable motor reflexes, and two gave motor reflexes with short and regular reaction times. In the first signaling system four could

TABLE 12
Periodic Catatonia

	Adequate Responses	Inadequate Responses	Too Difficult Tasks	No Information	Total Patients
Associations					
Reproduction	2	10	4	0	16
Mean reaction times	3	12	1	0	16
Median reaction times	2	13	1	0	16
Echolalic responses	2	13	1	0	16
Multiword responses	6	9	1	0	16
Higher responses	0	15	1	0	16
Primitive responses	7	8	1	0	16
Incoherent responses	6	9	1	0	16
Motor Conditional Reflexes					
First reflex in first system	4	12	0	0	16
Second reflex in first system	8	1	0	7	16
Reflex in second system	13	3	0	0	16
Reaction times	2	14	0	0	16
After-inhibitions	1	9	6	0	16
Extinction	8	3	5	0	16
Restoration	4	6	6	0	16
Differentiation	1	8	7	0	16
Reversal of negative reflexes	2	3	11	0	16
Reversal of positive reflexes	4	1	11	0	16
Description of performances	3	13	0	0	16
Unstable reflexes	7	9	0	0	16
Extrasignaling reactions	13	3	0	0	16
Continuous pressing	12	4	0	0	16
Autonomic Reactions					
Vascular curve	13	3	0	0	16
Respiratory curve	12	4	0	0	16
Respiratory and vascular dissociation	6	10	0	0	16
Vascular responses to cold	2	14	0	0	16
Vascular responses to calculation	7	9	0	0	16
Effects of pathodynamic structures	16	0	0	0	16
Defensive Reflexes					
Current tolerance	6	10	0	0	16
Motor exhaustion	5	11	0	0	16
Autonomic exhaustion	9	7	0	0	16
Dissociations	2	14	0	0	16
Number of inadequate responses		260			
Number of adequate responses	188				
Number of too difficult tasks			57		

rapidly form motor conditional responses in the first trials. The second reflex was formed rapidly in eight of nine cases studied. In the second signaling system the majority formed conditional reflexes rapidly. The ability to develop conditional responses in the second signaling system is not essentially inferior to that of the normal sample. One-half of the cases carried out extinction adequately, but only one succeeded with differentiation. In restoration four cases did adequately. The reversal of negative and positive reflexes was too difficult a task for most patients. Five cases had extra-signaling reactions or continuous pressing, which indicated a considerable inertia of the nervous processes. Three cases were able to describe their motor performances adequately.

Most cases had a strong tendency to exhaustion of the unconditional responses to electrical stimulation. Two cases could avoid the electrical stimulation after instruction in all trials. Most cases failed in several trials and seven of them in all trials.

The plethysmogram had a zero curve from the start in thirteen cases and a chaotic curve in three cases. Four had respiratory arrhythmias and ten dissociations between the respiratory curve and the respiratory oscillations of the plethysmogram. This shows a considerable tendency to autonomic dissociation. Two responded to unconditional cold stimulation and seven to calculation. The influence of pathodynamic structures on the vascular and respiratory curves was absent in most cases, and was never marked.

From the experimental data, the periodic catatonics show great variations, but most cases have severe disturbance of all three levels of the higher nervous activity and as pronounced dissociative phenomena as in the severe paranoid and hebephrenic defects. It will be seen from the following that the periodic catatonics have slighter disturbances of the higher nervous activity than the systematic catatonics ($P < 0.001$).

Eight patients received ataraxic drugs while they were studied experimentally. The experimental data do not show any differences for treated and untreated cases. Altogether sixteen cases had been treated with ataraxic drugs during the period observed. In only two was there no effect, in four a moderate effect and in ten considerable effect of the treatment. The periodic excitements and the aggressiveness were diminished, and this led to a much greater stability in work and general behavior.

The later parts of this chapter illustrate that the systematic catatonics benefit much less from ataraxic drugs.

It was found that the periodic catatonics not only had different clinical symptomatologies as compared with the systematic catatonics, but that the experimental disturbances were slighter, and the effects of ataraxic drugs better. They also had less hereditary loading with severe schizophrenic defects. Clinically not only the periodic course, but also a tendency to more acute onset with violent psychomotor symptoms seems to be more characteristic of this group than of the systematic catatonics.

13. Parakinetic Catatonia

The central symptoms of this defect form are the parakinesias, which are present from the onset of the disease, but in the beginning are so slight that the attention of the clinical observer is often not focused upon them (537). In the defect stages the parakinesias can be rich in variety, but certain forms reappear as bizarre actions. Voluntary actions are carried out in an unnatural awkward way, and the involuntary movements take place jerkily so that they are reminiscent of choreiform movements. The smooth connection between the complete acts of movements is absent. The special disorder of the completion of movements is often also expressed in the verbal utterances. The words are "cut up" and expressed as if in individual thrusts (234, 236, 537).

The parakinetic catatonics have in contrast to most other catatonic defects a certain disinhibition of motor phenomena. The author finds it practical to include all cases with parakinetic traits in this group, even if they may have traits from other catatonic defects. The differential diagnosis is mainly from the other catatonic forms where signs of disinhibition are observed. In the speech-prompt catatonic the prompt answering may resemble the verbal utterances of the parakinetics, but the parakinesia is lacking. Some proskinetic catatonics have some motor disinhibition which can be seen in their turning towards the examiner, but the jerky and awkward movements are lacking. The manneristic catatonics may also resemble the parakinetic catatonic, but the stereotyped repetition of the movements and extreme stiffness and rigidity differentiate these two illnesses. In negativistic catatonics awkward movements and positions are often observed, but the characteristic negativistic opposition makes the differential diagnosis possible.

In the present series there were sixteen cases with parakinetic catatonia. The average age of onset was 27.5 years and the average observation period 22.8 years. One case had a recurring course, and in nine cases the onset was insidious.

Three had self-assertive, seven schizoid and two balanced prepsychotic personalities. Precipitating factors were found in seven cases. One had hebephrenic and eleven paranoid traits. In six of the cases with paranoid traits feelings of passivity were present. Five had expansive ideas. All cases had hallucinations during the acute stage, but with the further course the hallucinations tended to disappear. The psychomotor symptoms were mostly severe during the acute stage. Ten cases were excited, seven negativistic, four stuporous and in two cases the parakinesics were so outspoken in the acute stage that they were specially mentioned in the case histories.

A large number of the parakinetic catatonics could answer simple questions adequately, and several showed greater interest in their relatives than other chronic systematic catatonics. The working ability was slight in most cases. Only three cases were so deteriorated that they needed care, in all ways, with eating, dressing and cleanliness. Half of the patients were in disturbed wards, and the others were able to live in wards for quiet chronic patients.

Although Leonhard found a strong hereditary loading in the parakinetic catatonic (537), the present sample has only six near relatives, who probably have been psychotic. Of the two case histories available, one had a slight paranoid defect and one a parakinetic catatonia.

The results of the experimental investigations are shown in Table 13.

Fourteen patients were studied experimentally. With the association test four gave no responses and one was unwilling to answer, but could otherwise communicate verbally. All had inco-

TABLE 13
PARAKINETIC CATATONIA

	Adequate Responses	Inadequate Responses	Too Difficult Tasks	No Information	Total Patients
Associations					
Reproduction	0	5	8	1	14
Mean reaction times	1	8	4	1	14
Median reaction times	1	8	4	1	14
Echolalic responses	1	8	4	1	14
Multiword responses	3	6	4	1	14
Higher responses	0	9	4	1	14
Primitive responses	0	9	4	1	14
Incoherent responses	0	9	4	1	14
Motor Conditional Reflexes					
First reflex in first system	5	9	0	0	14
No reflex in first system	9	5	0	0	14
Reflex in second system	12	2	0	0	14
Reaction times	0	14	0	0	14
After-inhibitions	0	6	8	0	14
Extinction	4	4	6	0	14
Restoration	2	5	7	0	14
Differentiation	0	1	13	0	14
Reversal of negative reflexes	1	0	13	0	14
Reversal of positive reflexes	0	1	13	0	14
Description of performances	0	14	0	0	14
Unstable reflexes	1	13	0	0	14
Extrasignaling reactions	6	8	0	0	14
Continuous pressing	5	9	0	0	14
Autonomic Reactions					
Vascular curve	8	6	0	0	14
Respiratory curve	7	7	0	0	14
Respiratory and vascular dissociation	2	12	0	0	14
Vascular responses to cold	2	12	0	0	14
Vascular responses to calculation	3	11	0	0	14
Effects of pathodynamic structures	14	0	0	0	14
Defensive Reflexes					
Current tolerance	3	11	0	0	14
Motor exhaustion	3	11	0	0	14
Autonomic exhaustion	6	8	0	0	14
Dissociations	1	13	0	0	14
Number of inadequate responses		244			
Number of adequate responses	100				
Number of too difficult tasks			96		

The more difficult and emotionally charged the questions become, the more certainly will the patient disregard the point of the question. Answers can be obtained to every question, and one can ask just what one likes. If left to themselves these patients do not speak, so that they are even falsely described as mute. In contrast to the abnormal readiness of speech, the motor activity has an element of constraint about it without there being any characteristic anomalies of posture. The facial expression is peculiarly empty and meaningless so that it can tell the examiner nothing about the psychological reactions of the patient (236, 537). In contrast with the strong inhibition of the general behavior, one can consider the promptness to answer as a speech disinhibition. The differential diagnosis is mainly from the other catatonics with signs of disinhibition. But when clearly defined parakinesia or proskinesia is found, these forms can be distinguished from the speech-prompt catatonia.

In the present series there are twelve patients with speech-prompt catatonia. The average age of onset was 23.8 years and the average observation period 26.7 years. This group tends to become sick early in life, and the observation period is comparatively long. In all cases there was an insidious onset, and none had a recurring course. Two had self-assertive, five schizoid and two balanced prepsychotic personalities. Precipitating factors were only noticed in two cases. In this group the catatonic symptoms were slight in the acute stage. In six cases there were catatonic-hebephrenic states in the beginning, and six had paranoid symptoms. Feelings of passivity were noticed in two cases and expansive ideas in two cases. In all but three cases severe emotional blunting was present from the start, and all cases had hallucinations, mainly auditory. Eleven cases had psychomotor excitations, two stupor, five negativism, and two mannerisms.

The patients with speech-prompt catatonia are clinically severely deteriorated. All but two needed help in every way with eating, dressing and cleanliness. Only one was able to carry out some simple work. All of them during the period of observation were mostly in the disturbed wards. Several could be impulsively aggressive.

Nine relatives were probably psychotic, and for four of them case histories were available. Two had affective psychoses, and two speech-prompt catatonias. There was a tendency in relatives to develop similiar defects.

The results of the experimental investigations are shown in Table 14.

All twelve were studied experimentally. With the association test there was a characteristic tendency to respond with echolalic reactions. In conversation these patients also often repeat the words of the examiner. Only one had higher associative reactions, and most reactions were of primitive type. As an experimental sign of disinhibition of speech, it was noticed that nine cases had either mean or median reaction times within the limits of the normal sample.

Two patients were not able to form motor reflexes in the first signaling system with the help of an instruction, but four rapidly developed conditional responses. In the second signaling system most cases formed conditional responses as rapidly as the normal sample. All patients had long and irregular reaction times, and none could give stable conditional reflexes. There is a severe inhibition of the first signaling system. Differentiation and reversal of the positive and negative reflexes were too complex tasks for all patients. Only seven were able to try extinction and restoration, and none of them succeeded in both these tasks. Gross phenomena of inertia such as extra-signaling reactions or continuous pressing were present in eight cases. Not one patient could describe adequately the motor performances.

For most patients the unconditional responses to electrical stimulation were severely inhibited. Seven cases in all trials were unable to avoid the electrical stimulation after instruction, and the remaining cases all had several unsuccessful trials. This shows that the dissociation between unconditional reflexes and the second signaling system is very marked in speech-prompt catatonia.

The plethysmogram in eight cases showed a zero curve, in three cases a chaotic curve. Respiratory arrhythmias were present in seven cases, and all cases had dissociation between the respiratory curve and the respiratory oscillations of the plethysmogram. Vascular reactions to unconditional cold stimulation were observed

TABLE 14
Speech-prompt Catatonia

	Adequate Responses	Inadequate Responses	Too Difficult Tasks	No Information	Total Patients
Associations					
Reproduction	0	2	10	0	12
Mean reaction times	8	4	0	0	12
Median reaction times	8	4	0	0	12
Echolalic responses	0	12	0	0	12
Multiword responses	6	6	0	0	12
Higher responses	0	12	0	0	12
Primitive responses	0	12	0	0	12
Incoherent responses	8	4	0	0	12
Motor Conditional Reflexes					
First reflex in first system	4	8	0	0	12
No reflex in first system	10	2	0	0	12
Reflex in second system	9	3	0	0	12
Reaction times	0	12	0	0	12
After-inhibitions	0	3	9	0	12
Extinction	5	2	5	0	12
Restoration	1	6	5	0	12
Differentiation	0	0	12	0	12
Reversal of negative reflexes	0	0	12	0	12
Reversal of positive reflexes	0	0	12	0	12
Description of performances	0	12	0	0	12
Unstable reflexes	0	12	0	0	12
Extrasignaling reactions	6	6	0	0	12
Continuous pressing	4	8	0	0	12
Autonomic Reactions					
Vascular curve	8	3	0	1	12
Respiratory curve	4	7	0	1	12
Respiratory and vascular dissociation	0	11	0	1	12
Vascular responses to cold	3	8	0	1	12
Vascular responses to calculation	4	7	0	1	12
Effects of pathodynamic structures	11	0	0	1	12
Defensive Reflexes					
Current tolerance	4	7	0	1	12
Motor exhaustion	3	8	0	1	12
Autonomic exhaustion	4	7	0	1	12
Dissociations	0	11	0	1	12
Number of inadequate responses		199			
Number of adequate responses	110				
Number of too difficult tasks			65		

in three and to calculation in four cases. Autonomic reactions to pathodynamic structures were negligible.

Summarizing the experimental data, the speech-prompt catatonics had severe dissociative phenomena, strong inhibitions of unconditional reactions and reactions in the first signaling system. Parallel with the disinhibitory speech promptness, a less pronounced inhibition of the second signaling system was observed, as compared with speech-inactive, manneristic and negativistic catatonics (P < 0.001).

Three cases received ataraxic drugs, when they were studied experimentally, but showed no experimental differences compared with the untreated cases. Altogether nine cases had received ataraxic drugs during the period observed, four showed no improvement and five moderate improvement. The effect of the treatment was mainly a reduction of the aggressiveness, but otherwise their clinical pictures were essentially unchanged.

The severe clinical deterioration of speech-prompt catatonics is paralleled by severe experimental disturbances of the higher nervous activity. Clinically it seems that the comparatively low age of onset and the gradual and often slight catatonic symptoms in the acute stages may favor the development of severe deterioration. A familial tendency to similiar psychoses may also be a factor of importance in determining the course of the disease.

15. Proskinetic Catatonia

The main characteristic of the proskinetic catatonics is the tendency to turn towards the examiner and allow themselves to be directed automatically. This is the direct opposite to the reaction pattern of negativistic catatonia. When examined, the proskinetic catatonics usually begin to murmur unintelligibly in a characteristic manner. If the murmuring can be heard adequately it turns out to be a verbigeration of isolated phrases. One can make the proskinetic behavior become very prominent by means of the appropriate orderly investigation. The patient will seize the examiner's hand untiringly when it is held out towards him, even if he repeatedly is instructed not to give his hand to the examiner. If one presses very lightly on any part of the body, then the body will move in the direction of the pressure and any attitude determined by the examiner will be taken up. In establishing the diagnosis it is important to ensure that there actually is an automatic grasping and a tendency to respond to external stimulation in the described manner. In order to ensure that the patients do not consciously try to please the examiner, it is necessary to give repeated instructions that the pressure should be resisted and the hand should not be given (236, 537).

In the present series there were fourteen patients with proskinetic catatonia. The average age of onset was 25.6 years and the average observation period 32.4 years, which is considerably longer than in most groups of defect schizophrenics. Two cases had recurring courses and in six cases the onset was comparatively acute. Two had self-assertive, eight schizoid and one balanced prepsychotic personalities. Precipitating factors were found in three cases. In this group also the catatonic symptoms initially often were slight. Four had hebephrenic-catatonic syndromes and eight paranoid symptoms during the acute stage. Feelings of passivity were present in five cases and expansive ideas in four cases. In most cases affective blunting was pronounced from the beginning of the disease. During the acute stage all cases had hallucinations, but with the further course of the illness the hallucinations apparently tended to disappear. As to psychomotor symptoms ten had excitation, two stupor, four negativism and one mannerisms during the acute stage. Clinically the proskinetic catatonics were severely deteriorated. They could only with exceptions answer questions adequately and had no working capacity. The majority needed care in all ways, with eating, dressing and cleanliness. Three were in wards with extensive nursing supervision and the rest in wards for disturbed patients. Often they would be aggressive or have attacks of abusive shouting.

Twenty-four relatives were probably psychotic, and eleven case histories from relatives were available. One had an affective psychosis, five paranoid defects and five catatonic defects. Among the catatonics two were periodic catatonics and three systematic catatonics. One of the relatives developed a typical proskinetic catatonia. There is a tendency among relatives to develop catatonic defects.

The results of the experimental investigations are shown in Table 15.

All the fourteen cases were studied experimentally. With the association test all patients reacted only with primitive reactions. Most cases had echolalic reactions, thirteen incoherent reactions, and nine cases in the association test also reacted with the murmuring verbigeration.

Ten were not able to give motor reflexes even after instruction, and only one rapidly developed a conditional motor reflex in the first signaling system. In the second signaling system four were able to give rapid conditional responses, and ten failed. Compared with the previously discussed catatonic defects, the ability to form conditional reflexes in the second signaling system is much inferior. The reaction times were irregularly prolonged in all cases and none could form stable motor reflexes. For this reason the more complex tasks could not be studied in the proskinetic catatonics, as they were too difficult for them. Eleven patients had gross signs of inertia in the form of extra-signaling reactions or continuous pressing. None was able to describe the motor performances adequately.

The unconditional responses to electrical stimulation were strongly exhausted in all but two cases. Ten patients failed in all attempts to avoid electrical stimulation after instruction, and the remaining three cases had more failures than successes in this task.

The plethysmogram gave a zero curve in twelve cases and a chaotic curve in one case. Five had respiratory arrhythmias and eleven dissociations between respiratory rhythms and the respiratory oscillations of the plethysmogram. Vascular reactions to unconditional cold stimulation were observed in two cases and to calculation also in two cases. Autonomic reactions to pathodynamic structures were slight or absent.

Experimental data show there are severe dissociative disturbances and strong inhibitions in all three levels of the higher nervous activity in proskinetic catatonia. The tendency to respond with primitive associations and verbigerating murmuring as experimental signs of disinhibition can be mentioned.

The proportion of too difficult tasks with the association test is much greater in the three following catatonic groups ($P < 0.001$).

TABLE 15
Proskinetic Catatonia

	Adequate Responses	Inadequate Responses	Too Difficult Tasks	No Information	Total Patients
Associations					
Reproduction	0	0	14	0	14
Mean reaction times	4	10	0	0	14
Median reaction times	3	11	0	0	14
Echolalic responses	2	12	0	0	14
Multiword responses	2	12	0	0	14
Higher responses	0	14	0	0	14
Primitive responses	0	14	0	0	14
Incoherent responses	1	13	0	0	14
Motor Conditional Reflexes					
First reflex in first system	1	11	2	0	14
No reflex in first system	4	8	2	0	14
Reflex in second system	4	8	2	0	14
Reaction times	0	12	2	0	14
After-inhibitions	0	1	13	0	14
Extinction	0	1	13	0	14
Restoration	1	0	13	0	14
Differentiation	0	0	14	0	14
Reversal of negative reflexes	0	0	14	0	14
Reversal of positive reflexes	0	0	14	0	14
Description of performances	0	12	2	0	14
Unstable reflexes	0	12	2	0	14
Extrasignaling reactions	4	8	2	0	14
Continuous pressing	3	9	2	0	14
Autonomic Reactions					
Vascular curve	12	1	0	1	14
Respiratory curve	8	5	0	1	14
Respiratory and vascular dissociation	2	11	0	1	14
Vascular responses to cold	2	11	0	1	14
Vascular responses to calculation	0	9	0	5	14
Effects of pathodynamic structures	13	0	0	1	14
Defensive Reflexes					
Current tolerance	2	11	0	1	14
Motor exhaustion	2	11	0	1	14
Autonomic exhaustion	6	7	0	1	14
Dissociations	0	13	0	1	14

Number of inadequate responses		247			
Number of adequate responses	76				
Number of too difficult tasks			111		

During the experimental investigation no patient received ataraxic drugs. Among seven patients treated with ataraxic drugs before and after, there were no effects in two and moderate improvement in five. The characteristic proskinetic symptomatology is not altered by the treatment, but aggressiveness and especially the scolding is reduced.

It is stressed that the severe clinical deterioration of the proskinetic catatonics is paralleled by the severe disturbances of the higher nervous activity. Among clinical factors related to the severe course, it was noted that the catatonic symptoms were slight in several cases in the acute stage. It is also possible that the long observation periods may to some degree be responsible for the severity of the defects. The family predisposition is mainly a nonspecific tendency to develop catatonic defects.

16. Speech-inactive Catatonia

Originally Leonhard contrasted speech-inactive catatonia with speech-prompt catatonia (526). The speech-inactive catatonics give answers slowly in the earlier stages. In the later stages as a whole they do not give answers. Also in their movements they are severely inhibited, and initiative is extinguished. In his later descriptions Leonhard has stressed that these patients apparently are constantly hallucinated (236, 537). During the examination one can regularly see that they are whispering, sometimes laughing, and at other times looking irritated. Their whispering is clearly different from the murmuring of the proskinetic catatonics. The latter turn towards the examiner and the speech-inactive catatonics seem to be completely uninterested in the examiner, look away and seem to be occupied by their hallucinations. If they are able to speak, they can confirm that they are listening and whispering to the voices. From time to time they can be markedly excited. They can only speak to themselves or have pronounced excitement in which they scream and gesticulate towards the empty air. Although the symptoms mentioned are very characteristic, hallucinations and excitements are so frequent in chronic catatonics that the author has limited the group of speech-inactive catatonics to cases without the characteristics of the other systematic catatonic defects.

In the present series there were twenty cases with speech-inactive catatonics. The average age of onset was 24.8 years and the average observation period 29.8 years. None had a recurring course, and the onset in most cases was insidious. One had a self-assertive, thirteen schizoid and three balanced prepsychotic personalities. Precipitating factors were noticed in five cases. The catatonic symptoms were slight in the beginning. Eight had hebephrenic-catatonic syndromes and nine had paranoid traits. According to Leonhard, speech-inactive catatonics in the beginning often have fantastic traits (537). In the present sample five had expansive ideas and seven feelings of passivity during the acute stage. Except for two cases auditory hallucinations were present from the start.

Clinically the speech-inactive catatonics seem to be the most severely deteriorated chronic catatonics. They have no contact with other patients and lead a completely vegetative existence. All but one were in the disturbed wards. They needed care in all ways with eating, dressing and cleanliness, and could not carry out the most simple forms of work.

Twenty relatives were probably psychotic, and thirteen case histories of relatives were available. One had an affective psychosis, and the remaining twelve were schizophrenics. There were three paranoid, one hebephrenic and eight catatonic defects. Three had periodic catatonias and five were probably speech-inactive catatonics. Thus the relatives show a marked tendency to develop similiar catatonic defects.

The results of the experimental investigation are shown in Table 16.

Eighteen cases were studied experimentally. With the association test 11 gave no responses at all, and in the remaining cases only primitive reactions, mainly echolalic and incoherent answers were obtained.

Twelve patients were not able to form motor reflexes in the first signaling system even with the help of an instructor. Three developed rapidly conditional responses. In the second signaling system ten rapidly formed conditional responses, while eight failed. None was able to form stable reflexes in the first signaling system, which indicates a severe passive inhibition. Even extinc-

TABLE 16
Speech-inactive Catatonia

	Adequate Responses	Inadequate Responses	Too Difficult Tasks	No Information	Total Patients
Associations					
Reproduction	0	0	18	0	18
Mean reaction times	0	7	11	0	18
Median reaction times	0	7	11	0	18
Echolalic responses	1	6	11	0	18
Multiword responses	2	5	11	0	18
Higher responses	0	7	11	0	18
Primitive responses	0	7	11	0	18
Incoherent responses	2	5	11	0	18
Motor Conditional Reflexes					
First reflex in first system	3	12	3	0	18
No reflex in first system	6	9	3	0	18
Reflex in second system	10	5	3	0	18
Reaction times	0	15	3	0	18
After-inhibitions	0	0	18	0	18
Extinction	1	1	16	0	18
Restoration	0	1	17	0	18
Differentiation	0	0	18	0	18
Reversal of negative reflexes	0	0	18	0	18
Reversal of positive reflexes	0	0	18	0	18
Description of performances	0	15	3	0	18
Unstable reflexes	0	15	3	0	18
Extrasignaling reactions	4	11	3	0	18
Continuous pressing	4	11	3	0	18
Autonomic Reactions					
Vascular curve	12	6	0	0	18
Respiratory curve	7	11	0	0	18
Respiratory and vascular dissociation	2	16	0	0	18
Vascular responses to cold	1	17	0	0	18
Vascular responses to calculation	0	13	0	5	18
Effects of pathodynamic structures	18	0	0	0	18
Defensive Reflexes					
Current tolerance	4	14	0	0	18
Motor exhaustion	4	14	0	0	18
Autonomic exhaustion	7	11	0	0	18
Dissociations	0	18	0	0	18
Number of inadequate responses		259			
Number of adequate responses	88				
Number of too difficult tasks			224		

tion and restoration tended to be too difficult for this group, and not one could even try differentiation and reversal of the reflexes. As gross signs of inertia of the nervous processes fourteen patients had either extra-signaling reactions or continuous pressing. No patient could give an adequate description of motor performances.

The unconditional responses to electrical stimulation were strongly exhausted in most cases. All patients were unable to avoid the electrical stimulation after instruction. Five of them succeeded in this task in a single trial, but this was obviously merely by chance.

The plethysmogram had a zero curve in twelve cases, and six had chaotic curves. Respiratory arrhythmias were noticed in eleven cases, and in sixteen cases there were dissociations between the respiratory rhythms and the respiratory oscillations of the plethysmogram. Only one patient had unconditional vascular responses to cold stimulation: vascular and respiratory reactions to calculation or to pathodynamic structures were practically absent.

In the experimental data, the *dissociative* phenomena as well as the inhibitions of all three levels of the higher nervous activity are more pronounced than in any other schizophrenic defect form. This corresponds to the clinical impression that this group consists of the most deteriorated patients. Just as there is clinically a deterioration in all aspects of behavior, the experimental data show severe impairment of all functions.

In seven patients who received ataraxic drugs during the time of the experimental investigations, no special differences as compared with the untreated cases could be established. Altogether sixteen cases had been treated with ataraxic drugs. In ten cases there was no effect and the treatment produced moderate improvement in six. The improvement was a reduction of the hallucinatory excitements, but there was no increase of initiative and contact.

Among the clinical factors related to the severe course can be mentioned the slight catatonic symptoms with hebephrenic traits during the acute stage, the comparatively low age of onset and the long observation period. Among near relatives there is also a marked tendency to develop catatonic defects.

17. Manneristic Catatonia

Originally Leonhard called this type stiff *("starr")* and pointed out that the psychomotor disturbance had some resemblances to Parkinsonism (526). Later he laid more stress on the mannerisms in this defect form (236, 537). In the manneristic catatonic an increasing impoverishment of involuntary motor activity occurs. This results in a stiffness of posture and movement. In addition there are mannerisms, which in the beginning are more prominent than the stiffness. As the illness develops the motor activity is restricted more and more to the forms of movements which are adhered to in a stereotyped way. The impoverishment of movement becomes greater when the mannerisms of movement diminish, and the mannerisms of omission become predominant. Often such patients stand in the same place in a stiff posture and with a stiff facial expression. During examination opposition *("Gegenhalten")* can be demonstrated. The differential diagnosis is mainly from the speech-inactive catatonia, which also shows extreme impoverishment of movement. This lacks the opposition and the stereotyped mannerisms and is distinguished from the manneristic catatonics by the characteristic behavior in relation to the hallucinations. Compared with the parakinetic catatonics, the movements are very slow and more stereotyped. Periodic catatonics with the most unfavorable outcome may also resemble the manneristic catatonics in their dullness and stiffness, but the mannerisms and opposition are lacking in the periodic catatonics.

In the present series there were seventeen cases with manneristic catatonia. The average age of onset was 23.3 years and the average observation period 28.3 years. The onset was insidious as a rule and only one case had a recurring course. Three had self-assertive, eight schizoid and four balanced prepsychotic personalities. Precipitating factors were noticed in six cases. In this group the catatonic symptoms were mostly pronounced from the onset. Only two had hebephrenic-catatonic syndromes and eight had paranoid traits. Expansive ideas were present in four cases, and four had feelings of passivity. The majority already had an emotional blunting in the acute stages. In three cases hallucinations were absent. As to psychomotor symptoms, fifteen had excitements, seven stupor, six negativism and one mannerisms during the acute stage.

Clinically the manneristic catatonics were severely deteriorated. Most of them did not even answer simple questions, and they were not able to carry out the most simple work. Fourteen were in disturbed wards and three in wards with much nursing supervision. Aggressiveness, abusive shouting or excited periods seldom occurred in these patients. The main reason for their being in disturbed wards was the great nursing problem. Practically all were unclean and with their stiffness of movements they were in need of help in every way.

Eighteen relatives were probably psychotic, and for eight case histories were available. Five had affective psychoses and three schizophrenics. One developed a severe paranoid defect, one had a periodic catatonia and one a negativistic catatonia. The family tendency to develop manneristic catatonia was slight. This is somewhat in contradiction to the findings of Leonhard and Faust (223, 537).

The results of the experimental investigations are shown in Table 17.

All seventeen cases were studied experimentally. Twelve gave no responses at all to the association test, and five gave only primitive responses, mainly echolalic and incoherent.

Fourteen patients could not form reflexes in the first signaling system even with instruction, one had stable reflexes, and not one was able to form conditional responses rapidly. In the second signaling system seven could form conditional responses rapidly, which indicates a less severe inhibition of the second than of the first signaling system. Extinction, restoration, differentiation and reversal of reflexes tended to be too difficult. Most of the ten cases who were able to give motor responses showed gross signs of inertia, such as extra-signaling reactions or continuous pressing. None could give an adequate description of the motor performances.

The unconditional responses to electrical stimulation in all but one case showed signs of inhibition. After instruction thirteen

TABLE 17
Manneristic Catatonia

	Adequate Responses	Inadequate Responses	Too Difficult Tasks	No Information	Total Patients
Associations					
Reproduction	0	0	17	0	17
Mean reaction times	0	5	12	0	17
Median reaction times	0	5	12	0	17
Echolalic responses	0	5	12	0	17
Multiword responses	2	3	12	0	17
Higher responses	0	5	12	0	17
Primitive responses	0	5	12	0	17
Incoherent responses	1	4	12	0	17
Motor Conditional Reflexes					
First reflex in first system	0	10	6	1	17
No reflex in first system	2	8	6	1	17
Reflex in second system	7	3	6	1	17
Reaction times	0	10	6	1	17
After-inhibitions	0	0	16	1	17
Extinction	0	2	14	1	17
Restoration	2	0	14	1	17
Differentiation	0	0	16	1	17
Reversal of negative reflexes	0	0	16	1	17
Reversal of positive reflexes	0	0	16	1	17
Description of performances	0	10	6	1	17
Unstable reflexes	1	9	6	1	17
Extrasignaling reactions	3	7	6	1	17
Continuous pressing	6	4	6	1	17
Autonomic Reactions					
Vascular curve	10	6	0	1	17
Respiratory curve	8	8	0	1	17
Respiratory and vascular dissociation	3	13	0	1	17
Vascular responses to cold	0	16	0	1	17
Vascular responses to calculation	0	5	0	12	17
Effects of pathodynamic structures	16	0	0	1	17
Defensive Reflexes					
Current tolerance	5	12	0	0	17
Motor exhaustion	2	15	0	0	17
Autonomic exhaustion	5	12	0	0	17
Dissociations	0	17	0	0	17
Number of inadequate responses		199			
Number of adequate responses	73				
Number of too difficult tasks			241		

cases were unable to avoid electrical stimulation in all trials. In the remaining four cases a few adequate reactions were found.

The plethysmogram in ten cases gave a zero curve and in six cases a chaotic curve. Respiratory arrhythmias were found in eight cases, and thirteen cases had dissociation between the respiratory rhythms and the respiratory oscillations of the plethysmogram. In all but one case the plethysmogram did not react to cold stimulation, calculation and pathodynamic structures. In nine cases stereotyped movements were also carried out during the experimental study, and motor discharges might set in periodically, making the evaluation of the plethysmographic responses difficult. If the patients were anxious, such discharges apparently increased.

The experimental findings show there are great similarities between speech-inactive and manneristic catatonics. These two groups have the most severe dissociations and inhibitions of all schizophrenic defects. There seems to be a basic inhibition of the unconditional centers, which spreads to the first and the second signaling system. The better formation of conditional responses in the second signaling system may indicate that the inhibition of speech functions is mainly determined by the inhibition of the deeper lying structures.

Four cases received ataraxic drugs during the experimental investigation. The only possible difference from the untreated cases was that three of the five patients who gave responses to the association test had received drugs. One of them had been mute for years and in connection with the treatment started to speak again. Among eleven drug-treated patients, in six there was no effect and in five moderate improvement. The improvement consisted mainly in a reduction of the stiffness. The mannerisms like Parkinsonism could become even more pronounced through the drug treatment. This was especially seen in the cases showing no improvement.

As to clinical factors related to the severe course, one can point to the comparatively low age of onset and the long observation periods. In the acute stages the symptoms in some cases resembled those of the prognostically more favorable periodic catatonics. In the family histories there was no great tendency to develop severe catatonic defects.

18. Negativistic Catatonia

Negativistic catatonia is to a great extent diametrically the opposite of proskinetic catatonia. The negativism in these patients seems to be of a rather automatic nature. Often one can observe an ambi-tendency which shows that it is more than an irritable rejection and that a true negativism is present. If it is possible to put the patient in a friendly mood, then he will carry out many requests, but often only partially. He will for instance put out the hand which one asks for, but only halfheartedly, and then draw it back again. If one tries to overcome the active opposition with force rather than with friendliness, then one can easily release a negativistic excitement which may be very violent. Excited states also appear in these patients without any detectable external causes. The motor behavior is impulsive and, due to this, operates awkwardly and jerkily. The posture of the patient is often peculiarly twisted (236, 537).

The differential diagnosis is primarily from the manneristic catatonia and periodic catatonia. In the manneristic cases the stiffness may give the impression of active resistance, but a close investigation shows that they have no active opposition but merely passive opposition ("*Gegenhalten*"). In periodic catatonics with severe defects sudden aggressiveness and irritability may give the impression of negativism, but during examination the more automatic tendency to opposition and ambi-tendency is lacking.

In the present series there were fifteen patients with negativistic catatonia. The average age of onset is 27.1 years and the average observation period was 26.6 years. No case had a recurring course, but in six cases the onset was comparatively acute. One had a self-assertive, eight schizoid and four balanced prepsychotic personalities. Precipitating factors were seen in five cases. During the initial stage some cases had only slight catatonic symptoms. Four cases had hebephrenic-catatonic syndromes. Eight had paranoid traits, three expansive ideas and three feelings of passivity. Emotionally most cases had an affective blunting from the start. Hallucinations were absent in three cases. As to psychomotor symptoms eleven had excitements, four stupor, two mannerisms and fourteen negativism.

Clinically the negativistic catatonics are severely deteriorated. Occasionally they could make remarks showing some ability to observe events in the surroundings. They could also have a lively instinctiveness, which manifested itself in greedy ingestion of food and erotic tendencies. But they could not perform the most simple work. Several were unclean. Because of negativism, periodic excitement or aggressiveness, fourteen were in disturbed wards and one in a ward for chronic cases requiring much supervision.

Eighteen relatives were probably psychotic, and in seven of them case histories were available. Three had affective psychoses and four schizophrenics. Two had hebephrenic defects and two negativistic catatonics. Although there are two close relatives with similiar defects, the family tendency to develop catatonic defects appears to be slight.

The results of the experimental investigations are shown in Table 18.

Ten cases were studied experimentally. Five cases, because of their negativistic behavior, could not be studied at all, and in the cases studied the cooperation was slight.

With the association test six gave no answers and four reacted only with primitive reactions, mainly echolalic and incoherent responses. Some of those who gave no answers could speak to the examiner, so that the results of the test were poorer than was expected from the behavior. Even after instruction none of the patients could give motor reflexes in the first or the second signaling systems. Only three pressed on command, but two with continuous pressing, and one with extra-signaling reactions. With motor reflexes the poor results must, to a great extent, be related to the negativistic attitude.

The unconditional responses to electrical stimulation were inhibited in six cases, and four showed no signs of inhibition. Three were so negativistic that their ability to avoid electrical stimulation after instruction could not be studied. The other seven cases failed in all trials on this task.

Only in six cases could the respiratory and plethysmographic reactions to various stimuli be studied. All cases had chaotic

TABLE 18
Negativistic Catatonia

	Adequate Responses	Inadequate Responses	Too Difficult Tasks	No Information	Total Patients
Associations					
Reproduction	0	0	10	0	10
Mean reaction times	0	4	6	0	10
Median reaction times	0	4	6	0	10
Echolalic responses	1	3	6	0	10
Multiword responses	1	3	6	0	10
Higher responses	0	4	6	0	10
Primitive responses	0	4	6	0	10
Incoherent responses	0	4	6	0	10
Motor Conditional Reflexes					
First reflex in first system	0	3	7	0	10
No reflex in first system	0	3	7	0	10
Reflex in second system	0	3	7	0	10
Reaction times	0	3	7	0	10
After-inhibitions	0	0	10	0	10
Extinction	0	0	10	0	10
Restoration	0	0	10	0	10
Differentiation	0	0	10	0	10
Reversal of negative reflexes	0	0	10	0	10
Reversal of positive reflexes	0	0	10	0	10
Description of performances	0	3	7	0	10
Unstable reflexes	0	3	7	0	10
Extrasignaling reactions	2	1	7	0	10
Continuous pressing	1	2	7	0	10
Autonomic Reactions					
Vascular curve	0	6	0	4	10
Respiratory curve	0	6	0	4	10
Respiratory and vascular dissociation	0	6	0	4	10
Vascular responses to cold	0	6	0	4	10
Vascular responses to calculation	1	2	0	7	10
Effects of pathodynamic structures	6	0	0	4	10
Defensive Reflexes					
Current tolerance	5	5	0	0	10
Motor exhaustion	4	6	0	0	10
Autonomic exhaustion	7	3	0	0	10
Dissociations	0	7	0	3	10
Number of inadequate responses		94			
Number of adequate responses	28				
Number of too difficult tasks			168		

plethysmographic curves, respiratory arrhythmias and dissociations between the respiratory rhythms and the respiratory oscillations of the plethysmogram. None of these cases gave vascular responses to unconditional cold stimulation, and only one case had marked respiratory and vascular reactions to calculation or pathodynamic structures.

In the experimental data, it is obvious that the poor performances were to a great extent due to the negativism. Compared with other catatonic defects, the tendency to inhibition of unconditional responses was smaller. The severe autonomic dissociations can also be regarded as signs of disinhibition of autonomic reactions. The complete failure to avoid electrical stimulation after instruction is probably a real sign of dissociation, as patients with strong motor and autonomic reactions to the unconditional stimuli also showed in their general behavior that the procedure was unpleasant, but nevertheless they were unable to avoid the stimulation. The strong inhibitions of the first and second signaling systems are probably mainly related to active negativism. The poor results in the few cases who responded to these tasks indicates that this cannot be the whole explanation. It is possible that the negativism and aggressiveness of the negativistic catatonics is related to less strong inhibition of unconditional reflexes than in other catatonic defects ($P < 0.02$).

One of the negativistic catatonics received ataraxic drugs when they were studied experimentally. Among nine cases treated with ataraxic drugs before and after, in five there was no effect and in four moderate improvement. The improvement was mainly due to a reduction of excitement and aggressiveness. The characteristic active opposition was practically unchanged.

Among clinical factors related to the severe course, it is demonstrated that all but one from the beginning had negativism. But as seen from other parts of this chapter, many catatonics with negativistic traits during the acute stage do not develop negativistic defect states. The family histories reveal no strong genetic tendency to develop catatonic defects.

Chapter VIII

CLINICAL AND EXPERIMENTAL STUDIES OF ACUTE AND SUBACUTE FUNCTIONAL PSYCHOSES

1. HEBEPHRENIC AND HEBEPHRENIC-PARANOID PSYCHOSES

THE PRESENT SERIES includes cases where affective blunting and autism were the most important symptoms. Most of them had some paranoid ideas, but mainly vague, unsystematic and short lasting delusions. Process symptoms such as depersonalization and feelings of passivity were usually present, but often for short periods and they did not dominate the clinical picture as they did in the paranoid group with the symptom complex of *"Gedanken-entzug."* As asserted by Carl Schneider, the hebephrenics show the symptom complex of *"Sprunghaftigkeit"* (803). In their behavior they may be inhibited or restless in a disorganized way.

In the group of hebephrenic-paranoid psychoses there were forty cases. None had recovered, nine had had social remissions, and thirty-one cases are probably developing schizophrenic deterioration. Clinically these cases are obviously a nuclear group of schizophrenia, where the prognosis, as emphasized by Langfeldt and co-workers is very poor (205, 513). In the followed-up cases from Gaustad hospital hebephrenic traits and emotional blunting were also prognostically unfavorable symptoms (331).

In the thirty-one cases with a progressive course several have already developed characteristics of the previously described types of chronic schizophrenia during the period of observation. Seven seem to have developed slight hebephrenic defects, nineteen severe hebephrenic defects and five slight paranoid defects. As severe paranoid defects usually need considerable time to develop, it is probable that the short observation period is the main reason why symptoms of such defects have not been observed.

188

For the whole group of hebephrenics the average age of onset was 24.2 years. At the time of the experimental investigation the average duration of disease was 2.8 years. The onset was insidious in thirty-seven cases and in three cases acute after prodromal symptoms. Only four had a recurring course. Three had self-assertive, twenty schizoid, two balanced and most of the remainder sensitive prepsychotic personalities. Precipitating factors were noticed in twenty-two cases, but no cases showed any acute mental trauma, bodily disease or childbirth, which in follow-up studies give a good prognosis (331). In thirty-one cases the initial symptoms were changes of character. At the onset eight cases had impulsiveness or tantrums and twelve cases suspiciousness, ideas of reference or jealousy. Purely hebephrenic syndromes were only found in four cases, whereas thirty-six had some paranoid traits. Psychomotor symptoms were regularly slight, but most cases had inhibition, blocking or some mannerisms. Typical schizophrenic delusions were present for a short time in ten cases. Only five cases had no hallucinations. Among patients with hallucinations eleven had the specific schizophrenic auditory hallucinations and nineteen haptic hallucinations (331). As to typical schizophrenic disturbances of thinking twenty-four had depersonalization and thirty-three feelings of passivity. Disturbance of symbolization was present in six cases.

The main clinical difference between the nine cases with social remissions and the progressive cases was the comparatively shorter duration of disease and less affective blunting. In seven of these cases it was doubtful if affective blunting was actually present, and all nine cases also had other affective changes such as depression, elation or perplexity.

Thirty-three relatives were probably psychotic, and for twenty-one case histories were available. There were five affective psychoses, three of manic-depressive and two of reactive types. In two of the affective psychoses there had been diagnostic doubt about the presence of schizophrenia. There remain sixteen certain schizophrenics. Two had developed hebephrenic, eight paranoid and six catatonic defects. It seems that the family background shows a slight genetic tendency to develop hebephrenic defects. There is a great tendency to schizophrenic deterioration in sixteen such cases as compared with five recurrent cases.

The results of the experimental investigations are shown in the Tables 19 and 20.

In the experiments all but one patient had several reactions not found in the normal sample. In the association test, nineteen had impaired reproduction. The mean reaction times were prolonged in twenty-nine and the median reaction times in twenty-five cases. It was also noticed that thirty-five had periodic prolongations of reaction times without any relations to complex words or difficult stimulus-words. Even these periodic prolongations could be considered as a correlate to the blocking and the "*Sprunghaftigkeit*," which is clinically characteristic of this group. Twenty-six had more echolalic and eleven more multiword responses than found in the normal sample. Twenty-four had less higher associations and fourteen more primitive responses than found in normals. In sixteen patients incoherent reactions were observed.

In the first signaling system the ability to form the first as well as the second conditional reflex was not essentially different from normals. In the second signaling system conditional responses were formed rapidly. There was a strong tendency to after-inhibitions, indicating a passive inhibition of the first signaling system. Twenty-two had irregular prolongations of the reaction times, which, in the same way as the irregular prolongations of association reaction times can be regarded as a physiological correlate to the clinical symptom complex of "*Sprunghaftigkeit*." Extinction occurred rapidly in most cases. Only ten succeeded in differentiation. There was a considerable impairment of internal inhibition in most cases. Restoration was impaired in seventeen cases. With the reversal of positive and negative reflexes only twelve had no signs of inertia of the excitatory or the inhibitory processes. Twenty-eight failed to describe their motor performances.

The unconditional responses to electrical stimulation showed signs of inhibition in thirteen cases, but pronounced inhibition only in 6 cases. Twenty-one cases failed in one or more trials to avoid electrical stimulation after instruction, but none failed in every attempt. This partial failing may correspond, just as the pro-

TABLE 19
PROGRESSIVE HEBEPHRENIAS

	Adequate Responses	Inadequate Responses	Too Difficult Tasks	No Information	Total Patients
Associations					
Reproduction	14	14	2	1	31
Mean reaction times	8	22	0	1	31
Median reaction times	9	21	0	1	31
Echolalic responses	9	21	0	1	31
Multiword responses	21	9	0	1	31
Higher responses	10	20	0	1	31
Primitive responses	18	12	0	1	31
Incoherent responses	17	13	0	1	31
Motor Conditional Reflexes					
First reflex in first system	14	17	0	0	31
Second reflex in first system	24	5	0	2	31
Reflex in second system	30	0	0	1	31
Reaction times	13	18	0	0	31
After-inhibitions	3	27	1	0	31
Extinction	25	6	0	0	31
Restoration	20	11	0	0	31
Differentiation	7	22	2	0	31
Reversal of negative reflexes	13	15	3	0	31
Reversal of positive reflexes	15	13	3	0	31
Description of performances	9	22	0	0	31
Unstable reflexes	29	2	0	0	31
Extrasignaling reactions	30	1	0	0	31
Continuous pressing	27	4	0	0	31
Autonomic Reactions					
Vascular curve	23	8	0	0	31
Respiratory curve	17	14	0	0	31
Respiratory and vascular dissociation	13	18	0	0	31
Vascular responses to cold	6	25	0	0	31
Vascular responses to calculation	13	16	0	2	31
Effects of pathodynamic structures	24	7	0	0	31
Defensive Reflexes					
Current tolerance	21	9	0	1	31
Motor exhaustion	21	9	0	1	31
Autonomic exhaustion	22	8	0	1	31
Dissociations	14	16	0	1	31
Number of inadequate responses		425			
Number of adequate responses	539				
Number of too difficult tasks			11		

TABLE 20
RECURRENT HEBEPHRENIAS

	Adequate Responses	Inadequate Responses	Too Difficult Tasks	No Information	Total Patients
Associations					
Reproduction	6	3	0	0	9
Mean reaction times	2	7	0	0	9
Median reaction times	5	4	0	0	9
Echolalic responses	4	5	0	0	9
Multiword responses	7	2	0	0	9
Higher responses	5	4	0	0	9
Primitive responses	7	2	0	0	9
Incoherent responses	6	3	0	0	9
Motor Conditional Reflexes					
First reflex in first system	5	4	0	0	9
Second reflex in first system	8	1	0	0	9
Reflex in second system	9	0	0	0	9
Reaction times	5	4	0	0	9
After-inhibitions	1	8	0	0	9
Extinction	7	2	0	0	9
Restoration	3	6	0	0	9
Differentiation	3	6	0	0	9
Reversal of negative reflexes	4	4	1	0	9
Reversal of positive reflexes	5	3	1	0	9
Description of performances	3	6	0	0	9
Unstable reflexes	9	0	0	0	9
Extrasignaling reactions	9	0	0	0	9
Continuous pressing	9	0	0	0	9
Autonomic Reactions					
Vascular curve	9	0	0	0	9
Respiratory curve	9	0	0	0	9
Respiratory and vascular dissociation	7	2	0	0	9
Vascular responses to cold	0	9	0	0	9
Vascular responses to calculation	6	3	0	0	9
Effects of pathodynamic structures	6	3	0	0	9
Defensive Reflexes					
Current tolerance	7	2	0	0	9
Motor exhaustion	7	2	0	0	9
Autonomic exhaustion	9	0	0	0	9
Dissociations	4	5	0	0	9
Number of inadequate responses		100			
Number of adequate responses	186				
Number of too difficult tasks			2		

longation of reaction times does, to the clinical symptom complex of "*Sprunghaftigkeit*" or psychologically to some kind of distractability.

The plethysmogram gave a zero curve in thirty cases, oscillations of the third order in two cases and chaotic curves in eight cases. Respiratory arrhythmias were noticed in fourteen cases and dissociations between the respiratory rhythms and the respiratory oscillations of the plethysmogram in twenty cases. In six cases vascular reactions to unconditional cold stimulation were noticed and nineteen responded to calculation. Most cases gave very slight or negative vascular and respiratory reactions to pathodynamic structures. In ten cases there were strong reactions to such structures. These ten cases in spite of the affective blunting, clinically show some affect in connection with their delusions. Three of them had social remissions, and two seemed to develop paranoid defects.

In the study of the initial stages of the defect schizophrenics, cases with mixed hebephrenic paranoid syndromes often develop paranoid defects during the further course of the illness. It may be that the experimental signs of strong pathodynamic structures can help to predict such courses.

Summarizing the experimental data, the hebephrenic group is characterized by the periodic inhibitions of associative and motor reactions and severe dissociative phenomena. Concerning prognostic factors it is noted that dissociation was less frequent in the cases with social remissions than in the progressive cases ($P < 0.02$). In the chronic hebephrenics a marked tendency to dissociation was also found. The progressive cases had a smaller proportion of adequate responses than the recurrent ones ($P < 0.01$).

During the experimental investigation seven cases received ataraxic drugs, five of these cases had signs of inhibition of the unconditional defensive reflexes. It is possible that this inhibition is due partially to the drugs. During the period of observation twenty-seven cases have been treated with ataraxic drugs. In seven cases there was no effect, in nine a moderate effect and in six a good effect of the treatment. Five had social remissions. Five of the patients with a good result, two of the patients with a moderate result and none with negative results showed a marked effect of pathodynamic structures in the experiments. This would mean that the presence of such structures indicates a better prognosis for drug treatment in hebephrenic-paranoid cases. The cases 254 and 514 are leucotomized and have comparatively great impairment of the higher nervous activity.

In conclusion it was found that the hebephrenics could be considered as a nuclear schizophrenic group with small chances of remissions. Clinically they had symptoms which according to follow-up studies are prognostically unfavorable (331). Experimentally there were severe dissociative disturbances and oscillating inhibitions of the two signaling systems, which can be correlated with the clinical symptom complex of *"Sprunghaftigkeit."* Their near relatives have a marked tendency to schizophrenic deterioration.

2. CATATONIC AND MIXED CATATONIC PSYCHOSES

This group comprises all cases where catatonic traits had been found during the acute stage.

In the present series there were altogether forty-four cases. Twenty-six are probably progressing towards schizophrenic deterioration, while eighteen had social remissions. All of these appeared to have some mild schizophrenic personality changes when they left the hospital. Since several of the progressive cases also had recurring courses, the longer term prognosis may be considerably different.

The average age of onset was twenty-seven years. If only the duration of the disease since the last remission was considered, the average duration of the disease at the time of the experimental investigation was 1.4 years. If the average observation period since the first attack of the disease was considered, the average observation period increases to six years. Thirty-four cases had social remissions previously to the experimental examination, and among the other ten, two recurred after the examination. In the systematic chronic catatonics, such pronounced tendency to remission was not found. One explanation might be that the modern therapeutic methods increase the tendency to remissions. Another possibility is that this sample consists of non-systematic catatonics with a tendency to a periodic course.

Among the progressive cases three appeared to develop severe and one slight paranoid defects. Only three had sharply defined traits of the systematic catatonics. In the remaining nineteen cases one could mainly observe the lameness and dullness found in periodic catatonics with a chronic course.

The onset of the disease was insidious in nine cases, acute after prodromal symptoms in twenty-four cases and acute without prodromal symptoms in eleven cases. Seven had balanced, eighteen schizoid, seven self-assertive and most of the remaining sensitive prepsychotic personalities. Twenty-three had precipitating factors in the case histories, and in seven cases acute mental trauma, somatic disease or childbirth. Compared with the hebephrenic group, definite external stresses played a greater role in the precipitation. The initial symptoms were mostly neurasthenic traits, depression, suspiciousness or ideas of reference. Thirteen had initially changes of personality and seven, tantrums or impulsiveness. The latter symptoms were mainly found in the progressive cases.

Six cases had hebephrenic-catatonic syndromes, and five of these had progressive courses. Thirty-four cases had paranoid traits, and only nine cases had purely catatonic syndromes. For psychomotor symptoms thirty-six had excitement, ten stupor, six mannerisms and seven negativism. The recurring cases mainly had excitements, and the other more characteristic catatonic symptoms were mostly found in the progressive cases. In fifteen cases emotional blunting was present from the start, and only three of them had social remissions. Typical schizophrenic delusions were found in nine cases, and just as often in the recurring as in the progressive cases. With regard to the typical schizophrenic disturbances of thinking, six had disturbances of symbolization, twenty-one feelings of passivity and twenty depersonalization. Feelings of passivity were more frequent in the progressive cases. Hallucinations were absent in ten cases. Seven had specific schizophrenic auditory hallucinations and fourteen haptic hallucinations. There were no essential differences between recurring and progressive cases with respect to the type of hallucination.

Fifty-two relatives had probably been psychotic, and thirty-eight case histories were available. Twenty had affective psychoses, eleven of the manic-depressive and nine of the reactive type. Among the remaining eighteen schizophrenics, two had paranoid defects, four hebephrenic defects, four systematic and eight periodic catatonics. There was a strong tendency among the relatives to suffer from catatonic schizophrenia. In the families of the progressive cases there were fourteen schizophrenics and seven affective psychotics, but in the families of the recurrent cases there were four schizophrenics and thirteen affective psychotics. This shows clearly that hereditary factors were of great importance for the prognosis of the catatonic cases.

The results of the experimental investigations are shown in the Tables 21 and 22.

With the association test the reproduction was severely impaired in twenty-seven cases. The mean reaction times were prolonged in twenty-seven cases and the median reaction times prolonged in twenty-nine cases. A tendency to periodic prolongations of the reaction times similiar to that in the hebephrenic sample was noticed in thirty-eight cases. Inadequate scores of echolalic and multiword responses are found in respectively twenty-eight and eleven cases. Less higher reactions than in the normal sample were found in twenty-five and more primitive reactions in thirteen cases. Incoherent reactions were noticed in eighteen cases and more often in the progressive than in the recurring cases.

The ability to form motor conditional reflexes in the first and second signaling system was in the majority of the cases not impaired. There was a strong tendency to after-inhibitions, and in twenty cases irregular prolongations of the reaction times were observed. Fifteen of these cases had a progressive course, which indicates that this type of inhibition is prognostically unfavorable. In most cases extinction was not impaired. Only twelve could adequately carry out differentiation, which shows that the internal inhibition is considerably weakened in most cases. Several cases had difficulties with restoration, and reversal of the positive and negative reflexes could be carried out adequately in nineteen cases. Most patients had an inertia of the nervous processes. Eighteen patients were able to describe their motor performances adequately. Only three of the progressive cases could give a completely adequate description of their reactions. It seems that in

TABLE 21
PROGRESSIVE CATATONIAS

	Adequate Responses	Inadequate Responses	Too Difficult Tasks	No Information	Total Patients
Associations					
Reproduction	9	14	3	0	26
Mean reaction times	9	17	0	0	26
Median reaction times	7	19	0	0	26
Echolalic responses	11	15	0	0	26
Multiword responses	19	7	0	0	26
Higher responses	12	14	0	0	26
Primitive responses	17	9	0	0	26
Incoherent responses	14	12	0	0	26
Motor Conditional Reflexes					
First reflex in first system	9	16	1	0	26
Second reflex in first system	19	3	1	3	26
Reflex in second system	23	2	1	0	26
Reaction times	10	15	1	0	26
After-inhibitions	5	17	4	0	26
Extinction	20	2	4	0	26
Restoration	12	10	4	0	26
Differentiation	7	15	4	0	26
Reversal of negative reflexes	15	6	5	0	26
Reversal of positive reflexes	13	8	5	0	26
Description of performances	8	17	1	0	26
Unstable reflexes	22	3	1	0	26
Extrasignaling reactions	21	4	1	0	26
Continuous pressing	22	3	1	0	26
Autonomic Reactions					
Vascular curve	23	3	0	0	26
Respiratory curve	21	5	0	0	26
Respiratory and vascular dissociation	13	13	0	0	26
Vascular responses to cold	4	22	0	0	26
Vascular responses to calculation	14	11	0	1	26
Effects of pathodynamic structures	25	1	0	0	26
Defensive Reflexes					
Current tolerance	16	9	0	1	26
Motor exhaustion	15	10	0	1	26
Autonomic exhaustion	23	2	0	1	26
Dissociations	13	12	0	1	26

Number of inadequate responses		316			
Number of adequate responses	471				
Number of too difficult tasks			37		

TABLE 22
RECURRENT CATATONIAS

	Adequate Responses	Inadequate Responses	Too Difficult Tasks	No Information	Total Patients
Associations					
Reproduction	8	10	0	0	18
Mean reaction times	8	10	0	0	18
Median reaction times	8	10	0	0	18
Echolalic responses	5	13	0	0	18
Multiword responses	14	4	0	0	18
Higher responses	7	11	0	0	18
Primitive responses	14	4	0	0	18
Incoherent responses	12	6	0	0	18
Motor Conditional Reflexes					
First reflex in first system	11	7	0	0	18
Second reflex in first system	18	0	0	0	18
Reflex in second system	18	0	0	0	18
Reaction times	13	5	0	0	18
After-inhibitions	5	13	0	0	18
Extinction	12	6	0	0	18
Restoration	11	7	0	0	18
Differentiation	5	13	0	0	18
Reversal of negative reflexes	13	5	0	0	18
Reversal of positive reflexes	12	6	0	0	18
Description of performances	10	8	0	0	18
Unstable reflexes	17	1	0	0	18
Extrasignaling reactions	18	0	0	0	18
Continuous pressing	18	0	0	0	18
Autonomic Reactions					
Vascular curve	18	0	0	0	18
Respiratory curve	17	1	0	0	18
Respiratory and vascular dissociation	13	5	0	0	18
Vascular responses to cold	5	13	0	0	18
Vascular responses to calculation	11	6	0	1	18
Effects of pathodynamic structures	12	6	0	0	18
Defensive Reflexes					
Current tolerance	10	8	0	0	18
Motor exhaustion	10	8	0	0	18
Autonomic exhaustion	15	3	0	0	18
Dissociations	9	9	0	0	18
Number of inadequate responses		198			
Number of adequate responses	377				
Number of too difficult tasks			0		

catatonics the absence of dissociation in the interactions of the signaling system is prognostically favorable.

In nineteen cases there were signs of inhibition of the unconditional responses to electrical stimulation. Twenty-one cases failed in one or more trials to avoid the electrical stimulation after instruction. With the reactions to electrical stimulation no essential differences between recurrent and progressive cases could be found.

The plethysmogram gave a zero curve in thirty-eight cases, oscillations of the third order in three cases and chaotic curves in three cases. Respiratory arrhythmias were noticed in six cases and dissociations between the respiratory curve and respiratory oscillations of the plethysmogram in eighteen cases. Signs of autonomic dissociation were considerably more frequent in the progressive than in the recurrent cases. Vascular reactions to unconditional cold stimulation and calculation were observed in respectively nine and twenty-five cases. In most cases the autonomic reactions to pathodynamic structures were slight or even absent. Violent autonomic reactions were only noticed in seven cases, and six of these had social remissions.

Reviewing the experimental data, the catatonic cases had severe dissociative phenomena, considerable impairment of internal inhibition, inertia of the nervous processes and inhibitions of all three levels of the higher nervous activity. The tendency to periodic swingings of the inhibition in the first and second signaling systems is characteristic. This is correlated with the clinical symptom complex of "*Sprunghaftigkeit*" in catatonia (803).

The severe dissociative phenomena and swinging inhibitions of the first signaling system were especially prognostically unfavorable. Prognostically favorable were absence of disturbances of the interactions of the two signaling systems and strong autonomic reactions to pathodynamic structures. The progressive cases had less adequate responses ($P < 0.01$) and more dissociative disturbances ($P < 0.05$) than the recurrent ones.

Compared with the series of chronic catatonics, the cases in this series had considerable less disturbances of the higher nervous activity. In particular there were less dissociative phenomena and less inhibition.

During the experimental investigation fourteen cases received ataraxic drugs. As only four of them had inhibitions of the unconditional responses to electrical stimulation, the drug treatment could not have been of importance in the tendency to inhibit such responses. Only two of the drug treated patients showed violent autonomic reactions to pathodynamic structures. For other types of disturbances there were no essential differences between treated and untreated cases. During the period observed altogether thirty-six cases have received ataraxic drugs. Fourteen responded with social remissions, thirteen had good improvement, six moderate and only in three was there no effect. It seems that most patients in this series benefited from the drug treatment. Those who benefited from the treatment had clinical symptoms and experimental findings which for the whole group were prognostically favorable.

In conclusion it was found that there were symptomatological, as well as hereditary and experimental differences, between the groups of progressive and recurrent catatonic cases. The clinical symptom complex of *"Sprunghaftigkeit"* is paralleled by oscillating inhibitions of the nervous activity in experimental investigations.

3. PARANOID PSYCHOSES DOMINATED BY PROJECTION SYMPTOMS

In the present series there were fifty-one paranoid cases, in whom the clinical picture was dominated by projection symptoms. In this group the prognosis is comparatively favorable with twenty-two progressive cases and twenty-nine with social remissions. Sixteen of the recurrent cases seemed to have some residual of the schizophrenic process in the form of personality changes, but thirteen had no such traits and could be considered as recovered when they left the hospital. In all the recovered cases there had been diagnostic doubts whether they actually were affective psychoses. Several of the progressive cases had previously had social remissions, so that it is probable that a longer observation period would lower the prognostic outlook for the recurrent psychoses.

The average age of onset was 34.5 years and slightly higher in the recurrent than in the progressive cases. The average duration of the disease since the first psychotic attack was at the time of experimental investigation 4.4 years. When remissions are not included, the average duration since the last psychotic attack was 1.6 years. Thirty-one cases had previously remitted from psychotic episodes, but twelve had later shown a schizophrenic deterioration. Among twenty-five cases with insidious onset seventeen had a progressive course, and among eleven cases with acute onset without prodromal symptoms only one case showed schizophrenic deterioration.

Seven had balanced, eleven schizoid, eight self-assertive, and most of the remaining sensitive prepsychotic personalities. Precipitating factors were observed in forty-two cases, but acute mental trauma in none of these, and somatic disease or childbirth only in seven. In thirty-two cases there had originally been diagnostic doubt whether the cases actually were schizophrenic, but only in eight of the progressive cases. In most cases the initial symptoms were ideas of reference, suspiciousness or jealousy. Changes of personality, impulsiveness or tantrums were only observed in a few cases. Emotional blunting was present in only eleven cases, mainly in the progressive cases. The emotional disturbances were predominantly in the direction of perplexity, depression, elation or ecstasy. Strong affective traits or confusion were present in twenty cases, and only two of these had progressive courses. The recurrent cases to a great extent can be considered to have schizoaffective syndromes. Typical schizophrenic delusions were present in thirty-four cases, but just as often in recurrent as in deteriorating cases. In nine cases there were combinations of such delusions (331). As to the typical schizophrenic disturbances of thinking, all patients in this group have feelings of passivity. Disorder of symbolization was present in thirty-five cases, and depersonalization also in thirty-five cases. These thought disturbances were as frequent in progressive as in recurrent cases. Hallucinations were absent in only three cases. Eighteen patients had specific schizophrenic auditory hallucinations and thirty-one haptic hallucinations. Such symptoms were also just as frequent in recurrent as in deteriorating cases.

Among symptoms, which in our follow-up studies were considered to be typically schizophrenic with the character of mental automatisms, the whole group had on the average 4.5 symptoms. This shows clearly that the feeling of passivity has a great tendency to be combined with other mental automatisms (331).

As to the clinical differences between the progressive and the recurrent cases, in the recurrent group affective and confusional syndromes are more frequent, and the onset tends to be more acute.

Fifty-one relatives had probably been psychotic, and for thirty-eight of them case histories were available. Seventeen had affective psychoses, nine of the manic-depressive and eight of the reactive type. There were twenty-one schizophrenics. Eleven had slight paranoid defects, two severe paranoid defects, one a slight hebephrenic defect, five were periodic and two systematic catatonics. This would mean that the relatives have a tendency to develop slighter schizophrenic defects, and especially slight paranoid defects. Among the progressive cases in this series all seemed to develop mild paranoid defects, probably phonemic and hypochondriacal paraphrenics in fourteen cases and in the remaining cases affect-laden paraphrenics and schizophasiacs. It may be noted that of the relatives of the recurrent cases thirteen had affective and five schizophrenic psychoses, whereas of the relatives of the progressive cases four had affective and sixteen schizophrenic psychoses. This shows that the relatives, with regard to remissions as well as with regard to types of defect, show great similiarities with the probands. It may be noted that our series of chronic phonemic and hypochondriacal paraphrenias mostly began in the acute stages as paranoid psychoses with projection symptoms, while the sample of acute paranoid psychoses with projection symptoms tended to develop phonemic and hypochondriacal paraphrenias.

The results of the experimental investigations are shown in the Tables 23, 24, 25.

In the association test fifteen cases had impairment of reproduction. The mean reaction times were prolonged in twenty-two and the median reaction times in twenty-three cases. The prolongations of reaction times did not, as in the hebephrenic and catatonic cases, have the periodic oscillating character. Pro-

TABLE 23
Progressive Psychoses with Projection Symptoms

	Adequate Responses	Inadequate Responses	Too Difficult Tasks	No Information	Total Patients
Associations					
Reproduction	14	8	0	0	22
Mean reaction times	9	13	0	0	22
Median reaction times	9	13	0	0	22
Echolalic responses	10	12	0	0	22
Multiword responses	16	6	0	0	22
Higher responses	11	11	0	0	22
Primitive responses	18	4	0	0	22
Incoherent responses	16	6	0	0	22
Motor Conditional Reflexes					
First reflex in first system	12	10	0	0	22
Second reflex in first system	22	0	0	0	22
Reflex in second system	22	0	0	0	22
Reaction times	17	5	0	0	22
After-inhibitions	10	12	0	0	22
Extinction	17	5	0	0	22
Restoration	12	10	0	0	22
Differentiation	9	13	0	0	22
Reversal of negative reflexes	14	7	1	0	22
Reversal of positive reflexes	18	3	1	0	22
Description of performances	14	8	0	0	22
Unstable reflexes	22	0	0	0	22
Extrasignaling reactions	22	0	0	0	22
Continuous pressing	22	0	0	0	22
Autonomic Reactions					
Vascular curve	22	0	0	0	22
Respiratory curve	22	0	0	0	22
Respiratory and vascular dissociation	13	9	0	0	22
Vascular responses to cold	4	18	0	0	22
Vascular responses to calculation	9	11	0	2	22
Effects of pathodynamic structures	22	0	0	0	22
Defensive Reflexes					
Current tolerance	8	14	0	0	22
Motor exhaustion	9	13	0	0	22
Autonomic exhaustion	14	8	0	0	22
Dissociations	16	6	0	0	22
Number of inadequate responses		225			
Number of adequate responses	475				
Number of too difficult tasks			2		

TABLE 24
IMPROVED PSYCHOSES WITH PROJECTION SYMPTOMS

	Adequate Responses	Inadequate Responses	Too Difficult Tasks	No Information	Total Patients
Associations					
Reproduction	11	3	0	2	16
Mean reaction times	10	4	0	2	16
Median reaction times	10	4	0	2	16
Echolalic responses	6	8	0	2	16
Multiword responses	5	9	0	2	16
Higher responses	3	11	0	2	16
Primitive responses	10	4	0	2	16
Incoherent responses	8	6	0	2	16
Motor Conditional Reflexes					
First reflex in first system	5	10	0	1	16
Second reflex in first system	14	1	0	1	16
Reflex in second system	15	0	0	1	16
Reaction times	12	3	0	1	16
After-inhibitions	3	12	0	1	16
Extinction	14	1	0	1	16
Restoration	9	6	0	1	16
Differentiation	5	10	0	1	16
Reversal of negative reflexes	11	4	0	1	16
Reversal of positive reflexes	8	7	0	1	16
Description of performances	7	8	0	1	16
Unstable reflexes	15	0	0	1	16
Extrasignaling reactions	15	0	0	1	16
Continuous pressing	15	0	0	1	16
Autonomic Reactions					
Vascular curve	15	0	0	1	16
Respiratory curve	15	0	0	1	16
Respiratory and vascular dissociation	12	3	0	1	16
Vascular responses to cold	6	9	0	1	16
Vascular responses to calculation	8	7	0	1	16
Effects of pathodynamic structures	15	0	0	1	16
Defensive Reflexes					
Current tolerance	9	5	0	2	16
Motor exhaustion	9	5	0	2	16
Autonomic exhaustion	11	3	0	2	16
Dissociations	9	5	0	2	16
Number of inadequate responses		148			
Number of adequate responses	320				
Number of too difficult tasks			0		

TABLE 25
Recovered Psychoses with Projection Symptoms

	Adequate Responses	Inadequate Responses	Too Difficult Tasks	No Information	Total Patients
Associations					
Reproduction	9	4	0	0	13
Mean reaction times	8	5	0	0	13
Median reaction times	7	6	0	0	13
Echolalic responses	6	7	0	0	13
Multiword responses	11	2	0	0	13
Higher responses	8	5	0	0	13
Primitive responses	12	1	0	0	13
Incoherent responses	13	0	0	0	13
Motor Conditional Reflexes					
First reflex in first system	10	3	0	0	13
Second reflex in first system	13	0	0	0	13
Reflex in second system	12	1	0	0	13
Reaction times	13	0	0	0	13
After-inhibitions	7	6	0	0	13
Extinction	11	2	0	0	13
Restoration	8	5	0	0	13
Differentiation	5	8	0	0	13
Reversal of negative reflexes	5	8	0	0	13
Reversal of positive reflexes	9	4	0	0	13
Description of performances	9	4	0	0	13
Unstable reflexes	13	0	0	0	13
Extrasignaling reactions	13	0	0	0	13
Continuous pressing	13	0	0	0	13
Autonomic Reactions					
Vascular curve	13	0	0	0	13
Respiratory curve	13	0	0	0	13
Respiratory and vascular dissociation	11	2	0	0	13
Vascular responses to cold	4	9	0	0	13
Vascular responses to calculation	9	4	0	0	13
Effects of pathodynamic structures	13	0	0	0	13
Defensive Reflexes					
Current tolerance	5	7	0	1	13
Motor exhaustion	5	7	0	1	13
Autonomic exhaustion	10	2	0	1	13
Dissociations	7	5	0	1	13
Number of inadequate responses		107			
Number of adequate responses	305				
Number of too difficult tasks			0		

longations were predominantly observed after stimulus-words having some connection with the delusions. Twenty-seven cases had an excessive number of echolalic and seventeen an excessive number of multiword responses. Only five cases responded predominantly with echolalic and multiword responses. Twenty-two had a number of higher associations, and forty a number of primitive associations within the limits of the normal sample. Incoherent responses were found in twelve cases, and in none of the recovered cases. Thus an absence of incoherent responses is prognostically favorable.

In the first as well as in the second signaling system the ability to form conditional motor reflexes was not essentially different from that of the normal sample. There was a strong tendency to after-inhibitions. Periodic prolongations of reaction times were noticed in eight cases, and in none of the recovered cases. There was a smaller tendency to such inhibitions than in the hebephrenic and catatonic psychoses, and, as in these cases, the periodic prolongations of reaction times were prognostically unfavorable. Extinction was impaired in a few cases. Only nineteen could differentiate adequately, which demonstrates a tendency to impairment of the internal inhibition. Restoration was impaired in twenty-one cases. With the changes of dynamic stereotypes nineteen failed in reversing a negative reflex into a positive reflex, whereas fourteen failed in reversing a positive reflex into a negative reflex. There was a considerable inertia of the nervous processes, especially of the inhibitory processes. Thirty were able to give an adequate description of their motor performances, a large proportion of those were recovered cases. For the whole group the dissociation between the two signaling systems was not so pronounced as in the hebephrenic and catatonic psychoses.

The unconditional reflexes to electrical stimulation showed signs of inhibition in twenty-nine cases, and there was a greater tendency to inhibition of the responses in these cases than in the hebephrenic and catatonic cases. After instruction sixteen cases failed to avoid the electrical stimulation in one or more trials.

The plethysmogram in forty-seven cases gave a zero curve, and in three cases oscillations of the third order were present. Chaotic plethysmographic curves or respiratory arrhythmias were found in none of the cases. Signs of dissociation between the respiratory curve and the respiratory oscillations of the plethysmogram were found in fourteen cases, mainly in the progressive group. Vascular responses to unconditional cold stimulation were seen in fourteen cases, and only four of those were deteriorating cases. Vascular responses to calculation were present in twenty-six cases, among which nine were progressive. This would mean that there is a greater tendency to inhibition of vascular responses to unconditional stimuli as well as to stimuli of the second signaling system in the progressive cases. Vascular or respiratory responses to pathodynamic structures were observed in twenty-six cases, but never the violent responses which are usually observed in paranoid cases with systematized delusions and several of the cases in the series of chronic paranoid schizophrenics. With regard to the influences of pathodynamic structures there were no differences between the progressive and the recurrent cases.

The experimental data here show the most characteristic disturbance was the tendency to inhibition, particularly of the unconditional reflexes. Compared with the other acute and subacute functional psychoses the tendency to inhibition of unconditional reflexes is statistically significant at the 0.001 level. It may be noted that the autonomic components of the pathodynamic structures tended to be small. Fluctuating inhibitions of the reaction times in the first and second signaling systems are as a rule absent. Internal inhibition tends to be weakened. In several cases there were only slight signs of inertia, and such cases mostly had a short duration. Compared with the paranoid cases with systematized delusions, the inertia is slighter ($P < 0.01$). Dissociative reactions were not so frequent as in hebephrenic and catatonic cases ($P < 0.001$) and were regularly lacking in the recovered cases. The recovered cases had less general impairment than the progressive ones ($P < 0.05$).

As pointed out by Carl Schneider, the symptom complex of
"*Gedankenentzug*" is characterized by a lability and impaired control of the stream of associations (803). This corresponds experimentally to some disinhibition of the second signaling system, which makes the rich production of typical schizophrenic
symptoms possible. The proportion of adequate associative responses is significantly greater than in the other acute psychoses
(P < 0.001). In relation to the inhibition of unconditional reflexes, and especially of the autonomic components of the pathodynamic structures, the affective coloring of the delusions is lacking. Yet the inhibition of unconditional reflexes runs parallel with
the general emotional changes such as perplexity, depression,
ecstacy and elation. It may be also noted that the recovered cases
with schizo-affective symptomatologies have disturbances of the
higher nervous activity similiar to those of the manic-depressive
cases (57). In the progressive cases dissociative phenomena are
more often found than in the recurrent cases. Clinically the
deterioration proceeds mainly in the direction of slight paranoid
defects. In chronic cases which started as paranoid cases with projection symptoms, the clinical changes were accompanied by an
increase of the effect of the pathodynamic structures in the experimental investigation. In a few progressive cases of this series,
repeated studies after one to two and one-half years showed increased vascular and respiratory reactions to pathodynamic structures.

Seventeen patients received ataraxic drugs during the experimental investigations. Compared with the untreated cases they
had a slightly greater tendency to inhibition of the unconditional
defensive reflexes. The dissociative phenomena were slighter in
the cases receiving drugs.

Altogether thirty-two patients had been treated with ataraxic
drugs before and after. Ten recovered, ten had social remissions,
seven cases considerable improvement, four cases moderate improvement and in only one was there negative effect of the treatment. The paranoid cases with projection symptoms seem to benefit very much from treatment with ataraxic drugs. Considering
the symptomatological, hereditary and experimental differences

between the groups of progressive and recurring cases, it is not possible to decide the specific curative effect of the treatment.

Case 507 is leucotomized and has comparatively great disturbances of the higher nervous activity.

In conclusion it seems that clinically as well as experimentally there is a great resemblance between the paranoid cases with projection symptoms and the manic-depressive psychoses. Experimentally, they have strong inhibitions of unconditional reflexes and slight influences of pathodynamic structures in common. The progressive schizophrenics have more dissociative disturbances than the recovered ones and the manic-depressive cases. Clinically, general disturbances of the affective life stand more in the foreground than affect-laden delusions. Recurrent cases with projection symptoms tend to have schizo-affective symptoms and more relatives with affective psychoses than the progressive cases. In chronic stages, the paranoid cases with projection symptoms are predominantly transformed into paraphrenics with affectively charged delusions. Experimentally this seems to be accompanied by stronger influences of pathodynamic structures.

4. PARANOID PSYCHOSES WITH SYSTEMATIZED DELUSIONS

The present series consists of forty-three cases. Twenty-nine are probably deteriorating, while fourteen have had social remissions. In none of the recurring cases are there complete recoveries. Although the delusions have disappeared, there is no full insight. A tendency to suspiciousness and slight feelings of reference may also appear periodically, which indicates that some residue of the delusions are left, and that the healing process had the character of encapsulation of psychotic ideas.

The average age of onset was 42.1 years, which is considerably higher than in the other schizophrenic symptom complexes. The average duration since the first psychotic attack was 5.5 years at the time of the experimental investigations. When remissions are not included, the average duration of the disease was 1.9 years. As several cases had had an insidious onset, and the remissions as a rule had been incomplete, the actual duration of the disease since the first prodromal symptoms of the psychosis may be considerably longer. In twenty-two cases there had been a recurring course, and in ten cases nervous episodes previous to the psychotic outbreak were noticed. The initial symptoms of the psychoses in most cases were suspiciousness, jealousy or ideas of reference. Twelve cases had an acute onset, and two of these without prodromal symptoms. Eight of the acute cases had social remissions. Four had balanced, three schizoid, nineteen self-assertive and most of the remaining sensitive prepsychotic personalities. Self-assertive personalities were frequent, and in the sensitive personalities there was regularly a sthenic component in the personality structure. Precipitating factors were found in thirty-four cases, but not acute mental trauma, and only in three cases somatic disease. Most cases were precipitated by prolonged mental conflicts, in which it was extremely difficult to decide to what extent the conflicts actually were of etiological importance or secondary to initial psychotic personality changes. As previously noted the diagnostic classification of these psychoses was difficult. In thirty-three cases non-schizophrenic conditions had at some time been diagnosed, affective psychoses in most cases, alcoholic in one and organic in two cases. Affective and confusional syndromes were present in five cases, and one had a progressive course. Psychomotor symptoms were regularly absent, but three cases had short-lasting excitations. Initially two cases had an emotional blunting. The emotional changes were mostly in the direction of depression, elation or irritability. Perplexity was present in eight cases and five of them had social remissions. Typical schizophrenic delusions were found in twenty-five cases, and eight had combinations of such delusions. These delusions were more frequent in progressive than in recurring cases. Emphasized in the definition of this group all cases showed disturbances of symbolization. Seventeen had feelings of passivity and eleven of depersonalization. Hallucinations were absent in twelve cases, which all had progressive courses. Specific schizophrenic auditory hallucinations were found in five cases, and twenty cases had haptic hallucinations.

The average number of typical schizophrenic symptoms in each case was 3.1 which is less than in the paranoid cases with projection symptoms. All the progressive cases are apparently developing paranoid defects, twenty-four slight defects and five severe defects of fantastic and expansive types. Among the slight defects sixteen seem to have non-systematic defects, mostly affect-laden paraphrenias.

Thirty-seven relatives were probably psychotic, and case histories were available in twenty-four cases. Eight had affective psychoses, four of the manic-depressive and four of the reactive type. Among sixteen schizophrenics one had a severe hebephrenic defect, one a systematic catatonia, one a periodic catatonia, one a severe paranoid defect, five had non-systematic and seven systematic slight paranoid defects. It is apparent that the probands, as well as their relatives, showed a tendency to develop slight paranoid defects. The main difference is that the probands resemble the non-systematic paraphrenias more. The probands have comparatively shorter observation periods, and the systematic paraphrenics must, as a rule, be present at least five years before they are recognized. The affective coloring of the delusions may especially give a false impression of an affect-laden paraphrenia. As an indicator of the slightness of the defects in the probands, it can be mentioned that since the experimental investigations eighteen of them have been discharged from the hospital, though five have been readmitted. Our follow-up studies indicate that the non-systematic schizophrenics to a great extent are able to live outside hospitals (64). This may explain the fact that a great proportion of the acute and subacute schizophrenics have non-systematic forms, while the majority of the chronic hospital cases have systematic schizophrenics. The relatives of the recurrent cases have the same tendency as the relatives of the deteriorating cases to develop slight paranoid defects, but do not develop more affective psychoses.

The results of the experimental investigations are shown in the Tables 26 and 27.

In the association test seventeen had an impairment of reproduction. The mean reaction times were prolonged in twenty-six cases and the median reaction times in thirty cases. It was noticed that the reaction times were comparatively longer in the improved than in the progressive cases. Thirty-six cases had more echolalic and twenty-six cases more multiword responses than

TABLE 26
Progressive Psychoses with Systematized Delusions

	Adequate Responses	Inadequate Responses	Too Difficult Tasks	No Information	Total Patients
Associations					
Reproduction	18	11	0	0	29
Mean reaction times	15	14	0	0	29
Median reaction times	11	18	0	0	29
Echolalic responses	5	24	0	0	29
Multiword responses	10	19	0	0	29
Higher responses	8	21	0	0	29
Primitive responses	23	6	0	0	29
Incoherent responses	23	6	0	0	29
Motor Conditional Reflexes					
First reflex in first system	18	11	0	0	29
Second reflex in first system	27	2	0	0	29
Reflex in second system	28	1	0	0	29
Reaction times	22	7	0	0	29
After-inhibitions	8	21	0	0	29
Extinction	25	4	0	0	29
Restoration	18	11	0	0	29
Differentiation	8	21	0	0	29
Reversal of negative reflexes	15	13	1	0	29
Reversal of positive reflexes	17	11	1	0	29
Description of performances	13	16	0	0	29
Unstable reflexes	29	0	0	0	29
Extrasignaling reactions	27	2	0	0	29
Continuous pressing	28	1	0	0	29
Autonomic Reactions					
Vascular curve	28	1	0	0	29
Respiratory curve	28	1	0	0	29
Respiratory and vascular dissociation	23	6	0	0	29
Vascular responses to cold	6	23	0	0	29
Vascular responses to calculation	24	4	0	1	29
Effects of pathodynamic structures	5	24	0	0	29
Defensive Reflexes					
Current tolerance	19	9	0	1	29
Motor exhaustion	19	9	0	1	29
Autonomic exhaustion	25	3	0	1	29
Dissociations	19	9	0	1	29
Number of inadequate responses		329			
Number of adequate responses	592				
Number of too difficult tasks			2		

TABLE 27
IMPROVED PSYCHOSES WITH SYSTEMATIZED DELUSIONS

	Adequate Responses	Inadequate Responses	Too Difficult Tasks	No Information	Total Patients
Associations					
Reproduction	8	6	0	0	14
Mean reaction times	2	12	0	0	14
Median reaction times	2	12	0	0	14
Echolalic responses	2	12	0	0	14
Multiword responses	7	7	0	0	14
Higher responses	3	11	0	0	14
Primitive responses	11	3	0	0	14
Incoherent responses	12	2	0	0	14
Motor Conditional Reflexes					
First reflex in first system	7	7	0	0	14
Second reflex in first system	14	0	0	0	14
Reflex in second system	14	0	0	0	14
Reaction times	11	3	0	0	14
After-inhibitions	5	9	0	0	14
Extinction	13	1	0	0	14
Restoration	11	3	0	0	14
Differentiation	7	6	0	1	14
Reversal of negative reflexes	9	4	0	1	14
Reversal of positive reflexes	9	4	0	1	14
Description of performances	11	2	0	1	14
Unstable reflexes	14	0	0	0	14
Extrasignaling reactions	14	0	0	0	14
Continuous pressing	14	0	0	0	14
Autonomic Reactions					
Vascular curve	12	2	0	0	14
Respiratory curve	12	2	0	0	14
Respiratory and vascular dissociation	11	3	0	0	14
Vascular responses to cold	5	9	0	0	14
Vascular responses to calculation	14	0	0	0	14
Effects of pathodynamic structures	3	11	0	0	14
Defensive Reflexes					
Current tolerance	9	5	0	0	14
Motor exhaustion	10	4	0	0	14
Autonomic exhaustion	12	2	0	0	14
Dissociations	8	6	0	0	14

Number of inadequate responses   148

Number of adequate responses   296

Number of too difficult tasks   0

found in the normal sample, and twenty-two responded predominantly with such responses. There are more signs of inertia of the second signaling system than in the paranoid cases with projection symptoms. Thirty-two had less of the higher reactions and nine had more of the primitive reactions than found in the normal sample. The lowered tendency to respond with higher associations was largely due to the great numbers of the intermediate types with echolalic and multiword responses. Incoherent responses were found in eight cases, and in no case were there more than five such responses. The tendency to dissociation in the second signaling system is slight.

In the first as well as in the second signaling system motor conditional reflexes were formed as rapidly as in the sample of normals. Most cases had considerable after-inhibitions. Irregular prolongations of the reaction times were only found in ten cases. Extinction was impaired in a few cases, and twenty-seven failed with differentiation. Restoration was impaired in fourteen cases. Only sixteen could carry out adequately a change of the dynamic stereotype. There was inertia of the inhibitory processes in eighteen cases and inertia of the excitatory processes in sixteen cases. Compared with the paranoid cases with projection symptoms there is a greater inertia of the nervous processes. Restoration was even more impaired in the paranoid cases with projection symptoms, which indicates the greater role of inhibition in these cases. Twenty-four were able to give an adequate description of their motor performances, and eleven of them belonged to the improved group. Only two of the improved patients gave completely inadequate descriptions as compared with sixteen of the progressive cases.

In fourteen patients the unconditional responses to electrical stimulation showed signs of inhibition. There was less tendency to inhibition of unconditional responses than in the group of paranoid cases with projection symptoms. Fifteen cases in one or more trials failed to avoid electrical stimulation after instruction.

The plethysmogram in thirty-seven cases showed a zero curve, in three cases oscillations of the third order and in three cases chaotic curves. Respiratory arrhythmias were present in three cases, and dissociations between the respiratory curve and the respiratory oscillations of the plethysmogram in nine cases. The signs of autonomic dissociations are as a rule lacking in this group. Vascular responses to unconditional cold stimulation were present in eleven and to calculation in all but four cases. All recurrent cases responded to calculation and five of them to cold stimulation. Compared with the cases with projection symptoms, the paranoid cases with systematized delusions respond more to calculation, which suggests a stronger influence of the second signaling system upon the vascular system. This influence is especially strong for the pathodynamic structures. Respiratory effects were found in all but one case. All gave vascular responses and in thirty-five cases stormy autonomic reactions indicating the presence of pathologically excited and inert subcortical structures. There is a fair parallellism between these experimental findings and the affect-laden delusions in the clinical picture.

Summarizing the experimental data, the paranoid cases with systematized delusions had disturbances of the higher nervous activity similiar to those of the slight paranoid defects in the series of chronic schizophrenics. They resembled the affect-laden paraphrenics, which clinically are very similar. The strong effect of pathodynamic structures was characteristic. There was a considerable tendency to inertia of the nervous processes, and dissociative phenomena were slight. Compared with the paranoid cases with projection symptoms, there is not only the difference with regard to pathodynamic structures, but the inertia of the nervous system is even less pronounced in paranoid cases with projection symptoms (P < 0.01). These cases also had more inhibition of the unconditional responses (P < 0.01). Previously mentioned there was a tendency for the paranoid cases with projection symptoms to develop into paraphrenics with systematized delusions. Here the inhibition is replaced by phenomena of inertia of a general character as well as localized to the pathodynamic structures. The latter phenomena are apparently more irreversible. This is also demonstrated by the differences with regard to outcome in the two groups of paranoid psychoses.

The paranoid psychoses with systematized delusions as a rule have their onset at higher ages than the paranoid cases with projection symptoms. This may be one of the factors explaining the weaker inhibitory phenomena and the stronger signs of inertia. As mentioned in Chapter IV, old age increases the inertia of the nervous processes, and in senile dementia there is a pronounced inertia of the nervous processes. The onset of the paranoid cases with systematized delusions is as a rule insidious, and it is possible that most of them have actually lasted so long that they are already chronic when they are admitted to the hospital. Their ability to live outside the hospital may delay their admission. By scrutinizing the case histories it is found that most of them had some nervous traits when young. It is questionable as to what extent their predominantly self-assertive and sthenic prepsychotic personalities may in fact be residual of a process of such a long duration so that they may give the false impression of being habitual personality patterns.

During the experimental investigations sixteen received ataraxic drugs. Among the drug-treated patients were four of the eight patients who gave no violent reactions to pathodynamic structures. It is possible that the drugs reduced the reactions to pathodynamic structures. There was also a stronger tendency to inhibition of unconditional defensive reflexes, as six of them showed signs of such inhibition.

Altogether thirty-one cases had been treated with ataraxic drugs. Ten had social remissions, sixteen much improvement, two moderate improvement and three no improvement. The treatment usually decreased the affective loading of the delusions, and during group treatment several such cases, as described in another paper, could modify their psychological attitude to their delusions (62).

The main conclusion is that the group of paranoid psychoses with systematized delusions showed many similiarities in the clinical symptomatology, as well as in the hereditary loading, and in experimental findings. When classifying these psychoses as schizophrenics, one must be aware that they are very different from the nuclear schizophrenic group of hebephrenic and hebephrenic paranoid cases.

5. REPEATED STUDIES OF PSYCHOSES WITH SCHIZOPHRENIC DETERIORATION

In Chapters VII and VIII the clinical and experimental factors related to schizophrenic deterioration have been analyzed. The severe schizophrenic defects had less adequate responses, more dissociative phenomena, inertia, impairment of internal inhibition, inhibitions of the signaling systems and the unconditional defensive reflexes than the slight defects (P < 0.001 for all comparisons). These disturbances were also more pronounced in the chronic than in the acute and subacute series (P < 0.001 for all comparisons). The severity of schizophrenic deterioration ran parallel with the severity of the experimental disturbances of the higher nervous activity.

In the series of acute and subacute functional psychoses the progressive psychoses had more general impairment (P < 0.001) and more dissociative reactions (P < 0.001) than the recurrent psychoses. The progressive cases had also more inertia (P < 0.01) and more passive inhibition of the reactions in the first and second signaling systems (P < 0.01). As to impairment of internal inhibition and inhibition of unconditional defensive reflexes there were no statistically significant differences between the progressive and recurrent psychoses.

The statistical comparisons indicate that the greater the general impairment and the dissociative disturbances, the worse the prognosis. The tendency to inhibition of unconditional defensive reflexes is correlated with schizophrenic deterioration, but may to some extent be prognostically favorable in the acute psychoses. It should be remembered from Chapter IV that manic-depressive psychoses had strong inhibitions of unconditional reflexes. The prognostically favorable psychoses with projection symptoms in the acute series to a great extent resembled the manic-depressive psychoses in their disturbances of the higher nervous activity.

In the series of acute and subacute functional psychoses, fifty of the cases with schizophrenic deterioration were re-examined after one to two and a half years. It is thought that this repeated study might throw more light upon the changes of the higher nervous activity related to the schizophrenic deterioration. As the control period was comparatively short, most cases had not progressed much clinically. The transition from the "active process stage" to the "defect stage" in several cases gives a reduction of the more alarming symptoms. It seems that ataraxic drugs, if not removing the psychotic symptoms, reduce much of the tension related to such symptoms. With repeated studies of patients with progressive courses of the illness it can be studied to what extent the ataraxic drugs could counteract the changes correlated with schizophrenic deterioration. One could also receive an impression as to what extent the experimental disturbances are reversible.

The results of the repeated experimental studies are presented in Table 28.

It is seen from the table that with the association test most signs show improvement ($P < 0.001$*). The improvement is mainly found in reproduction, reaction times, echolalic responses and the number of primitive responses. Multiword responses, the number of higher reactions and incoherent responses give an equal number of good and bad performances. In the last half of the test the reaction times tend to be longer.

For motor conditional reflexes there is less variation from the first examination and slightly more signs of worse performances. More patients had difficulties with the reversal of reflexes, generalized reactions in the two signaling systems and failures in the description of the performances.

The unconditional responses to electrical stimulation showed forty-seven signs of more inhibition as compared with twelve signs of less inhibition. With the sign test the tendency to increased inhibition of unconditional defensive reflexes is statistically significant at the 0.001 level.

The autonomic reactions in most patients were not changed. There were a few patients with less responses to buzzer, heat and cold. In the repeated investigations the dissociative phenomena were more pronounced, with thirty-five worse signs as compared with four improved signs ($P < 0.001$).

---

* The level of statistical significance is determined by the sign test for all comparisons of the tendency to improvement or unimprovement of responses in re-examined patients.

TABLE 28
REPEATEDLY STUDIED PSYCHOSES WITH SCHIZOPHRENIC DETERIORATION

Diagnostic Subgroup	Changes of Experimental Reactions	Associations									Motor Conditional Reflexes											
		Reproduction	Mean Reaction Times	Median Reaction Times	Speed in Last Half of the Test	Echolalic Responses	Multiword Responses	Higher Responses	Primitive Responses	Incoherent Responses	First Reflex in First System	Reaction Times	Generalization of Reflex in First System	Reflex in Second System	Generalization of Reflex in Second System	Extinction	Restoration	Second Reflex in First System	Differentiation	Reversal of Negative Reflexes	Reversal of Positive Reflexes	Description of Performances
Hebephrenic psychoses	No change	2	0	0	1	0	2	1	0	2	8	12	10	8	8	7	5	8	9	3	1	9
	Improved	6	9	9	5	10	6	8	10	4	2	0	0	2	2	4	5	2	2	5	1	1
	Worse	5	4	4	7	3	5	4	3	7	3	1	2	3	3	2	3	3	2	3	9	3
Catatonic psychoses	No change	2	0	0	2	1	4	0	1	5	7	10	11	7	9	8	2	5	5	2	3	8
	Improved	8	8	8	2	8	5	6	8	6	3	1	0	4	1	3	6	3	4	3	5	2
	Worse	4	6	6	10	5	5	8	5	3	4	3	2	3	4	2	5	5	4	7	4	4
Paranoid with projection symptoms	No change	0	0	1	0	1	1	0	0	6	3	4	5	5	4	4	1	5	3	1	0	5
	Improved	8	5	5	6	5	3	4	5	2	4	2	0	2	1	4	3	2	3	3	4	0
	Worse	0	3	2	2	2	4	4	3	0	1	2	3	1	3	0	4	1	2	4	4	3
Paranoid with systematized delusions	No change	2	1	2	3	1	2	1	4	8	6	12	9	6	6	7	4	4	6	1	2	7
	Improved	5	10	10	7	9	9	7	7	4	5	0	2	5	3	4	5	4	5	5	6	2
	Worse	7	3	2	4	4	3	6	3	2	2	1	2	2	4	2	4	5	2	7	5	4
Total repeatedly studied psychoses	No change	6	1	3	6	3	9	2	5	21	24	38	35	26	27	26	12	22	23	7	6	29
	Improved	27	32	32	20	32	23	25	30	16	14	3	2	13	7	15	19	11	14	16	16	5
	Worse	16	16	14	23	14	17	22	14	12	10	7	9	9	14	6	16	14	10	21	22	14
	Total signs	49	49	49	49	49	49	49	49	49	48	48	46	48	48	47	47	47	47	44	44	48

TABLE 28–Continued

REPEATEDLY STUDIED PSYCHOSES WITH SCHIZOPHRENIC DETERIORATION

Diagnostic Subgroup	Changes of Experimental Reactions	Automonic Reactions									Defensive Reflexes				Number of Unimproved Reactions	Number of Improved Reactions
		Vascular Curve	Vascular Reactions to Buzzer	Vascular Reactions to Cold	Vascular Reactions to Heat	Vascular Reactions to Calculation	Vascular Reactions to Pathodynamic Structures	Respiratory Reactions to Pathodynamic Structures	Respiratory and Vascular Dissociation	Respiratory Curve	Current Tolerance	Motor Exhaustion	Autonomic Exhaustion	Dissociations		
Hebephrenic psychoses	No change	10	12	12	9	10	8	8	4	10	6	8	9	3	125	107
	Improved	0	0	0	2	1	2	2	1	0	0	0	1	5		
	Worse	3	1	1	2	2	3	3	8	3	7	5	3	5		
Catatonic psychoses	No change	14	14	13	14	13	15	15	5	13	4	11	10	7	131	109
	Improved	1	1	2	1	1	0	0	2	0	3	0	0	4		
	Worse	0	0	0	0	1	0	0	8	2	8	4	5	4		
Paranoid with projection symptoms	No change	7	7	7	8	7	5	6	4	8	6	8	4	4	63	79
	Improved	0	1	1	0	1	0	0	0	0	1	0	2	2		
	Worse	1	0	0	0	0	3	2	4	0	1	0	2	2		
Paranoid with systematized delusions	No change	11	9	8	9	11	11	12	9	13	4	10	11	10	106	127
	Improved	0	0	1	0	2	1	1	0	0	3	1	1	3		
	Worse	2	4	4	4	0	1	0	4	0	7	3	2	1		
Total repeatedly studied psychoses	No change	42	42	40	40	41	39	41	22	44	20	37	34	24	425	422
	Improved	1	2	4	3	5	3	3	3	0	7	1	4	14		
	Worse	6	5	5	6	3	7	5	24	5	23	12	12	12		
	Total signs	49	49	49	49	49	49	49	49	49	50	50	50	50		

For all signs the re-examined patients had as many improved as unimproved reactions, with 422 and 425 respectively. In the first and second signaling systems there were 215 signs of less and 160 signs of more inhibition. The tendency to less inhibition is statistically significant at the 0.01 level. For internal inhibition there was a tendency to improvement, statistically significant at the 0.01 level with fifty-six better and thirty-two worse signs. There was a slight tendency to less inertia of the nervous processes, which was not statistically significant. As to dissociation, there were ninety-six unimproved and fifty-nine improved signs. This tendency to unimprovement is statistically significant at the 0.01 level.

As forty-six of the repeatedly studied patients had been treated with ataraxic drugs (chlorpromazine) it is possible that the changes of the higher nervous activity may be related to the treatment. The four cases who had not received ataraxic drugs showed forty unimproved and eighteen improved signs. This would mean a tendency to worse reactions (P < 0.01). They had four signs of more and no sign of less inhibition of the unconditional defensive reflexes. For dissociative reactions there were 11 poor and no improved signs. Thus there was tendency to more dissociative reactions (P < 0.001).

It appears that whether the patients have been treated with ataraxic drugs or not, a schizophrenic deterioration runs parallel with more dissociative phenomena and greater inhibition of the unconditional defense reflexes. This should be expected from the comparisons of slight and severe chronic defects, and from our comparisons of the series of acute and chronic schizophrenic psychoses. The ataraxic drugs have probably counteracted the tendency to more general impairment. In the re-examined psychoses the tendency to improved associative responses, less inertia, less impairment of internal inhibition and less inhibition of the two signaling systems is probably an effect of the drug treatment, as such disturbances tend to increase with a schizophrenic deterioration.

When divided into clinical subgroups, thirteen belonged to the hebephrenic, fifteen to the catatonic, eight to the group of paranoid psychoses with projection symptoms, and fourteen to the group of paranoid psychoses with systematized delusions.

In the hebephrenic group there were thirty-five poor and fifteen improved reactions with respect to dissociative phenomena (P < 0.01). They showed fifteen signs of increased inhibition of unconditional responses to electrical stimulation and one of decreased inhibition (P < 0.001). The hebephrenic psychoses have a pronounced increase of such disturbances. In all tests they revealed 107 improved and 125 unimproved signs.

The catatonic group had twenty-eight more and twenty less pronounced dissociative reactions. There were seventeen signs of increased and three signs of decreased inhibition of the unconditional responses to electrical stimulation (P < 0.01). In all tests they revealed 109 improved and 131 unimproved signs. Compared with the other cases who were studied repeatedly the catatonic had a greater tendency to impairment of associative responses (P < 0.05) and passive inhibition in the two signaling systems (P < 0.01).

In the group of paranoid psychoses with systematized delusions there were nineteen poor and seventeen improved signs of dissociation. They had twelve signs of increased inhibition of unconditional defensive reflexes and five signs of decreased inhibition. In all tests they revealed 127 improved and 106 unimproved signs. This improvement of experimental performances may be related to the drug treatment, as clinically these cases benefit much from the treatment. All of them were treated with *chlorpromazine*. Traugott also found improvement of the higher nervous activity in paranoid schizophrenics after treatment with chlorpromazine (989). The influence of pathodynamic structures is apparently very stable. In one case the autonomic responses were stronger, and in another one weaker.

In the paranoid group with projection symptoms there were fourteen unimproved and seven improved signs of dissociation. They had three signs of stronger and three signs of less inhibition of the unconditional defensive reflexes. In all tests they revealed seventy-nine improved and sixty-three unimproved signs. In four cases, where the projection symptoms clinically were replaced by systematized delusions, the repeated studies showed violent autonomic responses to pathodynamic structures. The repeated studies indicate that paranoid cases with projection symptoms tend to be associated with more dissociative phenomena and greater influences of pathodynamic structures. This can be expected from the analysis of clinical and experimental data in the series of chronic as compared with acute paranoid schizophrenias.

The results of the re-examinations show that the schizophrenic deterioration is accompanied by increased tendency to dissociative reactions and increased inhibition of the unconditional defensive reflexes. This tendency was most pronounced in the hebephrenic cases. The paranoid psychoses with projection symptoms tend to develop disturbances of the higher nervous activity similiar to those in the paranoid cases with systematized delusions. In the psychoses with systematized delusions, the experimentally established influences of pathodynamic structures are rather stable. Experimentally the paranoid cases showed more signs of improvement than of unimprovement of the experimental performances. They had less tendency to impairment of the higher nervous activity than the hebephrenic and catatonic cases ($P < 0.01$).

In the total material of re-examined schizophrenics, the experimental data, contrary to expectations, had given as much improvement as unimprovement of the disturbances of the higher nervous activity. This could indicate that the ataraxic drugs have counteracted some of the disturbances associated with schizophrenic deterioration. This would then apply to passive inhibition of the two signaling systems, impairment of internal inhibition, and to the functions of the second signaling system.

Chapter IX

DISCUSSION OF EXPERIMENTAL AND CLINICAL DATA

1. THE DISTURBANCES OF THE HIGHER NERVOUS ACTIVITY IN SCHIZOPHRENIA COMPARED WITH OTHER PSYCHIATRIC DISORDERS

From the preceding chapters it can be seen that there are great variations of disturbances of the higher nervous activity in schizophrenia. For the clinically separate subgroups the patients in each group reveal very similiar experimental data. There are more variations in the clinical pictures than in the experimental findings. Several subgroups, which clinically can be separated, show no essential differences in the tests. The obvious reason for this is that the clinical examination makes it possible to penetrate into the details of the complex subjective experiences of the patients, whereas the tests only give a crude measure of simple and elementary activities.

On the whole, the schizophrenics had several general disturbances at all levels of the higher nervous activity. The greater the clinical deterioration, the more pronounced was the general impairment of the higher nervous activity. Some types of disturbances of the higher nervous activity were especially frequent in schizophrenics, more pronounced in severe than in slight defects, more frequent in progressive than in recurrent cases and tended to increase in the repeated examination of deteriorating cases. They also seemed to be rare in non-schizophrenic disorders. This was markedly so for the dissociative phenomena. Among the signs of dissociation, incoherent responses in the association test were not found in non-schizophrenic disorders. One cannot entirely exclude a subjective element in the classification of such reactions, and a misunderstanding of the set tasks in the test may also give the false impression of incoherent reactions. With the association test periodic prolongations of the reaction times without relation to the character of the stimulus-words also seem to be characteristic of some types of schizophrenia. This type of inhibition could be regarded as a dissociative inhibition. It can, however, be difficult to decide whether such prolongations definitely are or are not related to complexes or difficult stimulus-words. In protocols with few higher responses, prolongations of the reaction times were also less important signs of inhibition than the lowered quality of the associative responses, so that this measure becomes less reliable.

For motor conditional reflexes irregular prolongations of the reaction times could also be regarded as a dissociative inhibition and were especially found in schizophrenics. In non-schizophrenic disorders disturbed or demented patients may also have similiar prolongations. The same is the case with failures in the description of motor performances, which can be considered as a sign for dissociation between the first and the second signaling system. Such disturbances are remarkably frequent in schizophrenics with well-ordered behavior. In group therapy it was noticed that schizophrenics who failed in the description of motor performances only vaguely describe their personal experiences, and in this way showed a defect of the ability to verbalize (62).

Failures in avoiding electrical stimulation after instruction were consistently found in schizophrenics, and regarded as a sign of dissociation between unconditional reflexes and the second signaling system. Also severely demented organics, oligophrenics and disturbed patients with affective psychoses could fail in this task. In schizophrenics, however, it was often noticed that patients were able to follow instructions for motor performances but nevertheless failed in avoiding the electrical current. Clinically this ran parallel with marked apathy such as insensivity to pain and temperature and extinction of basic biological instincts (interest in food and the opposite sex). Such symptoms can be regarded as signs of inhibition and dissociation of instinctual life, which is mainly subcortically determined.

The final group of dissociative phenomena are the signs of autonomic dissociation, which are also found predominantly in schizophrenics. One has the chaotic vascular or respiratory curves. Physiologically such phenomena can be regarded as signs of deficient cortical regulation and an autonomy of the subcortical autonomic centres. It was noticeable that the chaotic autonomic activity was found in the severe hebephrenic and catatonic defects. In the severe hebephrenic defects the affective blunting and disorganized behavior can be assumed to be related to insufficient cortical regulation of subcortical centres and thereby the instinctual life. Similarly, in the catatonic defects the psychomotor disturbances apparently have an autonomic character with impaired cortical regulation.

Dissociations between the respiratory curve and the respiratory oscillations of the plethysmogram can be considered as related to an autonomy of the vascular and respiratory centres, which normally are well coordinated in their activities. These disturbances were most pronounced in the severe hebephrenic and catatonic defects.

Among other disturbances of great importance in the schizophrenics are the effects of pathodynamic structures. Such disturbances were regularly found in paranoid schizophrenics with systematized and affect-laden delusions. In the author's experience violent plethysmographic and respiratory reactions to pathodynamic structures were not found in typical non-schizophrenic conditions. Such changes can be seen in paranoid psychoses, where it is clinically uncertain if they can be classified as schizophrenics. Complexes in neuroses may give strong autonomic responses, while in some cases with typical schizophrenic systematized delusions the autonomic responses can be slight. The differential diagnostic value of such responses should not be relied upon too much. Evaluating the great clinical differences in cases with systematized delusions as compared with neuroses, there is a probability that the application of several methods of investigation might show the differences more advantageously. It was noted for a series of neurotics that the vascular curves tended to be labile, and the reactivity in several cases increased. In schizophrenics with systematized delusions the vascular curves are as a rule rather inert and do not respond to unconditional stimuli.

In the neuroses the effect of complexes in the association test tend to be marked, and in schizophrenics with systematized delusions general disturbances of inhibition and inertia are most characteristic of the associative responses. For the neuroses the general disturbances of the higher nervous activity are small, mainly affecting the first and the second signaling systems, whereas the unconditional reactions are not affected. In schizophrenics there tends to be great impairment of the unconditional reflex activity. This would indicate that in neuroses the pathophysiological structure is predominantly of a cortical nature related to the psychodynamic complexes. The autonomic components of the complexes are parts of the general autonomic lability and exaggeration of the autonomic reactivity which is found in normals as a response to affect-charged experiences. Taking into consideration the general tendency to inertia and impairment of the subcortical activity in paranoid schizophrenia, it is likely that in these cases pathologically excited and inert autonomic structures in the subcortex play an important role. The tendency for paranoid cases with projection symptoms to be transformed into paranoid cases with systematized delusions would also indicate the process character of the systematized delusions. Clinically systematized delusions have a primary character which is not immediately understandable from personality structures and life experiences as are delusions in typical reactive psychoses. This splitting from reality is understood as related to pathologically excited and inert subcortical structures, which are not under cortical control and represent a dissociation of the integrated activity of the higher nervous functions. Even the contrast between the general decrease of autonomic reactivity and the violent autonomic reactions to the mention of delusions also indicates a kind of dissociation.

In most schizophrenics there is considerable inhibition of all three levels of the higher nervous activity. Among the psychiatrists, Carl Schneider has pointed out the analogy between the mental activity when falling asleep and the schizophrenic symptom complexes. Following Pavlov, Russian psychiatrists have stressed that the schizophrenic symptoms might be understood physiologically as due to sleep-like inhibitions of the higher nervous activity. From the studies of patients with various psychiatric disorders, it is seen that inhibitions are common to all kinds of mental disorders. Yet in oligophrenics, senile dementia, senile psychoses, organic psychoses, chronic alcoholism, alcoholic psychoses, infectious psychoses, reactive psychoses and neuroses, the inhibition affected the second signaling system. The inhibition tends to be slighter in the first signaling system, and the unconditional reflex activity is, on the whole, not interfered with. Only in the endogenous psychoses are strong tendencies to inhibition of the unconditional reflexes found. Pathophysiologically this might mean that in the non-endogenous conditions there is mainly a cortical disorder which predominantly affects the phylogenetically and ontogenetically more recent and more vulnerable second signaling system.

The experimental data do not allow any conclusions about the significance of external precipitating factors in the endogenous psychoses. Our detailed clinical studies of followed-up endogenous psychoses indicate that precipitating factors can be found in most of the acute cases (64, 331). Apart from the eventual significance of such external factors, their pathophysiological mechanisms are different from the non-endogenous conditions. In our analysis of clinical symptoms in previous studies, it was shown that in schizophrenics the symptoms were more of an automatic than a psychodynamic nature. In the manic-depressive psychoses the symptoms are also more understandable as biological forms of reactions than as related to psychodynamic complexes (64). The main experimental difference between the manic-depressive psychoses and progressive schizophrenics was the tendency to more dissociative reactions and strong effects of pathodynamic structures in the latter. In a group of schizo-affective cases with projection symptoms, with recurrent course of the disease, the clinical symptomatology as well as the hereditary loading and the experimental findings, resembled those of the manic-depressive psychoses.

Even for the endogenous psychoses the specificity of the tendency to inhibition of the subcortical centres cannot be regarded as certain, as other experimental studies indicate that such inhibitions may be found in other psychiatric disorders (Chapter IV).

In several endogenous psychoses no inhibition of the unconditional reflex activity could be found in the experiments.

In the schizophrenics, clinically as well as experimentally, disinhibitions are often found. Such disinhibitions as well as irregular distributions of the inhibitory phenomena seem to be related to the splitting phenomena. The periodic inhibitions of associative and motor reaction times have above even been labelled as dissociative inhibitions. With the experimental methods used in this study, only a few aspects of the unconditional reflex activity could be studied. Perhaps combinations with other methods for the study of unconditional reflex activity could give a more complete demonstration of the various types of impairment of subcortical activity in the schizophrenias.

On the basis of the experimental data it cannot be decided whether the schizophrenics start with impairment of cortical activity which spreads to the subcortical centres, or if the subcortical centres are primarily affected. Comparisons of the acute and chronic schizophrenics as well as repeated studies of progressive cases indicate that with a schizophrenic deterioration there is an increasing tendency to inhibition of the unconditional defensive reflexes. As the unconditional reflex activity is basic for the activity of the higher levels, an inhibition of the unconditional reflexes will regularly inhibit the functions of the higher levels. The marked tendency to exhaustion was characteristic of the inhibition of unconditional defensive responses. In assumption that there is a steady shift of exhaustion in the subcortical centres, this would induce shifting inhibitions of the higher levels. These could explain the irregular spontaneous prolongations of reaction times in the association test and with motor conditional reflexes. This would then stand in sharp contrast to the prolonged reaction times in connection with complexes in neuroses, where the psychodynamic character is obvious.

Among experimental data indicating that the impairment of cortical activity is to a great extent related to impairment of the subcortical activity, it is stressed that conditional motor reflexes in schizophrenics are formed as rapidly as in normals in the first as well as in the second signaling systems. The ability to form conditional reflexes would actually be less affected by an irradiated inhibition from the subcortex than reaction times and other signs involving speed in the performances. It is observed that schizophrenics as a rule condition best in the second signaling system. This might support the hypothesis that inhibition from the subcortex has less strength at the highest level. Several authors have found that in organic dementia, senile dementia and oligophrenics, where the cortical activity is impaired, the ability to form conditional reflexes is poor (Chapter IV). These findings illustrate differences in schizophrenic deterioration as compared with mental deficiency and organic deterioration.

The extent to which the dissociative phenomena in schizophrenics actually are related to impairment of the subcortical activity can be questioned, because the disturbances of the basic driving force interferes severely with a harmonious integration of the total nervous activity. Clinically it is obvious that the splitting phenomena are especially related to the changes in the affective and instinctual life.

In most schizophrenics internal inhibition is considerably impaired. However, internal inhibition, which is phylogenetically developed later, is easily disturbed, and tends to be strongly impaired in most forms of psychiatric disease. To some extent the impairment of internal inhibition is associated with marked dissociative phenomena in the schizophrenics. With the association test incoherent responses, especially the mediate responses, are often combined with a deficient ability to reproduce the associations. In normal persons the stream of associations is inhibited so that the common word connections, which are well established during life, are formed in free association. These responses are so firmly interconnected that they tend to be correctly reproduced. In schizophrenics with mediate associations this control of the stream of associations seems to be deficient, so that responses with only a remote or casual connection with the stimulus-word are given. When they must reproduce, they often give the first word which comes into their mind, without any evidence of selective inhibition. Also in the autonomic dissociative phenomena a lack of active cortical inhibition may be present.

It seems that with a schizophrenic deterioration the excitatory processes are weakened and a passive inhibition dominates, while active inhibition is weakened and dissociative and disinhibitory phenomena emerge. In animal neuroses also it can be found that disturbances of the inhibitory processes are accompanied by signs of dissociation. Gantt labelled the splitting phenomena *schizokinesis*, which he thought was a general principle in the development of pathological disorder of the functions of the nervous system. Another central factor Gantt labelled *autokinesis*. This was the tendency for functional disturbances of nervous activity to persist and develop their own patterns, related to the external factors which first started them but with a mass of material added from internal neural (?) mechanisms and elaborations (274, 275, 282, 283). The principles of autokinesis and schizokinesis may explain the development of the schizophrenic defects, and that the specific form is predominantly related to the impairment of subcortical activity is a possibility.

In schizophrenics signs of inertia of the nervous processes are regularly found. The longer the disease had lasted, and the more severe the deterioration, the greater the inertia of the nervous processes tends to be. It is also observed that among the acute and subacute patients, the paranoid psychoses with systematized delusions which start at a higher age are characterized by inertia of the nervous processes, while the inhibitory and dissociative changes are not marked. It is probable that age also is of importance in the development of inertia. From the animal experiments it is known that with increasing age there is a tendency to increasing inertia of the nervous processes, and in senile dementia such phenomena are pronounced (Chapter IV). Even in neuroses long-lasting conditions tend to show more signs of inertia of the higher nervous activity than the short-lasting cases, and similiar findings were obtained in other psychiatric and psychosomatic diseases (Chapter IV). There is also a tendency to develop the phenomenon of inertia the longer the pathological condition persists. Inertia can also be partially explained from the principle of autokinesis.

Hypothetically the following factors could be considered to be important neurophysiological mechanisms in schizophrenia:

1. Basic inhibition of subcortical centres.
2. Irradiation of inhibition to other structures.

3. Induced disinhibitions and excitations.
4. Induced inhibitions from pathologically excited structures.
5. Dissociations related to subcortical inhibition, disinhibitions, impairment of internal inhibition, excitation and inertia
6. Inertia of nervous processes related to stagnant excitation and inhibition.
7. Weakness of internal inhibition as the evolutional latest developed and most vulnerable processes.

Presented in a schema one could assume that there are disturbances between as well as within the three levels of the higher nervous activity (see Figure 4).

2. CLINICAL AND EXPERIMENTAL DIFFERENCES AND RESEMBLANCES OF CHRONIC SCHIZOPHRENIAS

Having discussed the general findings in schizophrenics, there is the problem of the clinical and experimental differences between the schizophrenic subgroups.

In the chronic schizophrenics one can start with the paranoid defects. It is noticed that in the slight paranoid defects the general disturbances of the higher nervous activity are not great. The dissociative phenomena are slighter than in most other chronic schizophrenics. Only in the schizophasics was there a pronounced tendency to dissociative reactions. This was in the second signaling system, which is correlated with their disturbances of speech. The vascular reactions to unconditional cold stimulation were inhibited. In most cases there were also some inhibitions of the unconditional reactions to electrical stimulation, less in the nonsystematic than in the systematic schizophrenics ($P < 0.01$).

The inhibitions of the first and second signaling systems were not great. Most cases were able to give several associative responses of the higher type and gave few primitive responses. Practically all could give stable motor conditional reflexes, only few had irregular prolongations of the reaction times, and most of them were able to attempt more complex tasks, such as differentiation and change of the dynamic stereotype.

There was a considerable inertia, of the associative as well as the motor reactions. In most cases autonomic responses to patho-

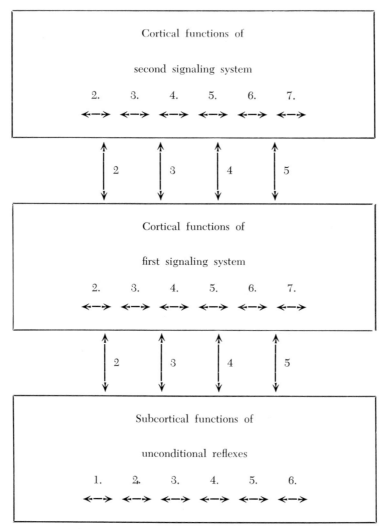

FIGURE 4. Schema of neurophysiological mechanisms in schizophrenia.

dynamic structures were observed, and often violent vascular reactions indicating pathologically excited subcortical structures with inertia. This was characteristic of the affect-laden paraphrenias, less of the schizophasiacs, where delusions are lacking, and far less in some of the systematic paranoid defects, where the symptomatology clinically had more the character of mental automatisms than of affect-laden delusions. It can be concluded that the slighter paranoid defects are characterized by the effect of pathodynamic structure, general inertia of nervous processes and general inhibition of subcortical structures. The experimental differences between the slight paranoid defects are considerably less than the resemblances.

The clinical differences between affect-laden, phonemic and hypochondriacal paraphreniacs are mainly related to the different associative connection (of complex delusions, simple verbal hallucinations or interoceptive changes of hypochondriasis) with the excited and inert subcortical structures. Present tests do not make it possible to demonstrate any such differences experimentally. Most schizophasiacs show effects of the pathodynamic structures. This may be a physiological correlate with the periodic outbursts of hallucinations and delusions in these patients. Because of the disturbances of speech these psychopathological phenomena cannot be so clearly analyzed as in the other slight paranoid defects.

Several symptomatological factors can be demonstrated in the acute stage which are of importance in the further course of illness in the slight paranoid defects. The clinical picture in the affect-laden paraphreniacs is dominated from the beginning by the systematized delusions with marked affective loading. Usually there are strong affective traits and often a tendency to good social remissions. In the schizophasiacs also there is a tendency to social remissions during the initial stages. The onset is often acute, accompanied by severe psychomotor symptoms in some cases. Typical schizophrenic delusions are often found. With the further course of the illness the delusions are overshadowed by the speech disturbances.

The phonemic and hypochondriacal paraphreniacs resemble each other closely during the acute stages. The onset tends to be more insidious than in the non-systematic schizophreniacs, the tendency to remissions less, and affective traits are of less importance. Several of these cases start with systematized delusions. Many start as paranoid psychoses with projection symptoms. In the acute stages the schizophrenic mental automatisms tends to be frequent. Clinically the specific schizophrenic auditory hallucinations in phonemic paraphrenia and the hypochondriacal sensations in hypochondriacal paraphrenia are very similiar to the corresponding acute symptoms and can often be traced to the beginning of the psychosis. In phonemic paraphrenia hypochondriacal sensations and haptic hallucinations are met so often in the acute stages that other factors than the initial symptomatology must decide why such cases do not develop into hypochondriacal paraphrenias.

The next group of paranoid psychoses are the more severe defects, such as confabulatory, expansive and fantastic paraphrenias. In these psychoses a common clinical feature is the delusions of expansive and fantastic character. The confabulatory cases tend to have some expansive traits. In the absurdness of their confabulations they also resemble the fantastic cases. In the experimental studies the influences of pathodynamic structures are mostly not as great as in the slight paranoid defects. The dissociative disturbances and the general impairment of the higher nervous activity are greater. It seems that a marked dissociation of the nervous activity is one link in the formation of expansive and fantastic ideas in chronic cases. In the fantastic cases, where the absurdness of ideas is greatest, the most severe impairment of nervous functions is also found.

Clinically, several cases of the fantastic-expansive group have expansive ideas during the initial stages. In the slight paranoid defects expansive ideas are frequent during the initial stage. The presence of expansive ideas during the initial stage does not allow any conclusions about the further course of the illness. It seems that the expansive ideas of acute psychoses have a different clinical and pathophysiological structure as compared with the expansive ideas in chronic stages.

In the acute stages the expansive ideas are usually accompanied by other typical schizophrenic symptoms, which can be regarded as projection phenomena or mental automatisms. They are frequent in the acute paranoid psychoses with projection symptoms, which tend to develop slight paranoid defects. In these cases the pathophysiological disturbances are generally inhibition of unconditional reflexes combined with comparatively good functions of the first and second signaling systems. After the initial process stage the expansive ideas in these cases as a rule disappear.

In the chronic expansive-fantastic cases, the characteristic expansive ideas, which dominate the clinical picture, usually need considerable time to develop, and are recognized as new symptoms. Some authors have argued that expansive ideas emerge because patients with the feelings of being persecuted believe that this is because they are important persons. Other authors have pointed out that expansive ideas are related to a dissolution of the psychic activity. From a reflexological point of view it seems that expansive ideas in the process stages are related to changes of subcortical structures, altering the general emotional balance and the feelings of self-importance which are connected with it. In the chronic stages the changes of the subcortical activity are also great, and clinically the patients tend to be euphoric. Most characteristic are the severe dissociative phenomena and the general impairment, which could explain why they do not understand the absurdity of their ideas. The pathodynamic structures seem to have lost their integrative control, which is present in the slightly deteriorated paranoids, who are somewhat reserved in talking about their delusions and hallucinations and often realize that others regard their ideas as abnormal. The strong pathodynamic structures may explain why, in spite of some intellectual understanding, the behavior is dominated by psychotic convictions.

It has been noted that in the expansive and fantastic group there are often hebephrenic or catatonic traits during the initial stages. As such syndromes in the acute stages tend to have greater disturbances of the higher nervous activity than the sharply defined paranoid cases, this may be one factor which explains why such cases develop severe defects. In other cases the initial stages were characterized by systematized delusions. In such cases no difference in the acute clinical symptomatology from that of psychoses developing slight paranoid defects could actually be found. This corresponds to the experience of Mayer in connection with the tendency of some paraphrenics to develop severe deterioration, and Leonhard's observation that affect-laden paraphreniacs may develop fantastic traits during long periods of observation (537, 591).

The incoherent paraphrenics are the last group of paranoid defects. These are clinically as severely demented as the most severe hebephrenic and catatonic defects. In these cases the dissociative phenomena (P < 0.01) and the general impairment of the higher nervous activity (P < 0.001) were considerably more pronounced than in the expansive-fantastic group. Effects of pathodynamic structures were practically absent. With the association test they reacted only with primitive responses, mainly with incoherent sentences. In this group the impairment of nervous activity and the disturbances of speech and thinking related to it are so great that they are not capable of describing such complex psychic experiences as are the expansive and fantastic cases. From the incoherent utterances of such patients one may sometimes get the impression of indications of expansive ideas. As these cases had very long observation periods, there may actually be a transition from expansive and fantastic cases to incoherent cases with the progress of deterioration.

During the acute stages most incoherent paraphrenics have catatonic or hebephrenic traits, and the psychosis usually begins in the younger age groups. The resemblance to the catatonic and hebephrenic cases may explain why the incoherent paraphrenics develop severe defects similiar to those in such psychoses.

For the whole group of paranoid defects it can be concluded that the mild defects have greater effects of pathodynamic structures than the severe defects (P < 0.01). The more pronounced the dissociative phenomena and general impairment of the higher nervous activity, the greater is the defect. In the milder paranoid defects the inhibition of the cortical processes is slight and a tendency to inertia is characteristic, the inhibitions of all three levels of the higher nervous activity are marked in the severe defects.

In the hebephrenics one could also distinguish between slight and severe defects. Clinically the autistic and eccentric hebephrenics have slight defects. In the experimental investigations these psychoses, like the slight paranoid defects, have comparatively good functions of the first and second signaling systems and a tendency to inertia of the nervous processes. The unconditional reactions are inhibited, but the dissociative phenomena are slight. In contrast to the slight paranoid defects, effects of pathodynamic structures are slight or lacking. During the acute stages the slight paranoid defects have some paranoid traits, but as a rule the projection symptoms are not pronounced. Observation revealed autistic hebephrenics in their acute stages predominantly had paranoid symptoms, and it is believed that these defects actually represent a natural healing process with respect to paranoid ideas, but accompanied by stronger emotional blunting. This is the main reason for classifying these psychoses as hebephrenic defects. Because of suspiciousness and autism, experimental studies of the autistic hebephrenics were only possible in a few cases.

The shallow and silly hebephrenics had clinically severe defects. In these psychoses also effects of pathodynamic structures were small or absent. There was a severe impairment of the functions of the first and second signaling systems. Most characteristic was a strong tendency to dissociative phenomena, and, in the silly hebephrenics especially an autonomic dissociation, which can be related to their silly and disorganized behavior. The general impairment of the higher nervous activity very much resembled that of the expansive and fantastic paranoid defects. Like these cases the severe hebephrenic defects also tended to have a euphoric mood. This indicates that euphoria in chronic schizophrenia tends to be associated with severe dissociative and inhibitory phenomena. In the slighter hebephrenic defects, where such disturbances are less pronounced, the mood is more sincere and irritable.

Among the catatonic defects all systematic catatonics were severely deteriorated clinically. The periodic catatonics varied clinically from slight to severe defects. In the same manner the experimental studies also showed great differences in the impairment of nervous activity in periodic catatonia. Effects of pathodynamic structures were slight and mostly absent in the non-systematic as well as in the systematic catatonics.

Among the periodic catatonics several cases resembled the slight hebephrenic defects experimentally and had comparatively good functions of the first and second signaling systems, a tendency to inertia of the nervous processes and slight dissociative phenomena. In other cases the general impairment of the higher nervous activity as well as the dissociative phenomena may have been even greater than in the severely deteriorated hebephrenics.

Outstanding clinical characteristics of the periodic catatonics was the tendency to remissions and to periodic catatonic shifts. When compared with the systematic catatonics the onset tended to be more acute with more violent psychomotor symptoms. Precipitating factors were found more often, the ages of onset were comparatively higher, and schizoid premorbid personalities were less frequent. Schizoid premorbid personalities were also often found in the hebephrenic cases. The paranoid cases tended to have more self-assertive premorbid personalities.

Among the systematic catatonics the speech-inactive and manneristic catatonics clinically had the most severe defects. In these cases all three levels of the higher nervous activity were severely inhibited. Most of them were unable to answer to the stimulus-words in the association test or to form stable motor conditional reflexes. Some of them had an ability to form conditional responses in the second signaling system, which may indicate that the inhibition of cortical functions is secondary to inhibition of subcortical centres. In the speech-inactive catatonics the abusive shouting during excitement also shows that the speech activity periodically may be liberated from the inhibition. The inability to avoid electrical stimulation after instruction is most striking. This indicates severe dissociation between the cortical and subcortical functions.

With regard to the clinical symptoms during the acute stages, it was noticed that these psychoses began insidiously with slight psychomotor symptoms. In the speech-inactive catatonics several cases actually had more hebephrenic than catatonic traits during the acute stages.

Because of the negativism, negativistic catatonics could only be incompletely studied, and several refused the experimental investigation. The experimental data indicate that the disturbances of the higher nervous activity are severe, to a great extent resembling those of the previously mentioned groups of systematic catatonics. The autonomic reactivity seems to be greater and the inhibition of unconditional defensive reflexes weaker. Usually it was found that clinically the negativism was already present in the acute stage.

In the remaining groups of systematic catatonics there are clinically some signs of disinhibition. In the parakinetic and speech-prompt catatonics associative responses were usually found, in speech-prompt catatonia even some associations of the higher type. Thus their associative responses resemble those of some severe hebephrenic defects. There were greater inhibitions of the first signaling system and the unconditional reflexes, with greater dissociations between the cortical and subcortical activity.

The proskinetic catatonics responded to the association test with a characteristic mumbling. Observation showed that their ability to form conditional responses in the second signaling system was poorer than their ability to form conditional responses in the first signaling system. Apart from these characteristics, the disturbances of a higher nervous activity were nearly as severe as in the manneristic and speech-inactive catatonics.

Generally it can be established that in the systematic catatonic defects there were severe inhibitions and dissociative phenomena. In the groups with some clinical signs of disinhibitions, there was also experimentally less inhibition of the second signaling system than in the groups with predominant inhibition in their general behavior.

Clinically the acute stages of the systematic catatonics did not show any concise differences between the subgroups. For catatonic psychoses it seems that acute and violent initial psychomotor symptoms give a fair chance of remission, as in periodic catatonics. In these cases insidiously developing catatonic symptoms in the course of years give rise to the deepest inhibitions and dissociations of the higher nervous activity.

3. CLINICAL AND EXPERIMENTAL FINDINGS IN ACUTE AND SUBACUTE FUNCTIONAL PSYCHOSES

For acute and subacute functional psychoses it is often difficult from the initial clinical pictures, to predict whether such psychoses will develop schizophrenic deterioration or not. If the experimental studies could contribute to this prediction, one could have a means of distinguishing between the more nuclear dementia pracox and the more benign schizophreniform cases.

A group of hebephrenic and hebephrenic-paranoid cases definitely had a nuclear character with no recoveries, and the majority progressed towards schizophrenic deterioration. In this group there were severe dissociative phenomena, notably for autonomic reactions in the progressive cases. All three levels of the higher nervous activity tended to be inhibited. The periodic inhibitions of associative and motor reactions were characteristic. As previously mentioned in this chapter, this may be secondary to inhibitions of subcortical structures. Clinically these psychoses show the symptom complex of *"Sprunghaftigkeit"* (desultoriness), which appears to be correlated with the periodic inhibitions experimentally. The progressive cases, like the patients in the series of chronic hebephrenics, generally have slight or no effect of the pathodynamic structures. The general impairment of nervous activity is not so great as in the deteriorated chronic patients ($P < 0.001$).

The hebephrenic psychoses have as a rule an insidious onset in younger age groups, and these factors seem to favor the development of dissociative inhibition. In repeated investigations the hebephrenics tended to have greater impairment of the higher nervous activity and in particular more signs of dissociation ($P < 0.01$) and more inhibition of the unconditional defensive reflexes ($P < 0.001$).

In the catatonic group there was a much greater tendency to remissions than in the hebephrenic group. At first this is somewhat in contrast to the finding among chronic catatonics, where the majority were systematic catatonics with predominantly steadily progressive course of the illness. The probable explanation is, partly, that the series of chronic catatonics consisted of severe defects accumulated in the hospital during several years. Here the periodic catatonics with remissions and slighter defects were able to live outside the hospital.

Experimentally the catatonics resembled the hebephrenics. Their clinical symptom complex of desultoriness ran parallel with periodic prolongations of associative and motor reaction times in the experiment. The progressive cases had less adequate responses ($P < 0.01$) and more signs of dissociation ($P < 0.05$) than the recurrent. Repeated studies of progressive catatonics showed more general impairment, more signs of dissociation, and more inhibition of unconditional defensive reflexes (P < 0.01).

In a group of paranoid psychoses with projection symptoms the prognosis was especially good with several recoveries and social remissions. Clinically the recurrent cases showed more affective and confusional syndromes, and the onset tended to be more acute than in the progressive ones. These psychoses were actually mixed schizophrenic and affective states.

Experimentally the most characteristic disturbances were the tendency to inhibition and comparatively more inhibition of the unconditional reflexes and of reactions in the first signaling system than of reactions in the second signaling system. It was noted that the vascular and respiratory components of the pathodynamic structures were slight or absent. Often effects of such structures were noted in the association test. Compared with the paranoid psychoses with systematized delusions, the inertia of the nervous processes was slighter (P < 0.01). Dissociative reactions were not so frequent as in hebephrenic and catatonic cases (P < 0.001), and were absent in some of the recovered cases. In contrast to the hebephrenic and catatonic cases, periodic inhibitions of the first and second signaling systems were not usually found. From the experimental data one can assume that some disinhibition of the second signaling system was present. This can be regarded as correlated with the clinical symptom complex of thought withdrawal. Even the associative disinhibition may make the rich production of typical schizophrenic symptoms of the nature of mental automatisms possible in these cases. Because of the inhibition of unconditional reflexes, and principally of the autonomic components of the pathodynamic structures, the affective loading of the delusions seems to be absent, and general affective changes are in the foreground. It was revealed that the recovered cases with schizo-affective symptoms had disturbances of the higher nervous activity similiar to those of the manic-depressive psychoses.

Clinically the symptom complex of thought withdrawal is mostly transient, either leading to remission or progressing to paranoid deterioration with affect-laden delusions. Most cases seem to develop in the direction of phonemic and hypochondriacal paraphrenics. In the analysis of these chronic defects it was found that several cases initially had paranoid psychoses with projection symptoms. The change in the direction of affect-laden delusions was accompanied in the experimental situation by stronger autonomic responses to pathodynamic structures. In repeated investigations of acute and subacute cases, increased effects of such structures in the experiments were also found in a few cases. It appears that in the paranoid cases with projection symptoms strong inhibitions affecting the deeper-lying subcortical structure were taking place. These inhibitions are to a great extent changeable, either giving place to remissions, or being more replaced by general inertia and inertia of pathological foci.

The last group of schizophrenic symptom complexes is the paranoid group with systematized and affect-laden delusions, where the differential diagnosis from non-schizophrenic psychoses could be very difficult. Clinically these cases very much resembled the chronic series of affect-laden paraphrenics, where there was also doubt in some cases as to whether they were actually schizophrenics. In these cases the chances of complete recoveries were small, but the chance of social remission was fair and even in the progressive cases the deterioration tended to be so slight that several were capable of living outside mental hospitals.

The paranoid cases with systematized delusions had disturbances of the higher nervous activity similar to the slight paranoid defects in the chronic series, and greatly resembled the affect-laden paraphrenics. The severe autonomic effects of pathodynamic structures were most characteristic, suggesting the presence of localized pathologically excited subcortical structures with inertia. There was a general tendency to inertia of the nervous processes. The dissociative phenomena were as a rule slight and less marked than in the hebephrenic and catatonic cases ($P < 0.001$). The progressive psychoses with systematized delusions had less inhibition of the two signaling systems than the progressive catatonic and hebephrenic psychoses ($P < 0.001$). It seems that even the slight tendency to dissociation and cortical inhibition distinguishes these psychoses from the more nuclear hebephrenic and hebephrenic-paranoid cases, where the schizophrenic nature of the disease is much more easily recognized.

Compared with the paranoid psychoses with projection symptoms, they have less signs of inhibtion of unconditional defensive reflexes (P < 0.01).

The paranoid psychoses with systematized delusions mostly begin in higher age groups, and this may be the one factor which explains why such psychoses show slight dissociation and predominantly show phenomena of inertia. With higher age the nervous processes become more inert, and one should also assume that the ability to react with strong inhibition of subcortical centres is reduced. Several of these cases had an insidious onset, and often had previous nervous periods and might actually at the time of the experimental investigations have been in a chronic stage. The tendency of the premorbid personalities to be of self-assertive and sthenic types might be related to process character changes of such a long duration that they had been assumed to be habitual personality patterns. These personality structures also predispose the individual to conflicts with the environment, so that it is difficult to decide to what extent precipitating factors are secondary to personality changes.

The absence of a tendency to recovery, as well as the repeated studies, indicates that in these psychoses, the pathodynamic structures clinically and experimentally are difficult to reverse. This is possibly related to experimentally established inertia of the nervous processes. Clinically there is an inertia in the thinking and the behavior of these patients, as described by Carl Schneider in the symptom complex of drivelling. In behavior and speech the same stereotyped patterns tend to be repeated, and in thinking these patients have difficulties in changing the stream of thought. Even their characteristic disturbance of symbolization with vague symbolic explanations of ordinary everyday experiences shows an inertia, preventing the stream of thoughts from finding adequate relations between perceptions and conceptual categories. In the paranoid cases with projection symptoms, the disturbance of symbolization has more the character of uncontrolled thoughts which come into the head without any reason and give things and words a new meaning.

Reviewing the findings in acute and subacute schizophrenic symptom complexes, the more nuclear hebephrenic and hebephrenic-paranoid group with poor prognosis is characterized experimentally by severe dissociation and cortical inhibition. Progressive catatonics resemble the hebephrenic cases experimentally, whereas in recurrent catatonics there are less dissociative phenomena (P < 0.01). They had also less cortical inhibition than the progressive hebephrenics and catatonics (P < 0.01).

It seems that insidious onset in younger age groups, as in progressive hebephrenic and catatonic psychoses is associated, experimentally with marked dissociation and cortical inhibition, and clinically with an unfavorable course of the illness.

In middle age, where the psychoses with projection symptoms (symptom complex of thought withdrawal) predominantly occur, subcortical inhibition is strong, but cortical inhibition and dissociative phenomena are slighter. Chances of remissions are good, and experimentally they resemble the manic-depressive psychoses.

At a more advanced age, paranoid psychoses with systematized delusions (symptom complex of drivelling) are most frequent. In these cases there is slight subcortical and cortical inhibition, no marked dissociation, and the phenomena of inertia come into the foreground. The chances of recovery are small, but the possibilities of social remission or only slight deterioration are fair.

4. HEREDITARY LOADING RELATED TO CLINICAL AND EXPERIMENTAL DATA

The present study has primarily been concerned with the relations between clinical symptomatology and experimental findings. From the various parts of Chapters VII and VIII it can be seen that in some clinical subgroups the relatives have a marked tendency to develop similiar schizophrenic defects, while in other subgroups this is not the case. In the following tables there is given a survey of the hereditary loading for all subgroups (see Tables 29, 30, and 31).

From Table 29 it is seen that for many probably insane relatives case histories have not been available. For the vast majority of the insufficiently known relatives there has been no hospitalization, but indication of peculiar behavior which might have been due to functional psychoses. The chronic schizophrenics

TABLE 29
DATA ON HEREDITARY LOADING

Proband Material	Relatives					
	Peculiar Behavior Living at Home	Unhospitalized Living in Family Care or Nursing Homes	Hospitalized Case Histories Not Available	Total Case Histories Not Available	Total Case Histories Available for Functional Psychoses	Total Probably Psychotic Relatives
Chronic schizophrenias	92	17	17	126	157	283
Acute and subchronic functional psychoses	38	4	10	52	121	173
Total	130	21	27	178	278	456

TABLE 30

HEREDITARY LOADING OF CHRONIC SCHIZOPHRENIAS

Clinical Groups	Probands	Relatives								
		Slight Paranoid Deterioration	Severe Paranoid Deterioration	Slight Hebephrenic Deterioration	Severe Hebephrenic Deterioration	Periodic Catatonia	Systematic Catatonia	Affective Psychoses	Total of Adequate Information	Case Histories Not Available
Slight paranoid deterioration	79	25	1	0	0	0	1	10	37	29
Severe paranoid deterioration	55	4	13	1	0	0	2	2	22	14
Slight hebephrenic deterioration	33	3	1	2	1	2	0	8	17	12
Severe hebephrenic deterioration	26	0	0	8	3	0	0	5	16	10
Periodic catatonia	19	0	1	0	0	16	1	2	20	11
Systematic catatonia	94	5	5	1	2	6	14	12	45	50
Total	306	37	21	12	6	24	18	39	157	126

TABLE 31

HEREDITARY LOADING OF ACUTE AND SUBACUTE FUNCTIONAL PSYCHOSES

Clinical Groups	Probands	Relatives								
		Slight Paranoid Deterioration	Severe Paranoid Deterioration	Slight Hebephrenic Deterioration	Severe Hebephrenic Deterioration	Periodic Catatonia	Systematic Catatonia	Affective Psychoses	Total of Adequate Information	Case Histories Not Available
Progressive paranoid psychoses	51	15	1	1	1	6	2	10	36	16
Remitted paranoid psychoses	43	8	2	0	0	0	1	15	26	10
Progressive hebephrenic psychoses	31	5	3	0	1	3	2	4	18	9
Remitted hebephrenic psychoses	9	0	0	1	0	0	1	1	3	3
Progressive catatonic psychoses	26	1	1	2	1	6	3	7	21	8
Remitted catatonic psychoses	18	0	0	1	0	2	1	13	17	6
Total	178	29	7	5	3	17	10	50	121	52

have more relatives with unknown clinical states than have the acute and subacute psychoses.

In the slight paranoid defects the subgroups showed a strong tendency to similar defects in the relatives. In the whole group of twenty-seven schizophrenic relatives, twenty-five had slight paranoid defects, and the affective psychoses were, as seen from Chapter VII, relatives of the non-systematic schizophrenics. The relatives of the severe paranoid defects also had a sharp tendency to develop severe paranoid defects with thirteen such cases, four with slight paranoid defects and three with other types of schizophrenia.

Among seventeen relatives of probands with slight hebephrenic defects only two had similar defects. Several relatives had affective psychoses. It is possible that the slight clinical deterioration is related to the prognostically favorable hereditary factor. Clinically it could be assumed that the autistic and eccentric hebephrenics resemble improved schizophrenics in our follow-up studies (331).

The relatives of the severely deteriorated hebephrenics had a clear tendency to develop hebephrenic defects, with more slight than severe deterioration. This could indicate that a hebephrenic hereditary factor tends to lower the resistance to severe hebephrenic deterioration.

The periodic catatonics had comparatively many relatives with available case histories, and sixteen out of twenty had similar psychoses.

Fourteen of the twenty-eight relatives with systematic catatonics were relations of probands with systematic catatonia. Thirty-one relatives of systematic catatonics had other types of psychoses. There were fifty probably psychotic relatives with no available case histories. Considering that the systematic catatonics were usually so demented that they had to live in disturbed wards, and that most of the probably psychotic relatives were not in hospitals, it was not likely that many of these psychotic relatives could have similar psychoses. It was probable that the severe deterioration of our systematic catatonics had to be related less to the hereditary factor than to other unfavorable factors.

In the acute catatonic series, the majority of the relatives had affective psychoses. Among eighteen schizophrenics eight had periodic and four systematic catatonia. The systematic catatonias are also rarer among the relatives of acute catatonics. The average observation periods of the probands with systematic catatonics were rather long. Probably the large series of such cases is related to a hospital accumulation over many years, and the incidence of such cases is low. Among the sick relatives with functional psychoses, only 10 per cent were systematic catatonics, and in progressive acute catatonics only a few cases developed characteristic symptoms of systematic catatonics. While there are few periodic catatonics in the chronic series of probands, they are found more often than the systematic catatonics among the relatives, and the patients in the acute series of catatonics mostly resemble the periodic catatonics.

Many of the relatives of probands with acute paranoid psychoses had affective psychoses, but the greater proportion of the relatives were recurrent cases. The schizophrenic relatives had mostly slight paranoid defects, and only a few had severe paranoid defects. In the acute stages the severe paranoid defects often have hebephrenic or catatonic traits. It was noted that among twenty-eight relatives with severe paranoid defects, eleven were relatives of probands with hebephrenic or catatonic psychoses. This would mean that the severe paranoid defects often develop when there is admixture with catatonia or hebephrenia either in the clinical picture or in the family history.

In the series of acute and subacute hebephrenics only two of twenty-one relatives had hebephrenic defects, and paranoid defects were most frequent among the relatives. Most of the acute hebephrenic probands had paranoid traits in the clinical pictures.

In the hereditary findings, it is obvious that the *constitutional* background plays an important role in the development of various types of schizophrenic deterioration.

In acute and subacute schizophrenic symptom complexes, the recurrent cases had more relatives with affective psychoses and the progressive cases more relatives with schizophrenic psychoses ($P < 0.001$). Experimentally also, the recurrent psychoses more than the progressive ones resemble the affective psychoses, with less signs of dissociation (P < 0.001).

In slight chronic paranoid defects there is a very great tendency to similar psychoses in the families. This might indicate that the formation of the more isolated pathodynamic structures is strongly dependent upon constitutional factors related to inertia of nervous processes. Even if the delusions may be set in relation to the personality structures and life experiences, or if the psychoses are apparently precipitated by external factors, the specific defect type is probably determined more by constitutional and process factors than by psychodynamic factors.

In periodic catatonia most relatives have similar psychoses. As in the slight paranoid defects, precipitating factors were often found. In periodic catatonia clinically there tended to be acute onsets with violent psychomotor symptoms, suggesting an ability to react with strong cortical inhibition. Possibly a constitutional tendency to react with stormy inhibitions to some extent represents a biological healing mechanism, which gives a greater chance of remissions than in the systematic catatonics, and in the defect states less deterioration, less general impairment of the higher nervous activity (P < 0.001) and fewer signs of dissociation (P < 0.001).

In the systematic catatonics there seems to be a greater tendency to similar defects in the subgroups, as well as in the whole group than could be expected from mere chance. Since they have so few relatives with systematized catatonia, the influence of the constitutional factors must be low. The severe clinical deterioration with the strong dissociations and inhibitions of all levels of the higher nervous activity seems to be related to a slowly progressive schizophrenic process. Even the lack of the constitutional tendency of the periodic catatonics to stormy inhibitions may indicate weaker biological defence mechanisms.

In the slight hebephrenic defects the relatives had a slight tendency to similar psychoses. Experimentally they had less dissociation (P < 0.001) and cortical inhibition (P < 0.001) than the severe hebephrenic defects whose relatives predominantly had hebephrenic defects. It is possible that the slight hebephrenic deterioration is related to a constitutional loading with affective psychoses, which have a slight tendency to dissociative inhibitions.

There is a pronounced family tendency to similar defects in psychoses with severe paranoid deterioration. Experimentally such psychoses, apart from the influence of pathodynamic structures, resemble the severe hebephrenic and catatonic defects with their severe dissociations and inhibitions. Clinically they also often have hebephrenic or catatonic traits in the acute stages, and several relatives of catatonic and hebephrenic probands had severe paranoid defects. This could suggest that the constitutional background of severe paranoid defects is a combination of tendencies to inertia and to dissociative inhibitions of the higher nervous activity.

In part one of this chapter the disturbances of the higher nervous activity in schizophrenia might be explained from the general principles of *autokinesis* and *schizokinesis*. The hereditary findings indicate that these biological reaction forms are related to the constitutional background. On the other hand the most hereditary types of schizophrenic deterioration tend to develop slight defects, are often precipitated by external factors, and, as seen in the following part of this chapter, seem to benefit from treatment with ataraxic drugs.

This stress on the importance of constitutional and process factors for the types of schizophrenic deterioration does not exclude the importance of social and psychological factors in the causation as well as in the treatment of schizophrenia. In other studies the author has pointed to the significance of such factors (54, 62, 331). As suggested by Adolf Meyer a multifactorial etiology and pathogenesis of schizophrenia seems probable (602). The present study is mainly concerned with symptomatological, hereditary and reflexological aspects of these factors.

5. THE EFFECTS OF ATARAXIC DRUGS RELATED TO CLINICAL AND EXPERIMENTAL DATA

In the present series 311 patients have been treated with ataraxic drugs, and among them 292 with *chlorpromazine*.

According to the literature referred to in chapter III, chlorpromazine acts on the unconditional as well as the conditional reflex activity.   Characteristic is the great inhibitory effect upon the unconditional responses.

It is seen from the Chapters VII and VIII that in most schizophrenic subgroups there are as a rule no essential differences in the disturbances of the higher nervous activity between patients treated and not treated with ataraxic drugs at the time of the experimental investigations.   This would suggest that the effect of the schizophrenic process predominates over that of the ataraxic drugs.

Altogether 130 patients received ataraxic drugs at the time of the experimental investigations.   Two patients received *meprobamate*, 14 *reserpine* and 114 *chlorpromazine*.

Those treated with reserpine had less adequate responses and more inhibition of unconditional defensive reflexes than clinically matched cases not treated with ataraxic drugs, but the differences were not statistically significant.

The 114 cases treated with chlorpromazine had more adequate responses than those who received no ataraxic drugs (P < 0.001). They had also less signs of dissociation (P < 0.01), less inertia (P < 0.01), less impaired internal inhibition (P < 0.02), less passive inhibition of the two signaling systems (P < 0.001), and more adequate responses in the second signaling system (P < 0.001).   They had more inhibition of the unconditional defensive reflexes than the untreated cases (not significant).

The statistical comparisons indicate that chlorpromazine has a slight inhibiting effect upon unconditional reflexes and improves the other aspects of the higher nervous activity.

In the series of chronic schizophrenics sixty-one received chlorpromazine at the time of the experimental investigations.   Compared with the others, there was a tendency to more inhibition of the unconditional defensive reflexes (not significant).   The treated cases had less general impairment of the higher nervous activity (P < 0.001).   This was largely due to better reactions in the paranoid cases, statistically significant at the 0.001 level.   In the drug-treated paranoid cases there was less autonomic effect of pathodynamic structures, but not statistically significant.

In the series of acute and subacute functional psychoses fifty-three received chlorpromazine at the time of the experimental investigations. Compared with the untreated cases there were no statistically significant differences as to general impairment, dissociation, inertia, impairment of internal inhibition, passive inhibition of the two signaling systems, and inhibition of the unconditional defensive reflexes.

In the predominantly drug-treated patients who were re-examined there was a tendency to more dissociation (P < 0.01), and inhibition of unconditional defensive reflexes (P < 0.001). But they had better reactions in the second signaling system (P < 0.001), less impairment of internal inhibition (P < 0.01), and less passive inhibition of the two signaling systems (P < 0.01).

The administration of single doses of ataraxic drugs, combined with experimental investigations, before and after the administration of the drug, can clearly demonstrate the effect upon the higher nervous activity. Treatment over longer periods will give rise to the question whether clinical and experimental changes are due to the drugs or to the spontaneous course of the disease. As the effects of the schizophrenic process upon the higher nervous activity seem to predominate over the effects of ataraxic drugs, it is also important to consider in detail the clinical pictures.

The chronic schizophrenics have fairly stable clinical pictures when untreated. The tendency to better reactions in drug-treated cases is probably an effect of the drug. It is probable that the improvement is related to inhibition of unconditional reflexes and slightly less autonomic effects of pathodynamic structures in the paranoid cases.

In the series of acute and subacute functional psychoses it is probable that the effects of drugs and changes in clinical conditions balance each other more than in the chronic series. It was noted that the drug-treated acute cases had less dissociative responses than the untreated cases. This would support the assumption that the tendency to more dissociative reactions in cases studied repeatedly is related to the schizophrenic deterioration in spite of treatment effects. The tendency to more inhibition of unconditional defensive reflexes in re-examined cases is probably not only related to the schizophrenic deterioration, but also to effects of drugs. From the analysis of the re-examined cases it was assumed that the tendency to better reactions in the second signaling system, less impairment of internal inhibition and less passive inhibition in the two signaling systems was due to the ataraxic drugs. The comparisons of all cases treated and not treated with ataraxic drugs at the time of the experimental investigations support this assumption.

A survey of the clinical effects of the ataraxic drugs is presented in the Tables 32 and 33 (see Tables 32 and 33).

In the chronic schizophrenics the best results are obtained in the non-systematic affect-laden paraphrenics (Chapter VII), schizophasiacs and some of the periodic catatonics. It is known that these cases have a tendency to periodic shifts in the clinical pictures. In the systematic schizophrenic defects, the characteristic defect symptoms were not essentially changed. The improvements were reduction of affective loading of delusions, hallucinations and periodic excitements. Clinically these changes may be considered as related to inhibition of subcortical centers. As a rule the clinical improvement was slightest in cases with severe dissociative phenomena and great general impairment of the higher nervous activity. This may indicate that the more severely nervous functions are distorted, the more difficult it is to modify the disturbed behavior.

Most cases with slight paranoid defects improved considerably and became less sensitive about their hallucinations and delusions. Experimentally these cases have strong influences of pathodynamic structures, slight dissociative phenomena and slight general disturbances of the higher nervous activity.

The severe paranoid defects benefited less from the treatment. Experimentally this was paralleled by less influences of pathodynamic structures, more general impairment and more dissociative disturbances.

Among the chronic hebephrenias, few improved considerably, the majority only improving a little. Considerable improvement was shown by only three slightly deteriorated hebephrenics, in whom experimentally the disturbances were mainly general

TABLE 32

EFFECT OF ATARAXIC DRUGS IN CHRONIC SCHIZOPHRENICS

Clinical Subgroups	Considerable Improvement	Slight Improvement	No Improvement	Total
Slight paranoid defects	40	8	0	48
Severe paranoid defects	0	10	13	23
Hebephrenic defects	3	21	7	31
Periodic catatonia	10	4	2	16
Systematic catatonia	0	37	30	67
Total	53	80	52	185

TABLE 33

Effect of Ataraxic Drugs in Acute and Subacute Schizophrenics and Schizophreniform Psychoses

Clinical Subgroups	Complete Remission	Social Remission	Considerable Improvement	Slight Improvement	No Improvement	Total
Hebephrenic and hebephrenic-paranoid psychoses	0	5	6	9	7	27
Catatonic psychoses	0	14	13	6	3	36
Paranoid psychoses with projection symptoms	10	10	7	4	1	32
Paranoid psychoses with systematized delusions	0	10	16	2	3	31
Total	10	39	42	21	14	126

inertia and inhibition. The severely deteriorated hebephrenics who had more general impairment of nervous functions and dissociative disturbances mostly showed moderate improvement.

In patients with chronic catatonia the best results were obtained in the periodic catatonics who experimentally showed less disturbances of the higher nervous activity than the systematic catatonics ($P < 0.001$). The systematic catatonics are clinically severely deteriorated, have great dissociative disturbances and more general impairment of the higher nervous activity than the other chronic schizophrenics. In nearly one-half of the patients the drug treatment had no effect, and not one improved considerably.

In the acute and subacute schizophrenic symptoms complexes, the hebephrenic group showed the least effect of the treatment. Such cases in our follow-up studies also had a poor prognosis with shock-treatment (331). Experimentally, this group was characterized by considerable dissociative disturbances and tendencies to periodic inhibitions of the functions of the first and second signaling systems. Repeated studies showed more unimproved than improved responses in spite of treatment. There was a pronounced tendency to increase of dissociative phenomena ($P < 0.01$) and inhibition of the unconditional defensive reflexes ($P < 0.001$).

In catatonic patients the majority had considerable improvement or social remissions. Cases with social remissions had less dissociative phenomena than the hebephrenic group ($P < 0.01$), but more inhibition of unconditional defensive reflexes (not statistically significant). Clinically the recurrent catatonics had symptoms which, according to our follow-up studies, were prognostically favorable (331). Repeated studies of progressive catatonics showed less tendency to increase of dissociative phenomena and inhibition of unconditional defensive reflexes than the hebephrenic psychoses.

In paranoid psychoses with projection symptoms the results of the treatment were very good. Experimentally these psychoses resembled the manic-depressive psychoses. They had less dissociative phenomena than the hebephrenic and catatonic psychoses (P < 0.001). They showed more signs of inhibition of the unconditional defensive reflexes than the other acute and sub-chronic psychoses (P < 0.001). Clinically the recurrent psychoses had symptoms which, according to our follow-up studies, were prognostically favorable (331). In contrast to the paranoid psychoses with systematized delusions, they had slight autonomic responses to pathodynamic structures. In repeated studies of progressive cases, there was a tendency to more signs of dissociation, but fewer signs of inhibition (P < 0.05). They also showed stronger autonomic responses to pathodynamic structures.

Most paranoid psychoses with systematized delusions had social remissions or considerable improvement, but no complete remissions, as in the paranoid psychoses with projection symptoms. In the experimental investigations they had, compared with the paranoid psychoses with projection symptoms, less inhibition of unconditional defensive reflexes (P < 0.01), but more signs of inertia (P < 0.01). This might indicate that general inertia and strong effects of pathodynamic structures mean small chances of complete remissions. In the repeated studies of progressive psychoses with systematized delusions, the autonomic effects of the pathodynamic structures were not much modified. Parallel with the clinical improvement, there was a general amelioration of the functions of the first and second signaling systems (P < 0.01). In this group there were clinically as well as experimentally no marked differences between progressive and recurrent cases.

In the series of chronic schizophrenics, the drug-treated cases with considerable improvement had less general impairment (P < 0.001) and fewer signs of dissociation (P < 0.001) than cases with no improvement. Sixteen of those with considerable improvement had violent autonomic responses to pathodynamic structures, but none were observed in those with no improvement.

For the series of drug-treated acute and subacute psychoses calculations show that the cases with complete and social remissions had a much greater number of adequate responses than those with slight or no improvement (P < 0.001). The recurrent cases in particular had fewer signs of dissociation (P < 0.001), less inhibition in the two signaling systems (P < 0.001), less inertia (P < 0.01), less impairment of internal inhibition (P < 0.01), and more adequate associative responses (P < 0.001).

The recovered cases had most inhibition of unconditional defensive reflexes, but not statistically significant differences compared with the others. Psychoses with slight or no improvement had fewer violent autonomic responses to pathodynamic structures than those with considerable improvement (P < 0.02).

In the clinical analysis of the effects of ataraxic drugs, it seems that in chronic schizophrenics the best results are obtained in cases which clinically are slightly deteriorated, or previously have had a great tendency to remissions. In particular the slightly deteriorated paranoid cases respond well to the treatment.

In acute and subacute psychoses, the symptom complexes which according to follow-up studies benefit most from shock-treatment, benefit most from ataraxic drugs. Only the paranoid psychoses with systematized delusions were an exception to this rule. As in the case of chronic slight paranoid defects, whom they resemble clinically and experimentally, the ataraxic drugs may give particular advantages.

Experimentally it seems that the chronic schizophrenics benefit most from the treatment when they have slight general impairment of the higher nervous activity, slight dissociative disturbances and strong autonomic responses to pathodynamic structures.

In the series of acute and subacute functional psychoses, the best results were obtained in cases which experimentally had slight impairment of the higher nervous activity. Slight dissociative disturbances or strong autonomic responses to pathodynamic structures seem to indicate favorable results. The group of paranoid psychoses with projection symptoms, which benefited much from the treatment, showed strong inhibitions of unconditional defensive reflexes. This indicates that such inhibitions in certain acute symptom complexes are favorable, although they ran parallel with severe schizophrenic deterioration.

The complexity of phenomena does not make definite conclusions about the effects of ataraxic drugs (especially chlorpromazine) possible. Some tentative hypotheses can be put forward.

The drugs, by increasing the inhibitions of subcortical centres, may help to counteract the tendency of such centres to exhaustion. The activity of the first and second signaling systems is then improved, especially the second signaling system, where the functions are most vulnerable, but also more reversible than at the deeper levels. In the pathodynamic structures the effect could also possibly be due to an inhibition of the unconditional defensive components. This could explain the clinical reduction of aggressiveness and affective loading of the delusions. An inhibition of the excited structures would then decrease the negative induction imposed on the cortical functions and give better responses in the two signaling systems. These effects were clearly patterned in the repeated studies of paranoid psychoses with systematized delusions.

As noted previously schizophrenic symptoms can to a great extent be interpreted neurophysiologically as due to pathological inhibitions of a protective nature. Taking into consideration that unconditional reflexes tend to be inhibited in schizophrenics, the possibility exists that chlorpromazine and other ataraxic drugs can strengthen protective inhibition of subcortical regions, and in this way support biological defense mechanisms. In the acute paranoid psychoses with projection symptoms there may be unconditional inhibition of a protective nature.

As the tendency to increasing inhibition of unconditional reflexes is apparently associated with schizophrenic deterioration, this inhibition is also a central pathological disturbance. The problem arises to what extent the ataraxic drugs can counteract the dissociative disturbances of schizophrenic deterioration.

6. THEORETICAL IMPLICATIONS OF THE CLINICAL AND EXPERIMENTAL STUDIES, AND FURTHER RESEARCH PROBLEMS

Details in the chapters on the experimental methods and the analysis of the clinical phenomena show there are many sources of error. It is obvious that the correlation between experimental data and clinical factors will not give sufficient data for definite conclusions.

The great amount of experimental data and the detailed clinical analysis make a great number of clinical-experimental comparisons possible. The statistical comparisons have been limited to what the author considered to be clinically relevant problems. No detailed statistical elaboration of the data has been carried out because this would give a false impression of exactness. By giving the experimental and clinical data, as they were found, it is possible for other authors to compare their findings.

Only simple statistical methods such as the chi-square test and the sign test were applied, and the P values must only be considered as a crude quantitative demonstration of the observed variations. With the chi-square test, comparisons of adequate and inadequate reactions in patient groups and normals, even for the least disturbed group of patients, give statistically significant differences at the 0.001 level ($X^2 = 228$). Only in four of the completely studied patients were there no greater inadequate reactions than in any of the 40 normals. Two of these had reaction types not found in the normal series. At the time of the experimental investigations not one of these four cases had active psychotic symptoms. It is very improbable that a schizophrenic, with the experimental methods selected for this study, would not give responses different from those of normals.

In spite of all the uncertainties, the experimental methods do furnish the opportunity of controlling hypotheses quantitatively, and may contribute to increasing the objectivity in psychiatric research. In the present study only correlations can be pointed out which need further study in order that definite conclusions can be reached. With these reservations in mind, some tentative hypotheses can be formulated.

Primarily it seems that *similar* clinical states tend to have similar disturbances of the higher nervous activity. The more the patients are *disturbed* and deteriorated, the *greater* is the impairment of the higher nervous activity.

The various schizophrenic subgroups showed very great differences in their higher nervous activity. Experimentally dissociative phenomena and disturbances of the subcortical activity were especially characteristic of schizophrenics. The severe schizophrenic deterioration was always accompanied by severe dissociations and inhibitions of all three levels of the higher nervous activity. The experimental as well as the clinical data indicate that the schizophrenic psychoses neurophysiologically are more of process than of psychodynamic character. The schizophrenic symptoms in the experimental studies had, to a great extent, the character of mental automatisms related more to general disturbances of nervous functions than to psychological complexes. Even the impairment of subcortical functions seemed to be of importance for the automatic character of the symptoms. Possibilities exist that the dissociative phenomena are secondary to consistent impairment of the subcortical activity.

There is some reason to believe that when the schizophrenic process has first started, the further development may be explained from the principles of *autokinesis* and *schizokinesis* found in animal experiments. This indicates that disturbances of the higher nervous activity tend to develop along certain paths relatively independent of the originally precipitating factors. The hereditary findings indicate that constitutional factors are of great significance in this process.

Although there are several cases with admixtures of symptoms of the typical systematic schizophrenics, the majority of the schizophrenic defects could easily be classified into a limited number of groups with very similar symptoms. This shows that the chronic schizophrenics do not have a vast number of individual forms, but are concentrated on certain symptom complexes. The hereditary findings show that in the subgroups also the similarity of clinical pictures in relatives is too great to be attributed to chance. There is good reason to believe that the schizophrenic defect on the basis of constitutional predispositions tends to disturb a limited number of neurophysiological systems. With the experimental studies it was not possible to find such sharply defined experimental as clinical differences between the subgroups. Perhaps the refinements of experimental technique might reveal differences more clearly. One entertains the idea that the clinical differences have been overestimated compared with the resemblances.

With the present methods only a limited experimental study of the complex higher nervous activity has been carried out. It is probable that complexes with other methods could give more information about the correlations between clinical symptoms and experimental data. In particular, the investigation of dissociative phenomena with batteries of psychological tests, and the disturbances of the subcortical activity with physiological and biochemical methods might give more detailed information about the pathophysiological structure, as well as diagnostic, prognostic and therapeutic aspects. The great clinical and experimental differences in the schizophrenic subgroups would suggest that a detailed clinical subgrouping is advantageous for such studies. Presumably the disturbances of subcortical functions are either caused by biochemical changes or, secondarily, give rise to such changes. Studies of the relations between the disturbances of the higher nervous activity in combination with biochemical research might be especially fruitful.

Independent of what biochemical research may yield in connection with treatment, experimental studies of the higher nervous activity may be of value in the evaluation of the effects of treatment in schizophrenia. In a previous study the author set out the results of group psychotherapy in relation to experimental findings (62). In the present study and in a congress report based on this study, the author has related the effects of the ataraxic drugs to the types of disturbances of the higher nervous activity (65). It was felt that chlorpromazine, through inhibition of subcortical centres, could have beneficial effects upon pathodynamic structures and inhibitory disturbances of the two signaling systems, but could modify the dissociative phenomena less. Through systematic studies it should be possible to find out how various ataraxic drugs act upon basic nervous processes in animals and man under normal as well as under pathological conditions. There are marked views that such studies might contribute to a more adequate selection of drugs in the treatment of various types of schizophrenia.

Chapter X
SUMMARY AND CONCLUSIONS

CHAPTERS I AND II deal with theoretical and methodological problems in studies of the higher nervous activity in man. The experimental methods selected for this study are described, and the neurophysiological interpretations of experimental findings discussed. Through experimental investigations of a series of normals, the limits of normal variation could be established for comparisons with series of patient groups.

Chapter III surveys our present knowledge of how drugs and other treatments influence the higher nervous activity.

Chapter IV deals with studies of disturbances of the higher nervous activity in other mental disorders than schizophrenia. These studies make it possible to judge what type of impairment is common to the various mental disorders and what is characteristic of schizophrenia.

Chapter V reviews previous studies of the higher nervous activity in schizophrenia. The experimental data, and the theoretical conceptions of neurophysiological mechanisms common to all groups of schizophrenia, as well as those typical of various individual symptoms and symptom complexes are referred to here. The results obtained with the methods selected for the present study are described. It is demonstrated that these studies as well as studies with other methods indicate that disturbances of subcortical activity and dissociative phenomena are important pathophysiological factors in the schizophrenics.

In Chapter VI problems of clinical analysis and classification are discussed. In order to be able to correlate the experimental and clinical data for relatively homogeneous groups, the clinical material is divided into precisely defined subgroups. The chronic schizophrenics are classified according to the principles of Leonhard. The acute and subacute functional psychoses are analyzed and divided into subgroups on the basis of personal experiences from follow-up studies, with special reference to the theories of Langfeldt and Carl Schneider. The principles of evaluating the hereditary loading are also discussed, and the selected clinical material is presented.

Chapter VII gives the experimental, clinical and hereditary characteristics, and the effects of ataraxic drug treatment for each subgroup of chronic schizophrenia. Similarly the subgroups of acute and subacute functional psychoses are analyzed in Chapter VIII. The findings in chronic schizophrenics are compared with those in acute and subacute cases. Repeated studies of progressive schizophrenics yield further information about the experimental changes related to schizophrenic deterioration.

The experimental and clinical data are summarized and discussed in Chapter IX. The more disturbed the behavior appeared, and the more pronounced the schizophrenic deterioration, the greater was the impairment of the higher nervous activity. Within the clinical subgroups, there was a tendency toward similar disturbances of the higher nervous activity.

Although the experimental findings for the subgroups varied much, inhibition of unconditional reflexes and dissociative phenomena seem to be largely associated with the schizophrenic deterioration. Most schizophrenics also showed impairment of internal inhibition and inertia of the nervous processes. The major role of sleep-resembling inhibitions in schizophrenia, which pathophysiologically has been stressed by Pavlov and clinically by Carl Schneider, was confirmed. It was assumed that the disturbances of the higher nervous activity in schizophrenia might be explained from the general neurophysiological principles of autokinesis and schizokinesis postulated by Gantt.

Neurophysiologically the various types of schizophrenic symptom complexes may be regarded as dependent upon general disturbances of the higher nervous activity. The clinical symptoms can more easily be interpreted as mental automatisms (Kandinsky and Clérambault) related to such disturbances than as the result of psychodynamic mechanisms.

From the present studies it must be left an open question whether the schizophrenics, as argued by Adolph Meyer, are unspecific reaction types of the nervous system to the most varied forms of stress. When the schizophrenic process is first started, the development of the deterioration can be described in physiological terms. It seems that the principles of autokinesis and schizokinesis, which are strongly dependent on constitutional factors, can give a model of the mechanisms of the schizophrenic deterioration.

The effects of chlorpromazine are supposed to be related to inhibition of subcortical centres, supporting biological healing mechanisms. It is suggested that experimental studies of the higher nervous activity might contribute to a more adequate selection of ataraxic drugs for the treatment of various types of schizophrenia.

REFERENCES

The index of subjects gives both a page number relative to reference of various topics of conditioning and an index of bibliography.

1. Abaskuliev, A. A. & M. I. Fel (1956) Clinical and pathophysiological problems of neuroses and pseudoneurotic types of schizophrenia. (Rus.) Tes. Dokl. Sess. Inst. M. Asatiani. 35-35.

2. Abaskuliev, A. A. & M. I. Fel (1958) Clinical and pathophysiological problems of neuroses and pseudoneurotic schizophrenia. (Rus.) Sb. nauch. Inst. M. Asatiani. Tiflis. 155-158.

3. Abramson, D. I., N. Schkloven & K. H. Katzenstein: (1941) Peripheral blood flow in schizophrenia and other abnormal mental states. Arch. Neurol. Psychiat. (Chicago) 45, 973-979.

4. Abramson, D. I. (1944) Vascular responses in the extremities of man in health and disease. Chicago.

5. Ackner, B. (1956) Emotions and the peripheral vasomotor system. J. psychosom. Res. 1, 3-20.

6. Agafonov, V. G. (1956) Inhibitory influences of aminazine on the central effect of pain stimuli. (Rus.) Z. Nevropat. Psihiat. (Korsakoff.) 56, 94-103.

7. Akhmerov, Y. S. (1956) Cortical regulation of muscular chronaxy. (Rus.) Z. vyss. nerv. Dejat. Pavlova. 6, 226-233.

8. Akhmerov, Y. S. (1956) Attempts to analyze the dynamics of the cortical processes in man with chronaximetry. (Rus.) Z. vyss. nerv. Dejat. Pavlova. 6, 365-369.

9. Aksentiev, S. B., J. V. Yermulovich, L. F. Zhmudskaya & L. G. Reznichenko (1957) Study of vascular conditional and unconditional reflexes as a method of analyzing cortico-visceral relations in various diseases. (Rus.) Z. vyss. nerv. Dejat. Pavlova. 7, 49-57.

10. Aleksandrova, L. I. (1952) Clinical physiological analysis of neurotic syndromes in the initial stages of hypertensive disease, and the significance of inhibition. (Rus.) Z. Nevropat. Psihiat. (Korsakoff.) 52, 42-48.

11. Aleksandrova, L. I. & R. A. Tkacheva (1958) Problems of the pathogenesis, clinic and treatment of neuroses. (Rus.) Moscow.

12. Aleksanjants, R. A. (1957) Some clinical characteristics and the disturbances of the higher nervous activity in simple forms of schizophrenia. (Rus.) Vopr. Klin. Patogenez. Schiz. Moscow. 32-41.

13. Aleksejev, M. A., A. A. Asknazy, A. I. Zotov & N. J. Lipatova (1955) Some characteristics of the formation of complex motor reactions in man. (Rus.) Z. vyss. nerv. Dejat. Pavlova. 5, 773-782.

14. Alpern, E. B., N. Finkelstein & W. H. Gantt (1943) Effect of amphetamine (benzedrine) sulfate upon higher nervous activity. I. Animal experiments. Bull. Johns Hopk. Hosp. 73, 287-299.

15. Alpern, E. B., N. Finkelstein & W. H. Gantt (1945) Effect of amphetamine (benzedrine) sulfate upon higher nervous activity compared with alcohol. II. Human experiments. Bull. Johns Hopk. Hosp. 76, 61-74.
16. Altman, J. A. (1955) Some disturbances of the higher nervous activity in the Korsakoff syndrome in typhoid fever. (Rus.) Tr. nauch. Konf. posv. Ioo Let. S. S. Korsakoff. 70-72.
17. Altschule, M. D. (1953) Bodily physiology in mental and emotional disorders. New York.
18. Angyal, A. & N. Blackman (1940) Vestibular reactivity in schizophrenia. Arch. Neurol. Psychiat. (Chicago) 44, 611-620.
19. Ángyán, A. J., I. Husár & J. Nyirö (1958) Angaben zur Pathophysiologie der Zwangsneurose auf Grund objektiv—experimenteller Beobachtungen. Psychiat. Neurol. med. Psychol. (Lpz.) 10, 253-260.
20. Apter, I. M. & B. V. Tshukher (1952) The influence of electroshock on the motor defensive conditional reflexes in dogs. (Rus.) Z. vyss. nerv. Dejat. Pavlova. 2, 396-410.
21. Apter, I. M. (1955) The characteristics of the higher nervous activity in patients with epilepsy. (Rus.) Z. Nevropat. Psihiat. (Korsakoff.) 55, 321-325.
22. Apter, I. M., Z. N. Bolotova & N. G. Sineiko (1955) The effects of combined ECT and prolonged sleep on the higher nervous activity of dogs. (Rus.) Z. vyss. nerv. Dejat. Pavlova. 5, 70-75.
23. Apter, I. M. (1957) Comparisons of the effects of ECT, camphor and a combination of ECT and prolonged sleep on the higher nervous activity of dogs. (Rus.) Z. Nevropat. Psihiat. (Korsakoff.) Suppl. 57, 89-90.
24. Apter, I. M. (1958) Clinical-physiological analysis of neuroses with disturbances of cardiovascular activity. (Rus.) Konf. Vopr. Patofiziol. vyss. nerv. Dejat. Moscow. 8-10.
25. Apter, I. M. (1958) The dynamics of the higher nervous activity of neurasthenic patients during treatment. (Rus.) Z. Nevropat. Psihiat. (Korsakoff.) 58, 1321-1325.
26. Arieti, S. (1945) Primitive habits and perceptual alterations in the terminal stage of schizophrenia. Arch. Neurol. Psychiat. (Chicago) 53, 378-384.
27. Arnold, O. H. (1955) Schizophrener Prozess und schizophrene Symptomgesetze. Wien & Bonn.
28. Artjukh, E. I. (1957) Disturbances of perception in schizophrenics and their pathophysiological basis. (Rus.) Psihiat. klin. Probl. Patol. vyss. nerv. Dejat. 2, 104-109.
29. Ås, A. (1958) Mutilation fantasies and autonomic response. Oslo. Diss.
30. Asatiani, L. M. (1956) Characteristics of speech incoherence of schizophrenics in association experiments. (Rus.) Tes. Dokl. Sess. Inst. M. Asatiani. Tiflis (8-9.)
31. Asatiani, L. M. (1958) Characteristics of speech activity in incoherent schizophrenics in association experiments. (Rus.) Sb. nauch. Inst. M. Asatiani. Tiflis. 33-39.
32. Asatiani, N. M. (1955) The influence of therapeutic doses of caffein on the cortical dynamics of some neuroses. (Rus.) Tr. Inst. vyss. nerv. Dejat. Ser. Patofiziol. 1, 193-211.

33. Asatiani, N. M. (1958) Disturbances of the mobility of the cortical processes in psychasthenic patients. (Rus.) Konf. Vopr. Patofiziol. vyss. nerv. Dejat. Moscow. 10-11.

34. Asatiani, N. M. (1958) Effect of different doses of serpasil on the cortical dynamics and some autonomic functions in neurotic patients (Rus.) Konf. Itog. nauch. issl. Rab. 1957 Moscow, 29-30.

35. Asatiani, N. M. (1958) The influence of various psychotherapeutic procedures on the combined activity of the signaling systems in patients with neuroses. (Rus.) Tr. Inst. vyss. nerv. Dejat. Ser. Patofiziol. 5, 273-292.

36. Aschaffenburg, G. (1896) Experimentelle Studien über Associationen. 1 Teil. Die Associationen im normalen Zustande. Psychol. Arb. 1, 209-299.

37. Aschaffenburg, G. (1904) Experimentelle Studien über Associationen. 3 Teil. Die Ideenflucht. Psychol. Arb. 4, 235-373.

38. Aslanov, A. S. (1955) Characteristics of induced inhibition in patients with sequelae of closed head injury. (Rus.) Tr. Inst. vyss. nerv. Dejat. Ser. Patofizol. 1, 109-136.

39. Aslanov, A. S. (1955) The influence of prolonged sleep on some disturbances of the cortical dynamics in patients with sequelae of closed head injury. (Rus.) Tr. Inst. vyss. nerv. Dejat. Ser. Patofiziol. 1, 267-285.

40. Aslanov, A. S. (1957) Some characteristics of the combined activity of the first and second signaling systems in closed head injury with late sequelae. (Rus.) Nauch. Konf. Dejat. Sign. Sist. Norm. i Patol. 5-6.

41. Aslanov, A. S. (1957) The influences of aminazine on the first and second signaling systems in schizophrenic patients. (Rus.) Nauch. Konf. Dejat. Sign. Sist. Norm. i Patol. 6-7.

42. Aslanov, A. S. (1958) Disturbances of the analysis and synthesis in patients with traumatic injury of the brain. (Rus.) Konf. Vopr. Pathofiziol. vyss. nerv. Dejat. Moscow. 13-14.

43. Aslanov, A. S. (1958) Some disturbances of the higher nervous activity in patients with hypochondriacal type of schizophrenia, and the effects of single doses of serpasil. (Rus.) Konf. Itog. nauch. issl. Rab. 1957 Moscow. 30-31.

44. Aslanov, A. S. (1958) The analysis of the mechanisms of aminazine effect on the higher nervous activity. (Rus.) Tes. 18 Sov. Probl. vyss. nerv. Dejat. 2, 32-33.

45. Aslanov, A. S. (1958) Characteristics of passive and active inhibition in patients with late sequelae of closed head injury. (Rus.) Tr. Inst. vyss. nerv. Dejat. Ser. Patofiziol. 5, 212-231.

46. Aslanov, A. S. (1958) Characteristics of the combined activity of the first and second signaling systems in late sequelae of closed head injury. (Rus.) Tr. Inst. vyss. nerv. Dejat. Ser. Patofiziol. 5, 196-211.

47. Aslanov, A. S. (1958) Characteristics of pathodynamic structures in the paranoid type of schizophrenia. (Rus.) Tr. Inst. vyss. nerv. Dejat. Ser. Patofiziol. 5, 85-100.

48. Asofov, B. D. & V. M. Smirnov (1956) The registration of spoken and written conditional responses by the study of speech and movements. (Rus.) Z. vyss. nerv. Dejat. Pavlova. 6, 333-337.

49. Asratyan, E. A. (1953) The physiology of the central nervous system. (Rus.) Moscow.

50. Astrup, C. (1954) The first and second signaling systems. (Nor.) Nord. psykiat. Medlemsbl. 8, 188-193.

51. Astrup, C. (1955) Untersuchungen mit der Assoziationsmethodik über Störungen im zweiten Signalsystem bei verschiedenen psychopathologischen Zuständen. Psychiat. Neurol. med. Psychol. (Lpz.) 7, 326-334.

52. Astrup, C. (1956) Erfahrungen mit verschiedenen bedingtreflektorischen Untersuchungsmethoden an Neurotikern. Psychiat. Neurol. med. Psychol. (Lpz.) 8, 161-172.

53. Astrup, C. (1956) Über Korrelationen zwischen klinischen Bildern und experimentell gefundenen Störungen der höheren Nerventätigkeit. Arb. tag. zent. Regulat. Funkt. Organism. Berlin. 314-322.

54. Astrup, C. (1956) Nervöse Erkrankungen und soziale Verhältnisse. Berlin.

55. Astrup, C. (1957) Experimentelle Untersuchungen über die Störungen der höheren Nerventätigkeit bei Defektschizophrenen. Psychiat. Neurol. med. Psychol. (Lpz.) 9, 9-14.

56. Astrup, C. (1957) Experimentelle Untersuchungen über die Störungen der höheren Nerventätigkeit bei akuten und subchronischen Schizophrenien. Psychiat. Neurol. med. Psychol. (Lpz.) 9, 33-38.

57. Astrup, C. (1957) Experimentelle Untersuchungen über die Störungen der höheren Nerventätigkeit bei manisch-depressiven Psychosen. Psychiat. Neurol. med. Psychol. (Lpz.) 9, 369-372.

58. Astrup, C. (1957) Experimentelle Untersuchungen über die Störungen der höheren Nerventätigkeit bei reaktiven (psychogenen) Psychosen. Psychiat. Neurol. med. Psychol. (Lpz.) 9, 373-377.

59. Astrup, C. (1957) Experimentelle Untersuchungen über die Störungen der höheren Nerventätigkeit bei Oligophrenen. Psychiat. Neurol. med. Psychol. (Lpz.) 9, 377-380.

60. Astrup, C. (1957) Experimentelle Utersuchungen über die Störungen der höheren Nerventätigkeit bei organisch Dementen und organischen Psychosen. Psychiat. Neurol. med. Psychol. (Lpz.) 9, 380-384.

61. Astrup, C. (1957) Disturbances of the higher nervous activity in schizophrenia. (Nor.) Nord. psykiat. Medlemsbl. 11, 208-212.

62. Astrup, C. (1958) Group therapy in a mental hospital with special regard to schizophrenics. Acta psychiat. scand. 33, 1-20.

63. Astrup, C. (1958) Klinisch-experimentelle Untersuchungen bei verschiedenen Formen von Schizophrenie. Psychiat. Neurol. med. Psychol. (Lpz.) 10, 355-356.

64. Astrup, C., A. Fossum & R. Holmboe (1959) A follow-up study of 270 patients with acute affective psychoses. Acta psychiat. scand. Suppl. 135.

65. Astrup, C. (1959) The effects of ataraxic drugs on schizophrenic subgroups related to experimental findings. Acta psychiat. scand. Suppl. 136, 388-393.

66. Astrup, C. & N. G. Harzstein (1960) The influence of psychotherapy on the higher nervous activity of schizophrenics. Internat. J. Grouppsychotherapy. 10, 394-407.

67. Astrup, C. (1961) A note on clinical and experimental observations of the application of group therapy. Internat. J. Grouppsychotherapy. 11, 74-77.

68. Atajev, M. M. (1954) Pupillary reflexes and electroencephalography in the study of the unconditional reflexes in man. (Rus.) Erevan. Diss.

69. Atajev, M. M. (1955) Attempts to use the pupillary reflex and EEG for the study of the conditional reflex activity in man. (Rus.) Z. vyss. nerv. Dejat. Pavlova. 5, 104-109.

70. Avakyan, R. V., M. A. Gershuny & M. A. Ratenberg (1957) Studies of the functions of the auditory analyser in patients with hysterical deafness. (Rus.) Z. vyss. nerv. Dejat. Pavlova. 7, 325-334.

71. Avakyan, R. V., and R. A. Felberbaum (1957) Study of the function of the auditory analyser in cases of suggested deafness. (Rus.) Z. vyss. nerv. Dejat. Pavlova. 7, 637-641.

72. Azbukina, V. D. (1955) The visual analyser in schizophrenia. (Rus.) Tr. nauch. Konf. posv. loo Let. S. S. Korsakoff. 392-394.

73. Azbukina, V. D. (1956) The dynamics of the processes of abstraction and generalization in schizophrenics during aminazine treatment. (Rus.) Tes. Dokl. 20 Ukrain. psikonevrol. Inst. Charkow. 56-58.

74. Azbukina, V. D. (1956) The neurodynamics of conditional reflexes and stable differentiation of the visual analyser in schizophrenics. (Rus.) Vopr. Psihiat. Moscow. 162-163.

75. Azbukina, V. D. (1956) The dynamics of interactions between the first and second signaling systems in schizophrenic patients in the process of treatment with aminazine, electrosleep and insulin. (Rus.) Avtoref. Dokl. issl. Psihiat. MZSSR. 15-17.

76. Azerkovich, N. N. & V. G. Levit (1955) Vascular reactions in schizophrenic patients refusing food. (Rus.) Tr. nauch. Konf. posv. loo Let. S. S. Korsakoff. 289-392.

77. Babkin, B. P. (1948) Origin of the theory of conditional reflexes. Sechenov; Hughlings Jackson; Pavlov. Arch. Neurol. Psychiat. (Chicago) 60, 520-535.

78. Balabanova, V. K. (1938) Experimental studies of the cortical dynamics of schizophrenics. (Rus.) Tr. 1 Moscow. psihiat. Boln. 197-214.

79. Balashova, L. N. (1958) Pathophysiological characteristics of the higher nervous activity in schizophrenic patients in remission. (Rus.) Konf. Vopr. Patofiziol. vyss. nerv. Dejat. Moscow. 15-16.

80. Balonov, L. J., A. E. Lichko & N. N. Traugott (1953) On the pathophysiological analysis of stupor in infectious psychoses. (Rus.) Z. Nevropat. Psihiat. (Korsakoff.) 53, 167-181.

81. Balonov, L. J. (1954) Disturbances in the nervous regulation of heart activity in acute psychoses. (Rus.) Tr. Inst. Fiziol. Im. I. P. Pavlov. 3, 355-368.

82. Balonov, L. J. & A. E. Lichko (1955) The physiological analysis of delusions, the symptoms of cerebral automatisms and hallucinations during insulin treatment. (Rus.) Z. vyss. nerv. Dejat. Pavlova. 5, 686-696.

83. Balonov, L. J. (1956) Studies of the regulation of cardiac conditional reflexes under normal and pathological circumstances. (Rus.) Nauch. Sess. vozrast. Fiziol. Chel. Moscow & Leningrad. 3-4.

84. Balonov, L. J. & A. E. Lichko (1956) The dynamics of conditional and unconditional autonomic reflexes during insulin coma in psychiatric patients. (Rus.) Tes. 17 Sov. Probl. vyss. nerv. Dejat. 16-17.

85. Balonov, L. J. (1957) Characteristics of the interactions of the signaling systems by studies of conditional and unconditional cardiac reflexes. (Rus.) Nauch. Konf. Dejat. Sign. Sist. Norm. i Patol. 7-9.

86. Balonov, L. J., A. E. Lichko & N. N. Traugott (1957) Oppression and restoration of the higher nervous activity in some pathological conditions. (Rus.) Z. vyss. nerv. Dejat. Pavlova. 7, 335-343.

87. Balonov, L. J. (1957) Characteristics of conditional reflex regulation of cardiac activity by extrasystolic arrhythmia. (Rus.) 3 nauch. Sov. vozrast. Fiziol. Patol. Leningrad. 4-6.

88. Balonov, L. J. & N. N. Traugott (1958) Disturbances of the higher nervous activity in various depressive states. (Rus.) Tes. 18 Sov. Probl. vyss. nerv. Dejat. 2, 36-38.

89. Balonov, L. J. (1958) The "sore points" of the cerebral cortex connected with pathological changes of cardiac activity. (Rus.) Tes. 18 Sov. Probl. vyss. nerv. Dejat. 2, 39-41.

90. Balonov, L. J. (1959) Conditional reflex regulation of cardiac activity in man. (Rus.) Moscow & Leningrad.

91. Balonov, L. J. (1959) On the evolution of conditional cardiac reflexes. (Rus.) 2 nauch. Sov. evolut. Fiziol. Leningrad. 26-28.

92. Bambas, B. S., G. D. Glod, L. I. Lando, A. P. Levkovich, G. K. Tarasov & I. M. Khazen (1956) The mechanisms of the aminazine effect. (Rus.) Z. Nevropat. Psihiat. (Korsakoff.) 56, 121-138.

93. Baranov, V. G. (1955) Data about the higher nervous activity in thyreotoxicosis and hypothyreosis. (Rus.) Z. vyss. nerv. Dejat. Pavlova. 5, 336-343.

94. Barnacle, C. H., F. G. Ebaugh & F. Lemere (1935) Association-motor investigation of the psychoneuroses. Amer. J. Psychiat. 91, 925-937.

95. Baruk, M. H., R. Welzer & M. P. Joubert (1950) Un test psychovasculaire spécial: l'indice oscillométrique. Son écrasement dans certains schizophrénies et dépressions. Ann. méd.-psychol. 108, 243-248.

96. Baryshnikov, I. I., V. M. Vinogradov, M. I. Nikiforov & Y. N. Shanin (1956) The influence of aminazine on some functions of the central nervous system. (Rus.) Z. vyss. nerv. Dejat. Pavlova. 6, 881-890.

97. Baskina, N. F. (1953) Concerning peculiarities of the auditory analyser during auditory hallucinations. (Rus.) Z. Nevropat. Psihiat. (Korsakoff.) 53, 840-846.

98. Baskina, N. F. (1955) Experimental investigations into the functions of the auditory analyser during auditory hallucinations. (Rus.) Eksp. issl. psihiat. nevrol. Klin. Leningrad. 23-29.

99. Baskina, N. F. (1959) The characteristics of the autonomic reactivity in neuroses and pseudoneurotic schizophrenia. (Rus.) Vopr. Psikonevrol. Leningrad. 59-60.

100. Batsha, T. (1957) Studies of vasomotor reflexes in cerebral arteriosclerosis. (Rus.) Z. Nevropatol. Psihiat. (Korsakoff.) Suppl. 57, 2-2.

101. Baumann, R. (1955) Die Schlaftherapie. Arb. tag. Kortiko. viz. Regulat. Berlin. 145-169.

102. Bekhterev, V. M. (1918) General foundations of reflexology. (Rus.) Leningrad.
103. Bekhterev, V. M. (1921) Collective reflexology. (Rus.) Leningrad & Moscow.
104. Bekhterev, V. M. (1926) The brain functions. (Rus.) Leningrad.
105. Bell, J. E. (1948) Projective techniques. New York.
106. Bellak, L. (1958) Schizophrenia. New York.
107. Belousova, M. T. (1954) The syndromes of anancastic conditions. (Rus.) Z. Nevropat. Psihiat. (Korsakoff.) 54, 919-927.
108. Bender, L. & P. Schilder (1930) Unconditional and conditional reactions to pain in schizophrenia. Amer. J. Psychiat. 10, 365-384.
109. Benedetti, G., H. Kind & F. Mielke (1957) Forschungen zur Schizophrenielehre 1951 bis 1955. Fortschr. Neurol. Psychiat. 25, 101-179.
110. Benjaminsh, L. A. (1955) An attempt to correlate the clinical and pathophysiological data in acute stages of schizophrenia. (Rus.) Tr. nauch. Konf. posv. loo Let. S. S. Korsakoff. 352-355.
111. Benjaminsh, L. A. (1956) Neurodynamic disturbances in acute stages of schizophrenia. (Rus.) Sb. Nevropat. Psihiat. Riga. 7-40.
112 Benua, N. N. (1957) The role of the second signaling system in the process of differentiation in adult man. (Rus.) Z. vyss. nerv. Dejat. Pavlova. 7, 642-650.
113. Binswanger, L. (1917) Über das Verhalten des psychogalvanischen Phänomens beim Assoziationsexperiment. Leipzig. Diss.
114. Binswanger, L. (1957) Schizophrenie. Pfullingen.
115. Birkengof, N. L., E. F. Roshevskaya & N. F. Suvorov (1954) Vascular reflexes in patients with neurasthenia and hysteria. (Rus.) Tr. Inst. Fiziol. Im. I. P. Pavlov. 3, 369-376.
116. Birnbaum, K. (1912) Über den Einfluss von Gefühlsfaktoren auf die Assoziationen. Mschr. Psychiat. Neurol. 32, 95-123, and 194-220.
117. Bischoff, A. (1953) Experimental-psychologische Untersuchungen über die Wirkung der Weckamine auf die schizophrene Sprachstörung. Mschr. Psychiat. Neurol. 125, 300-309.
118. Bitol, V. J. (1956) Changes of EEG in schizophrenic patients during insulin treatment. (Rus.) Sb. Nevropat. Psihiat. Riga. 41-53.
119. Blagosklonnaya, Y. V., E. I. Kalnina & G. P. Panina (1955) Some characteristics of the vascular reactions in neurasthenia. (Rus.) Klin. Med. (Mosk.) 33, 45-50.
120. Blednova, O. F. (1956) Unconditional and conditional reflexes in hypochondriacal syndromes of various origin. (Rus.) Tes. Konf. Ukrain. psikonevrol. Inst. 63-64.
121. Bleuler, E. (1911) Dementia praecox. In. Aschaffenburg, G. (edit.) Handbuch der Psychiatrie. Leipzig & Wien.
122. Bleuler, E. (1923) Lehrbuch der Psychiatrie. Berlin.
123. Bleuler, M. (1941) Krankheitsverlauf, Persönlichkeit und Verwandtschaft Schizophrener und ihre gegenseitgen Beziehungen. Leipzig.
124. Bleuler, M. (1943) Die spätschizophrenen Krankheitsbilder. Fortschr. Neurol. Psychiat. 15, 259-290.

125. Bobrova, I. N. (1958) Clinical and pathophysiological characteristics of patients with early mental disturbances in cerebral arteriosclerosis. (Rus.) Konf. Vopr. Patofiziol. vyss. nerv. Dejat. Moscow. 18-20.

126. Bogachenko, L. S., N. G. Harzstein & M. I. Seredina (1957) Theory of the higher nervous activity of man. (Rus.) Z. vyss. nerv. Dejat. Pavlova. 7, 794-804.

127. Bokin, I. V. (1954) Characteristics of the higher nervous activity in patients with hypertensive psychoses. (Rus.) Z. vyss. nerv. Dejat. Pavlova. 4, 339-347.

128. Bokser, O. J. & P. N. Karpenko (1954) Methods for the investigation of reactions to verbal stimuli. (Rus.) Z. Nevropat. Psihiat. (Korsakoff.) 54, 1024-1028.

129. Bokser, O. J. (1957) Studies of the interactions of the first and second signaling systems in Parkinsonism and chorea. (Rus.) Nauch. Konf. Dejat. Sign. Sist. Norm. i Patol. 14-16.

130. Bostoganashvili, N. I. (1956) The characteristics of the higher nervous activity in protracted types of schizophrenia. (Rus.) Tes. Dokl. Sess. Inst. M. Asatiani. Tiflis. 35-36.

131. Bostoganashvili, N. I. (1958) The characteristics of the higher nervous activity in protracted types of schizophrenia. (Rus.) Sb. nauch. Inst. M. Asatiani. Tiflis. 159-161.

132. Boumann, L. (1908) Assoziationen bei Geisteskranken. Klin. psych. nerv. Krank. 2, 505-523.

133. Brady, J. V. (1957) A comparative approach to the evaluation of drug effects upon affective behavior. Ann. N. Y. Acad. Sci. 64, 632-643.

134. Breiger, E. (1913) Plethysmographische Untersuchungen an Nervenkranken. Z. ges. Neurol. Psychiat. 17, 413-444.

135. Bridger, W. H. & W. H. Gantt (1955) The effect of mescaline on higher nervous activity (differentiated conditional reflexes). J. Pharmacol. exp. Ther. 113, 7-8.

136. Bridger, W. H. & W. H. Gantt (1956) The effect of mescaline on differentiated conditional reflexes. Amer. J. Psychiat. 113, 352-358.

137. Britvan, J. M., I. A. Mizrukhin & G. B. Safronova (1957) Vascular reactions in schizophrenic patients. (Rus.) Vopr. Klin. Nevropat. Psihiat. 47-59.

138. Britvan, J. M. & E. S. Kozhinskaya (1957) The functional adaptation of the cardiovascular system in catatonic schizophrenia, as measured by arterial oscillometry. (Rus.) Vopr. Klin. Nevropat. Psihiat. 60-67.

139. Brogden, W. J. (1939) Higher order conditioning. Amer. J. Psychol. 52, 579-591.

140. Brown, C. C., M. Rudo & W. H. Gantt (1955) Autonomic responses to methacholine and epinephrine injections in schizophrenic patients. J. Pharmacol. exp. Ther. 113, 8-9.

141. Brown, C. C. (1957) Changes in avoidance conditioning following psychotherapeutic treatment. J. nerv. ment. Dis. 125, 487-489.

142. Brunnschweiler, H. (1912) Über Assoziationen bei organisch Dementen. Zürich. Diss.

143. Brzezicki, E. (1956) Ultraparadoxical phase in form of paragnomen as initial stage of schizophrenia. (Pol.) Neurol. Neurochir. Psychiat. pol. 6, 669-680.

144. Bumke, O. (1904) Die Pupillenstörungen bei Geistes-und Nervenkrankheiten. Jena.

145. Bumke, O. & F. Kehrer (1910) Plethysmographische Untersuchungen an Geisteskranken. Arch. Psychiat. Nervenkr. 47, 945-946.

146. Bykov, K. M. (1957) The cerebral cortex and the internal organs. New York.

147. Calkins, M. W. (1892) A suggested classification of cases of association. Philos. Rev. 1, 389-402.

148. Cantor, E. (1911) Ergebnisse von Assoziationsversuchen mittels blossen Zurufs bei Schwachsinnigen. Mschr. Psychiat. Neurol. 29, 335-342.

149. Chapman, W. P. (1944) Measurements of pain sensitivity in normal control subjects and in psychoneurotic subjects. Psychosom. Med. 6, 252-257.

150. Chernachek, I. (1956) A study of the pathophysiology of hysterical symptoms by the method of conditional reflexes. (Rus.) Z. Nevropat. Psihiat. (Korsakoff.) 56, 858-865.

151. Cheyman, I. M. (1957) The natural conditional reflexes of chronic alcoholics as signs of their treatment progress. (Rus.) Z. Nevropat. Psihiat. (Korsakoff.) 57, 1235-1241.

152. Chistovich, A. S. (1938) Pathophysiological studies of respiration in psychoses. (Rus.) Sb. Tr. Boln. Im. Balinskogo. Leningrad. 2, 115-126.

153. Chistovich, A. S. (1938) Contributions to the study of catatonia. (Rus.) Sb. Tr. Boln. Im. Balinskogo. Leningrad. 2, 183-194.

154. Chistovich, A. S. & F. M. Semernitskoi (1938) Pathophysiological studies of the depressive syndrome. (Rus.) Sb. Tr. Boln. Im. Balinskogo. Leningrad. 2, 5-41.

155. Chistovich, A. S. (1939) The pathophysiology and the pathogenesis of some types of delusions. (Rus.) Novosibirsk. Diss.

156. Chistovich, A. S. (1948) The physiological analysis of electroshock. (Rus.) Tes. Dokl. 13 Sov. Fiziol. posv. I. P. Pavlov. 105-106.

157. Chistovich, A. S. (1949) The opinions of Pavlov on schizophrenia. (Rus.) Nevropat. i Psihiat. 18, 52-55.

158. Chistovich, A. S. (1950) The physiological analysis of electroshock. (Rus.) Tr. vsesoj. Sjesd. Nevropatol. Psihiat. Moscow. 369-370.

159. Chistovich, A. S. (1950) The neurophysiological mechanisms of electroshock. (Rus.) Bjul. eksp. Biol. Med. 29, 108-110.

160. Chistovich, A. S. (1951) The pathophysiological mechanisms of catatonic psychoses after extracerebral injury. (The problem of the significance of chronic interoceptive stimulation). (Rus.) Nevropat. i. Psihiat. 20, 35-39.

161. Chistovich, A. S. (1952) Some data on the pathophysiological understanding of acute infectious psychoses. (Rus.) Z. vyss. nerv. Dejat. Pavlova. 2, 78-84.

162. Chistovich, A. S. (1952) Experiences with physiological elucidation of some speech disturbances in psychoses, with the help of hypnotic experiments. (Rus.) Tr. Inst. Fizol. Im. I. P. Pavlov. 1, 425-435.

163. Chistovich, A. S. (1954) Psychiatric textbook. (Rus.) Leningrad.

164. Chistovich, A. S. (1955) The role of infections in the development of some mental disorders. (Rus.) Z. Nevropat. Psihiat. (Korsakoff.) 55, 843-850.

165. Chuchmareva, N. I. (1947) The problems of conditional inhibition in schizophrenics. (Rus.) Probl. Patofiziol. Ter. Schiz. Kieff. 191-202.
166. Chugunov, S. A. (1950) Clinical electroencephalography. (Rus.) Moscow.
167. Chugunov, S. A. (1952) The significance of electroencephalography for the clinical analysis of the disturbances of the higher nervous activity. (Rus.) Z. Nevropat. Psihiat. (Korsakoff.) 52, 26-33.
168. Clarke, A. D. B. (1955) Motor and memory responses of neurotics and normals in the Luria association-motor technique. Brit. J. Psychol. 46, 38-43.
169. Clausen, J. (1951) Respiration movement in normal, neurotic and psychotic subjects. Acta psychiat. scand. Suppl. 68.
170. Clérambault, G. (1927) Psychoses a base d'automatisme et syndrome d'automatisme. Ann. méd.-psychol. 85, 193-236.
171. Coderch, J., J. M. Costa Molinari & A. M. Sarró (1957) Contributción al estudio de la concepción pluralista de la esquizofrenia. Rev. psiquiat. psicol. méd. 5, 137-157.
172. Copelman, L. S. (1958) La conception actuelle sur la schizophrénie dans la lumière du psychodiagnostic de Rorschach d'après les lois des réflexes conditionnels. Ann. méd.-psychol. 116, 815-822.
173. Corwin, W. & H. Barry (1940) Respiratory plateaux in "daydreaming" and in schizophrenia. Amer. J. Psychiat. 97, 308-318.
174. Crown, S. (1947) A controlled association test as a measure of neuroticism. J. Personality. 16, 198-208.
175. Dahl, N. L. & J. Odegard (1956) On hereditary factors in functional psychoses. Acta psychiat. scand. Suppl. 106, 320-335.
176. Danilenko, E. T. (1956) The dynamics of conditional reflex activity during insulin treatment of schizophrenics. (Rus.) Tes. Dokl. 20 Ukrain. psikonevrol. Inst. Charkow. 60-61.
177. Danilenko, E. T. (1957) Catamnestic investigations of the cortical dynamics of schizophrenics after insulin treatment. (Rus.) Vopr. Klin. Nevropat. Psihiat. 23-33.
178. Danilenko, E. T. (1957) The influence of insulin treatment on the cortical dynamics of schizophrenics. (Rus.) Vopr. Klin. Nevropat. Psihiat. 34-46.
179. Danilenko, E. T. (1958) The influence of insulin treatment on the cortical dynamics of schizophrenics. (Rus.) Odessa. Diss.
180. Das, J. P. (1958) The Pavlovian theory of hypnosis: an evaluation. J. ment. Sci. 104, 82-90.
181. Das, J. P. (1958) Conditioning and hypnosis. J. exp. Psychol. 56, 110-113.
182. De, B. (1953) A study of the validity of the word association technique for the differentiation of normal and abnormal persons. London. Diss.
183. Dmitriev, A. S. (1956) Contribution to the methods of studying higher nervous activity in man. (Rus.) Z. vyss. nerv. Dejat. Pavlova. 6, 906-912.
184. Dmitriev, A. S. & A. T. Zhidkova (1956) The influence of a day of learning on the interactions of the first and second signaling systems. (Rus.) Z. vyss. nerv. Dejat. Pavlova. 6, 378-386.
185. Dmitriev, L. I. (1957) Characteristics of the combined activity of the first and second signaling systems in patients with Korsakoff's psychosis. (Rus.) Nauch. Konf. Dejat. Sign. Sist. Norm. i Patol. 34-35.

186. Dmitriev, L. I. (1957) The influence of tropazine on the higher nervous activity and in particular the combined activity of the signaling systems in catatonic stupor. (Rus.) Nauch. Konf. Dejat. Sign. Sist. Norm. i Patol. 35-36.

187. Dmitriev, L. I. (1957) Studies of the combined activity of the signaling systems in the dynamics of catatonic stupor. (Rus.) Nauch. Konf. Dejat. Sign. Sist. Norm. i Patol. 37-39.

188. Dmitriev, L. I. (1958) Studies of the higher nervous activity in various types of catatonic stupor. (Rus.) Konf. Vopr. Patofiziol. vyss. nerv. Dejat. Moscow. 38-40.

189. Dmitriev, L. I. (1958) The influences of aminazine on the higher nervous activity of patients with catatonic schizophrenia. (Rus.) Konf. Itog. nauch. issl. Rab. 1957. Moscow. 31-32.

190. Dmitriev, L. I. (1958) The interactions of somatic and autonomic conditional and unconditional reactions in the stuporous form of catatonic schizophrenia. (Rus.) Tr. Inst. vyss. nerv. Dejat. Ser. Patofiziol. 5, 21-37.

191. Dmitriev, L. I. (1958) Studies of the combined activity of the cortical signaling systems in the stuporous form of catatonic schizophrenia. (Rus.) Tr. Inst. vyss. nerv. Dejat. Ser. Patofiziol. 5, 38-54.

192. Dmitrieva, A. F. (1958) The higher nervous activity in various types of neurasthenia. (Rus.) Tr. Inst. Fiziol. Im. I. P. Pavlov. 7, 97-105.

193. Dmitrieva, A. F., M. A. Zhilinskaya, N. A. Kryshova & L. G. Pervov (1958) The determination of the type of higher nervous activity in patients with neuroses. (Rus.) Tr. Inst. Fiziol. Im. I. P. Pavlov. 7, 106-113.

194. Dneprovskaya, S. V. (1958) Studies of the inhibitory processes in schizophrenic patients during treatment. (Rus.) Konf. Vopr. Patofizol. vyss. nerv. Dejat. Moscow. 42-42.

195. Dneprovskaya, S. V. (1959) Internal inhibition and mobility of the nervous processes in schizophrenics treated with ataraxic drugs. (Rus.) Vopr. Psikonevrol. Leningrad. 99-100.

196. Dobrzhanskaya, A. K. (1953) Studies of the higher nervous activity in Ichenko-Cushing's disease. (Rus.) Z. vyss. nerv. Dejat. Pavlova. 3, 119-129.

197. Dobrzhanskaya, A. K. (1954) The cortical functions and the interaction of the signaling systems in the acute stage of schizophrenia. (Rus.) Z. vyss. nerv. Dejat. Pavlova. 4, 502-511.

198. Dobrzhanskaya, A. K. (1955) The study of the neurodynamics of acute schizophrenia. (Rus.) Tr. nauch. Konf. posv. loo Let. S. S. Korsakoff. 223-225.

199. Dobrzhanskaya, A. K. (1956) Dynamics of restoring disturbances of interaction between the first and second signaling systems in cases of reactive states. (Rus.) Z. vyss. nerv. Dejat. Pavlova. 6, 663-671.

200. Dobrzhanskaya, A. K. (1957) The interactions of the signaling systems in aminazine treatment of patients with hysterical excitation. (Rus.) Nauch. Konf. Dejat. Sign. Sist. Norm. i Patol. 39-39.

201. Dobrzhanskaya, A. K. (1959) Effect of aminazine on the higher nervous activity during reactive states involving excitation phenomena. (Rus.) Z. vyss. nerv. Dejat. Pavlova. 9, 22-29.

202. Dokuchajeva, O. N. (1955) Characteristics of the associative reactions and their changes in schizophrenics under the influence of caffein. (Rus.) Tr. nauch. Konf. posv. loo Let. S. S. Korsakoff. 280-283.

203. Dougan, C. & L. Welch (1948) A study of elation, making use of the Rorschach test and an association test. J. Psychol. 26, 363-366.

204. Eastman, F. C. & A. J. Rosanoff (1912) Association in feeble-minded and delinquent children. Amer. J. Insan. 69, 125-142.

205. Eitinger, L., C. L. Laane & G. Langfeldt (1958) The prognostic value of the clinical picture and the therapeutic value of physical treatment in schizophrenia and the schizophreniform states. Acta psychiat. scand. 33, 33-53.

206. Elgazina, L. M. (1954) The Kandinsky syndrome with mental automatisms. (Rus.) Z. Nevropat. Psihiat. (Korsakoff.) 54, 707-709.

207. Elgazina, L. M. (1958) Clinical variations of paranoid schizophrenia. (Rus.) Z. Nevropat. Psihiat. (Korsakoff.) 58, 453-461.

208. Elizarova, K. A. & N. I. Gerasimov (1957) Peculiarities of the vascular reflexes in neuroses in the involutional age. (Rus.) Z. Nevropat. Psihiat. (Korsakoff.) Suppl. 57, 73-74.

209. Enukidze-Likhovidova, S. S. (1957) The problems of neurodynamic disturbances in sensory and motor aphasia. (Rus.) Nauch. Konf. Dejat. Sign. Sist. Norm. i Patol. 40-42.

210 Enukidze, S. S. (1958) Autonomic reactions in schizophrenia. (Rus.) Sb. nauch. Inst. M. Asatiani. Tiflis. 189-192.

211. Erlikh, V. & Z. Garantova (1957) Treatment of hypertensive diseases with prolonged sleep. (Rus.) Z. vyss. nerv. Dejat. Pavlova. 7, 547-553.

212. Ey, H. (1954) Études psychiatriques. Structure des psychoses aigues et déstructuration de la conscience. Paris.

213. Ey, H. (1959) Unity and diversity of schizophrenia: clinical and logical analysis of the concept of schizophrenia. Amer. J. Psychiat. 115, 706-714.

214. Eysenck, H. J., G. W. Granger & J. C. Brengelmann (1957) Perceptual processes and mental illness. London.

215. Eysenck, S. B. G. (1955) A dimensional analysis of mental abnormality. London. Diss.

216. Faddeyeva, V. K. (1941) Changes in the higher nervous and autonomic activity in depressive states. (Rus.) Tes. Dokl. 9 Sov. Fiziol. posv. I. P. Pavlov. 92-94.

217. Faddeyeva, V. K. (1945) An attempt to study experimentally the cortical dynamics of the manic and depressive phases of the circular psychosis. (Rus.) Leningrad. Diss.

218. Faddeyeva, V. K. (1947) An experimental investigation of the cortical dynamics during the manic and depressive phases of circular psychosis. (Rus.) Ref. nauch. issl. Rab. med. biol. Nauk. SSSR. 80-81.

219 Faddeyeva, V. K. (1949) The effect of phenamine on the cortical dynamics of animals. (Rus.) Ref. nauch. issl. Rab. med. biol. Nauk. SSSR. 112-115.

220. Faddeyeva, V. K. (1951) The effect of phenamine on conditional reflexes of the first and second signaling systems. (Rus.) Z. vyss. nerv. Dejat. Pavlova. 1, 926-933.

221. Faddeyeva, V. K. (1953) Experimental investigations of the effect of phenamine on the brain functions. (Rus.) Moscow. Diss.

222. Faust, C. (1941) Die paranoiden Schizophrenien auf Grund katamnestischer Untersuchungen. 1 Teil. Die progressive Halluzinose. Z. ges. Neurol. Psychiat. 172, 308-393.

223. Faust, E. (1953) Zur Frage der latenten Schizophrenien in den Sippen manifest Schizophrener. Mschr. Psychiat. Neurol. 125, 65-84.

224. Fedotov, D. D., N. N. Stanishevskaya & V. V. Borinevich (1958) Preliminary data about the treatment of some psychiatric diseases with meratran. (Rus.) Z. Nevropat. Psihiat. (Korsakoff.) 58, 592-599.

225. Feilbach, W. (1914) Zur Untersuchung der Assoziationen bei Dementia paralytica. Klin. psych. nerv. Krank. 9, 97-173.

226. Fel, M. I. (1953) The clinic and pathophysiology of hysteric psychoses with disturbed consciousness. (Rus.) Baku. Diss.

227. Fel, M. I. (1957) The interactions of the first and second signaling systems in involutional psychoses. (Rus.) Nauch. Konf. Dejat. Sign. Sist. Norm. i Patol. 130-131.

228. Fel, M. I. (1958) Paranoid psychoses in the involutional age. (Rus.) Sb. nauch. Inst. M. Asatiani. Tiflis. 137-141.

229. Fillipicheva, N. A. (1952) Inertia of the higher cortical processes after local lesions of the brain. (Rus.) Moscow. Diss.

230. Finesinger, J. E., G. F. Sutherland & F. F. McGuire (1942) The positive conditional salivary reflex in psychoneurotic patients. Amer. J. Psychiat. 99, 61-74.

231. Finesinger, J. E. (1943) The spirogram in certain psychiatric disorders. Amer. J. Psychiat. 100, 159-169.

232. Finesinger, J. E. (1944) The effect of pleasant and unpleasant ideas on the respiratory pattern (spirogram) in psychoneurotic patients. Amer. J. Psychiat. 100, 659-667.

233. Fischgold, H. & H. Gastaut (1957) Conditionnement et réactivité en électroéncephalographie. Electroenceph. clin. Neurophysiol. Suppl. 6.

234. Fish, F. J. (1957) The classification of schizophrenia. J. ment. Sci. 103, 443-463.

235. Fish, F. J. (1958) A clinical investigation of chronic schizophrenia. J. ment. Sci. 104, 34-54.

236. Fish, F. J. (1958) Leonhard's classification of schizophrenia. J. ment. Sci. 104, 943-971.

237. Fleck, S. & W. H. Gantt (1951) Conditional responses in patients receiving electric shock treatment. Amer. J. Psychiat. 108, 280-288.

238. Fleck, S. (1953) Vigilance (orienting behavior), conditional reactions, and adjustment patterns in schizophrenic and compulsive patients. Ann. N. Y. Acad. Sci. 56, 342-379.

239. Franks, C. M. (1956) Conditioning and personality: a study of normal and neurotic subjects. J. abnorm. soc. Psychol. 52, 143-150.

240. Franks, C. M., D. S. Trouton & S. G. Laverty (1958) The inhibition of a conditional response following arecoline administration in man. J. clin. exp. Psychopathol. 19, 226-233.

241. Freierov, O. E. (1954) Problems of the dynamics of oligophrenia. (Rus.) Z. Nevropat. Psihiat. (Korsakoff.) 54, 143-148.

242. Freierov, O. E. (1956) Pathophysiological mechanisms of oligophrenia. (Rus.) Z. vyss. nerv. Dejat. Pavlova. 6, 812-821.

243. Freierov, O. E. (1957) Some characteristics of the disturbances of the interactions of the signaling systems in oligophrenics. (Rus.) Nauch. Konf. Dejat. Sign. Sist. Norm. i. Patol. 132-133.

244. Freierov, O. E. (1958) Experimental studies of the neurodynamic disturbances in psychopaths. (Rus.) Konf. Vopr. Patofiziol. vyss. nerv. Dejat. Moscow. 142-144.

245. Frenkel, G. M. (1958) Electroencephalographic studies of schizophrenics with hypochondriacal syndromes. (Rus.) Z. vyss. nerv. Dejat. Pavlova. 8, 509-516.

246. Fufligina, T. P. (1954) Scientific conference about the problems of interaction of the first and second signaling systems. (Rus.) Z. zyss. nerv. Dejat. Pavlova. 4, 924-929.

247. Fufligina, T. P. (1958) Formation and reversal of complex dynamic structures in oligophrenics. (Rus.) Konf. Vopr. Patofiziol. vyss. nerv. Dejat. Moscow. 144-146.

248. Funkenstein, D. H., M. Greenblatt & H. C. Solomon (1951) Autonomic changes paralleling psychologic changes in mentally ill patients. J. nerv. ment. Dis. 114, 1-18.

249. Gabashvili, V. M. (1956) The clinic, pathophysiology and treatment of the writing cramp. (Rus.) Moscow. Diss.

250. Gabashvili, V. M. (1956) The clinic and pathophysiology of the writing cramp. (Rus.) Z. vyss. nerv. Dejat. Pavlova. 6, 234-241.

251. Gaftek, J., G. Koznevskaya, B. Seletsky, S. Serpinsky, L. Stempen & S. Tochek (1955) Studies of the pathophysiological mechanisms of speech disturbances after lesions of the dominant cerebral hemisphere. (Rus.) Z. Nevropat. Psihiat. (Korsakoff.) 55, 922-927.

252. Gakkel, L. B. (1938) Pathophysiological mechanisms and the clinic of anancastic syndromes. (Rus.) Leningrad. Diss.

253. Gakkel, L. B. (1940) Changes of the reaction times in neuroses. (Rus.) Tes. Dokl. 7 Sov. Fiziol. posv. I. P. Pavlov. 21-22.

254. Gakkel, L. B. (1951) The investigation method of speech reflexes. (Rus.) Fiziol. Z. (Mosk.) 37, 547-552.

255. Gakkel, L. B. (1953) Comparative studies of the higher nervous activity in patients with oligophrenia and with senile dementia. (Rus.) Z. vyss. nerv. Dejat. Pavlova. 3, 92-98.

256. Gakkel, L. B. & N. V. Zinina (1953) Changes in the higher nervous activity in persons older than 60 years. (Rus.) Fiziol. Z. (Mosk.) 39, 533-539.

257. Gakkel, L. B. (1956) Pathophysiological mechanisms in anancastic syndromes. (Rus.) Leningrad.

258. Gakkel, L. B. & N. M. Trofimov (1956) Experimental studies of the interaction of the signaling systems in neuroses. (Rus.) Tr. Konf. Probl. Nevros. Petrozavodsk. 166-171.

259. Gakkel, L. B. (1957) Changes in the higher nervous activity of man in old age. (Rus.) 3 nauch. Sov. vozrast. Fiziol. Patol. Leningrad. 20-20.

260. Gakkel, L. B., I. A. Molotkova & N. M. Trofimov (1957) Experimental investigation of disturbances of cortical nervous processes in patients suffering from oligophrenia. (Rus.) Z. vyss. nerv. Dejat. Pavlova. 7, 494-500.

261. Galton, F. (1879) Psychometric experiments. Brain. 2, 149-162.

262. Gamburg, A. L. (1954) Orienting and defensive reactions in some psychiatric diseases. (Rus.) Saratov. Diss.

263. Gamburg, A. L. (1956) The role of verbal suggestion in the effective action drugs. (Rus.) Z. vyss. nerv. Dejat. Pavlova. 6, 87-92.

264. Gamburg, A. L. (1958) Some characteristics of the higher and lower nervous activity in imbecile oligophrenics. (Rus.) Konf. Vopr. Patofiziol. vyss. nerv. Dejat. Moscow. 27-28.

265. Gantt, W. H. (1935) Effect of alcohol on cortical and subcortical activity measured by the conditional reflex method. Bull. Johns Hopk. Hosp. 56, 61-83.

266. Gantt, W. H. (1936) An experimental approach to psychiatry. Amer. J. Psychiat. 92, 1007-1021.

267. Gantt, W. H. (1938) A method of testing cortical function and sensitivity of the skin. Arch. Neurol. Psychiat. (Chicago) 40, 79-85.

268. Gantt, W. H. (1938) Impairment of the function of adaptability as measured by a simple conditional reflex test in certain psychogenic contrasted with organic diseases. Sth. med. J. (Birmingham, Ala.) 31, 1219-1225.

269. Gantt, W. H. & W. Muncie (1942) Analysis of the mental defect in chronic Korsakov's psychosis by means of the conditional reflex method. Bull. Johns Hopk. Hosp. 70, 467-487.

270. Gantt, W. H. (1944) Experimental basis for neurotic behavior. London & New York.

271. Gantt, W. H. (1948) Physiological psychology. Ann. Rev. Physiol. 10, 453-478.

272. Gantt, W. H. & W. Fleischmann (1948) Effect of thyroid therapy on the conditional reflex function in Hypothyroidism. Amer. J. Psychiat. 104, 676-681.

273. Gantt, W. H. (1952) The conditional reflex function as an aid in the study of the psychiatric patient. In. Hoch, P. H. & J. Zubin (edit.) Relation of psychological tests to psychiatry. New York.

274. Gantt, W. H. (1953) The physiological basis of psychiatry: the conditional reflex. In. Wortis, J. (edit.) Basic problems in psychiatry. New York.

275. Gantt, W. H. (1953) Principles of nervous breakdown: Schizokinesis and autokinesis. Ann. N. Y. Acad. Sci. 56, 143-163.

276. Gantt, W. H. (1956) Pharmacological agents in the study of higher nervous activity. XX internat. Physiol. Cong. Brussels. 2, 322-323.

277. Gantt, W. H. (1957) The use of pharmacological agents in the study of higher nervous activity. In. Probl. Fiziol. tsent. nerv. Sist. posv. 70 Let. K. M. Bykov. 175-179

278 Gantt, W. H. (1957) Pavlovian principles and psychiatry. Progress in psychotherapy. 2, 140-146.

279. Gantt, W. H. & W. G. Reese (1957) Neurological and psychological factors in adaptive behavior. VI internat. Cong. Neurol. July 1957. 110.

280. Gantt, W. H. & R. A. Dykman (1957) Experimental psychogenic tachycardia. In. Hoch, P. & J. Zubin (edit.) Experimental psychopathology. New York & London

281. Gantt, W. H. (1957) Pharmacological agents in study of higher nervous activity. Dis. nerv. Syst. 18, 339-341.

282. Gantt, W. H. (1957) Normal and abnormal adaptations-homeostasis, schizokinesis and autokinesis. Dis. nerv. Syst. 18, 30-33.

283. Gantt, W. H. (1960) Pavlov and Darwin. Darwin Centennial. 219-238.

284. Garlanova, T. T., A. F. Dmitrieva, M. A. Zhilinskaya, N. A. Kryshova, L. G. Pervov & T. I. Tolstova (1958) Clinical-physiological data on some types of internal inhibition in neurasthenic and hysteric patients. (Rus.) Tr. Inst. Fiziol. Im. I. P. Pavlov. 7, 72-77.

285. Gasanov, K. A. (1955) The neurodynamic disturbances in Korsakoff's psychosis. (Rus.) Tr. nauch. Konf. posv. 100 Let. S. S. Korsakoff. 59-62.

286. Gavrilova, N. A. (1960) Studies of the cortical mosaic in various types of schizophrenia. (Rus.) Z. Nevropat. Psihiat. (Korsakoff.) 60, 453-460.

287. Geier, T. A. (1954) The problems of the pathogenesis of manic-depressive psychosis. (Rus.) Z. Nevropat. Psihiat. (Korsakoff.) 54, 928-933.

288. Gellhorn, E. (1946) Is restoration of inhibited conditional reactions by insulin coma specific for Pavlovian inhibitions? Arch. Neurol. Psychiat. (Chicago) 56, 216-221.

289. Gellhorn, E. (1953) Physiological foundations of neurology and psychiatry. Minneapolis.

290. Gerard, K. (1956) Speech disorders during catatonic stupor. (Pol.) Neurol. Neurochir. Psychiat. pol. 6, 737-746.

291. Gershekovich, M. (1930) Investigations of salivary reflexes in schizophrenic patients. Sovr. Psikonevrol. 10, 329-339.

292. Giliarovsky, V. A. (1948) Studies of hallucinations. (Rus.) Moscow.

293. Giliarovsky, V. A., N. M. Liventsev, J. E. Segal & Z. A. Kirillova (1953) Electrosleep. (Rus.) Moscow.

294. Giliarovsky, V. A. (1954) Textbook of psychiatry. (Rus.) Moscow.

295. Gjessing, G. (1953) Beiträge zur Somatologie der periodischen Katatonie. VIII. Arch. Psychiat. Nervenkr. 191, 297-326.

296. Gleser, G. A. (1955) Vascular reactions in patients with coronary insufficiency. (Rus.) Sovetsk. Med. 3, 47-54.

297. Gliedman, L. H. & W. H. Gantt (1956) The effects of reserpine and chlorpromazine on orienting behavior and retention of conditional reflexes. Sth. med. J. (Birmingham, Ala.) 49, 880-889.

298. Gliedman, L. H., W. H. Gantt & H. A. Teitelbaum (1957) Some implications of conditional reflex studies for placebo research. Amer. J. Psychiat. 113, 1103-1107.

299. Golovina, V. P. & G. I. Vopilkina (1934) Observations on the vegetative nervous activity in the catatonic form of schizophrenia. (Rus.) Ark. biol. Nauk. Ser. B. 36, 325-338.

300. Golovina, V. P. (1941) Modifications of the cortical dynamics in involutional psychoses. (Rus.) Tes. Dokl. 9 Sov. Fiziol. posv. I. P. Pavlov. 25-26.

301. Golubkov, O. Z. (1957) Some disturbances of interaction of the signaling systems in epileptics with a severe course of illness. (Rus.) Nauch. Konf. Dejat. Sign. Sist. Norm. i Patol. 29-31.

302 Golubykh, L. I. (1956) New method of studying respiratory conditional and unconditional reflexes in man. (Rus.) Z. vyss. nerv. Dejat. Pavlova. 6, 919-925.

303. Gorbov, F. D. (1955) The problems of the treatment of compulsive pathological reflexes. (Rus.) Z. vyss. nerv. Dejat. Pavlova. 5, 370-375.

304. Grandjean, E. & K. Bättig (1957) Die Wirkung von Serotonin auf eine konditionierte Fluchtreaktion der Ratte. Helv. physiol. pharmacol. acta. 15, 366-370.

305. Grecker, L. A. (1911) Tactile reactions in catatonics studied by the method of associated reflexes. (Rus.) Leningrad. Diss.

306. Grindel, O. M. & B. G. Spirin (1958) Changes in the lability of basic cortical processes after closed head injury. (Rus.) Z. vyss. nerv. Dejat. Pavlova. 8, 482-490.

307. Gubina, G. P. (1958) Disturbances of the higher nervous activity in patients with hypertensive disease. (Rus.) Konf. Vopr. Patofiziol. vyss. nerv. Dejat. Moscow. 33-35.

308. Guk, E. D. (1934) Concerning the conditional reflex action in schizophrenia (Rus.) Sovetsk. Psikonevrol. 10, 76-84.

309. Guljamov, M. G. (1957) Disturbances of interaction of the first and second signaling systems in pseudodementia. (Rus.) Nauch. Konf. Dejat. Sign. Sist. Norm. i Patol. 31-32.

310. Gurevich, M. I. (1957) Experimental data on the functional condition of the higher nervous activity in hypertensive disease. (Rus.) Kieff. Diss.

311. Hall, K. R. L. & E. Stride (1954) The varying response to pain in psychiatric disorders: A study in abnormal psychology. Brit. J. med. Psychol. 27, 48-60.

312. Harzstein, N. G. (1939) The changes of cortical functions in schizophrenics treated with prolonged narcosis. (Rus.) Tes. Dokl. 5 Sov. Fiziol. posv. I. P. Pavlov. 22-23.

313. Harzstein, N. G. & N. N. Traugott (1940) Changes of the cortical functions of schizophrenics in prolonged narcosis. (Rus.) Tr. Psihiat. Klin. I. P. Pavlov. 2, 227-243.

314. Harzstein, N. G. (1941) Changes of the neurodynamics after cardiazol convulsive treatment in schizophrenics. (Rus.) Tes. Dokl. 9 Sov. Fiziol. posv. I. P. Pavlov. 22-24.

315. Harzstein, N. G. (1954) Phasic phenomena and their emergence in the cerebral cortex of patients suffering from reactive depression. (Rus.) Ref. nauch. issl. Rab. med. biol. Nauk. SSSR. 140-141.

316. Harzstein, N. G. (1951) Phasic states in the cerebral cortex of patients suffering from reactive depressions. (Rus.) Z. vyss. nerv. Dejat. Pavlova. 1, 280-289.

317. Harzstein, N. G. (1952) Disturbances of interaction between the first and second signaling systems in reactive depressions. (Rus.) Z. vyss. nerv. Dejat. Pavlova. 2, 868-885.

318. Harzstein, N. G. (1953) The influence of prolonged sleep on the disturbances of interaction of the first and second signaling systems and the associated cardiovascular activity in reactive depressions. (Rus.) Z. vyss. nerv. Dejat. Pavlova. 3, 562-583.

319. Harzstein, N. G. (1955) The connections between disturbances of interaction of the signaling systems and some autonomic disturbances in reactive depressions. (Rus.) Tr. Inst. vyss. nerv. Dejat. Ser. Patofiziol. 1, 97-108.

320. Harzstein, N. G. (1955) Treatment of reactive depression with prolonged sleep. (Rus.) Tr. Inst. vyss. nerv. Dejat. Ser. Patofizol. 1, 314-329.

321. Harzstein, N. G. & A. S. Aslanov (1956) Scientific conference on the problems of higher nervous activity in the neurological and psychiatric clinic. (Rus.) Z. vyss. nerv. Dejat. Pavlova. 6, 501-507.

322. Harzstein, N. G. (1957) Studies of nervous mechanisms of reactive depression and some types of treatment. (Rus.) Moscow. Diss.

323. Harzstein, N. G. (1957) The influences of psychotherapy on the higher and autonomic nervous activity in anancastic neuroses and reactive depression. (Rus.) Nauch. Konf. Dejat. Sign. Sist. Norm. i Patrol. 24-25.

324. Harzstein, N. G. (1957) The types of functional interaction of motor and autonomic reactions in the investigation of patients with reactive depression. (Rus.) Nauch. Konf. Dejat. Sign. Sist. Norm. i Patol. 26-27.

325. Harzstein, N. G. (1958) The study of pathodynamic structures in some neuro-psychiatric diseases. (Rus.) Tes. 18 Sov. Probl. vyss. nerv. Dejat. 1, 38-39.

326. Hemphill, R. E., K. R. L. Hall & T. G. Crookes (1952) A preliminary report on fatigue and pain tolerance in depressive and psychoneurotic patients. J. ment. Sci. 98, 433-440.

327. Henschel, A., J. Brozek & A. Keys (1951) Indirect vasodilatation in normal man and in schizophrenic patients. J. appl. Physiol. 4, 340-344.

328. Hilgard, E. R. & D. G. Marquis (1940) Conditioning and learning. New York & London.

329. Hill, D., P. St. J. Loe, J. Theobald & M. Waddell (1951) A central homeostatic mechanism in schizophrenia. J. ment. Sci. 97, 111-131.

330. Hoeven, H. van (1908) De invloed der affectieve Meerwaarde van Voorstellingen in het Woordreaktieexperiment. Hertogenbosch. Diss.

331. Holmboe, R. & C. Astrup (1957) A follow-up study of 255 patients with acute schizophrenia and schizophreniform psychoses. Acta psychiat. scand. Suppl. 115.

332. Holzinger, J. (1908) Über Assoziationsversuche bei Epileptikern. Erlangen. Diss.

333. Hoskins, R. G. (1946) The biology of schizophrenia. New York.

334. Howe, E. S. (1958) G.S.R. conditioning in anxiety states, normals and chronic functional schizophrenic subjects. J. abnorm. soc. Psychol. 56, 183-189.

335. Hunt, H. F. (1956) Some effects of drugs on classical (type S) conditioning. Ann. N. Y. Acad. Sci. 65, 258-267.

336. Hunt, H. F. (1957) Some effects of meprobamate on conditional fear and emotional behavior. Ann. N. Y. Acad. Sci. 67, 712-723.

337. Hunt, J. McV. (1936) Psychological experiments with disordered persons. Psychol. Bull. 33, 1-58.

328. Huston, P. E. (1934) Sensory threshold to direct current stimulation in schizophrenic and in normal subjects. Arch. Neurol. Psychiat. (Chicago) 31, 590-596.

339. Igersheimer, W. W. (1953) Cold pressor test in functional psychiatric syndromes. A.M.A. Arch. Neurol. Psychiat. 70, 794-801.

340. Ilina, I. I. (1958) Some characteristics of conditional and unconditional alimentary leucocyte reflexes in schizophrenic patients. (Rus.) Konf. Vopr. Patofizol. vyss. nerv. Dejat. Moscow. 43-44.

341. Iliynsky, B. V. (1954) Comparative studies of vascular reactions in patients with hypertension and gastric ulcer. (Rus.) Tr. Inst. Fiziol. Im. I. P. Pavlov. 3, 428-446.

342. Iliynsky, B. V. (1957) Unconditional and conditional vascular reactions in patients suffering from angina pectoris. (Rus.) Z. vyss. nerv. Dejat. Pavlova. 7, 231-240.

343. Isajev, D. N. (1958) Some characteristics of the influenza psychoses and their neurodynamic basis. (Rus.) Konf. Vopr. Patofiziol. vyss. nerv. Dejat. Moscow. 55-55.

344. Ischlondsky, N. E. (1930) Neuropsyche und Hirnrinde. Berlin & Wien.

345. Isserlin, M. (1907) Psychologische Untersuchungen an Manisch-depressiven. Mschr. Psychiat. Neurol. 22, 302-355.

346. Isserlin, M. (1907) Über Jung's "Psychologie der Dementia praecox." Zbl. Nervenheilk. 29, 329-343.

347. Ivanov, E. S. (1957) Clinical-pathophysiological studies of the higher nervous activity in delirium tremens. (Rus.) Vopr. Psihiat. Nevropat. Leningrad. 108-124.

348. Ivanova, M. P. (1953) Disturbances of interaction of the two signaling systems in the formation of complex motor reactions after brain lesions. (Rus.) Moscow. Diss.

349. Ivanova, M. P. (1957) Study of higher nervous activity in juveniles engaged in sports. (Rus.) Z. vyss. nerv. Dejat. Pavlova. 7, 519-524.

350. Ivanov-Smolensky, A. G. (1921) The theory of psychasthenia and attempts at experimental psychological studies of psychasthenia. (Rus.) Leningrad. Diss.

351. Ivanov-Smolensky, A. G. (1922) The biogenesis of speech reflexes and the fundamental methodological principles of investigation. (Rus.) Psihiat. Nevropatol. eksp. Psikol. 2, 231-242.

352. Ivanov-Smolensky, A. G. (1925) Experimentelle Untersuchungen über sprachliche und mimische Reflexe in der manischen Phase der Cyklophrenie. Z. ges. Neurol. Psychiat. 98, 680-707.

353. Ivanov-Smolensky, A. G. (1927) Études expérimentales sur les enfants et les aliénés selon la méthode des réflexes conditionnels. Ann. méd.-psychol. 85, 140-150.

354. Ivanov-Smolensky, A. G. (1927) Neurotic behavior and teaching of conditional reflexes. Amer. J. Psychiat. 84, 483-488.

355. Ivanov-Smolensky, A. G. (1927) On the methods of examining the conditional food reflexes in children and in mental disorders. Brain. 50, 138-141.

356. Ivanov-Smolensky, A. G. (1928) Methodology of the study of higher nervous activity in man. (Rus.) Moscow.

357. Ivanov-Smolensky, A. G. (1928) Über pathophysiologische Grundmechanismen der Psychoneurosen. Schweiz. Arch. Neurol. Psychiat. 22, 13-34.

358. Ivanov-Smolensky, A. G. (1928) Pathology of conditional reflexes and so-called psychogenic depression. J. nerv. ment. Dis. 67, 346-350.

359. Ivanov-Smolensky, A. G. (1933) On the pathophysiological substratum of schizophrenia. (Rus.) Sovr. Probl. Schiz. 157-165.

360. Ivanov-Smolensky, A. G. (1933) Fundamental problems of the pathophysiology of the higher nervous activity. (Rus.) Moscow & Leningrad.

361. Ivanov-Smolensky, A. G. (1934) An attempt at pathophysiological study of mutism in schizophrenia. (Rus.) Ark. biol. Nauk. Ser. B. 36, 107-126.

362. Ivanov-Smolensky, A. G. (1934) Concerning different forms and neurodynamics of catatonic stupor. (Rus.) Ark. biol. Nauk. Ser. B. 36, 85-106.

363. Ivanov-Smolensky, A. G. (1934) On the neurodynamic structure of eidetic and verbal delusions. (Rus.) Ark. biol. Nauk. Ser. B. 36, 145-164.

364. Ivanov-Smolensky, A. G. (1934) An attempt at pathophysiological investigation of speech incoherence in schizophrenia. (Rus.) Ark. biol. Nauk. Ser. B. 36, 127-144.

365. Ivanov-Smolensky, A. G. (1936) On the pathogenesis of epilepsy in terms of cerebral pathophysiology. (Rus.) Probl. klin. eksp. Nevropat. Psihiat. Charkow. 85-92.

366. Ivanov-Smolensky, A. G. (1949) Certain age periods and certain pathological derangements of the first and second signaling systems. (Rus.) Ref. nauch. issl. Rab. med. biol. Nauk. SSSR. 134-136.

367. Ivanov-Smolensky, A. G. (1949) Concerning the pathophysiological aspect of the pathogenesis and therapy of schizophrenia. (Rus.) Ref. nauch. issl. Rab. med. biol. Nauk. SSSR. 136-137.

368. Ivanov-Smolensky, A. G. (1949) The interactions of the first and second signaling systems in some physiological and pathological conditions. (Rus.) Fiziol. Z. (Mosk.) 35, 571-581.

369. Ivanov-Smolensky, A. G. (1951) Concerning the study of the joint activity of the first and second signaling systems. (Rus.) Z. vyss. nerv. Dejat. Pavlova. 1, 55-66.

370. Ivanov-Smolensky, A. G. (1953) Investigations into the interactions of the first and second signaling systems. (Rus.) Z. vyss. nerv. Dejat. Pavlova. 3, 481-494.

371. Ivanov-Smolensky, A. G. (1954) Essays on the patho-physiology of the higher nervous activity. Moscow.

372. Ivanov-Smolensky, A. G. (1955) General disturbances of the higher nervous activity and the pathodynamic structures in neuroses and reactive conditions. (Rus.) Tr. Inst. vyss. nerv. Dejat. Ser. Pathofiziol. 1, 350-368.

373 Ivanov-Smolensky, A. G. (1955) The fundamental traits of the pathophysiology of the higher nervous activity in the clinic of psychoses and neuroses. (Rus.) Tr. Inst. vyss. nerv. Dejat. Ser. Patofiziol. 1, 3-10.

374. Ivanov-Smolensky, A. G. (1956) Some new data from the study of nervous mechanisms in the interaction of the cortical signaling systems. (Rus.) Tr. Inst. vyss. nerv. Dejat. Ser. Patofiziol. 2, 315-334.

375. Ivanov-Smolensky, A. G. (1956) Ways and perspectives in the development of the physiology and pathophysiology of the higher nervous activity in children. (Rus.) Tr. Inst. vyss. nerv. Dejat. Ser. Patofiziol. 2, 335-346.

376. Ivanov-Smolensky, A. G. (1957) Some problems of the pathophysiology of the higher nervous activity in experimental therapy and disturbances related to infections and intoxications. (Rus.) Tr. Inst. vyss. nerv. Dejat. Ser. Patofiziol. 3, 3-20.

377. Ivanov-Smolensky, A. G. (1958) The study of physiologically based treatment of neuropsychiatric diseases. (Rus.) Tr. Inst. vyss. nerv. Dejat. Ser. Patofiziol. 5, 343-371.

378. Ivanov-Smolensky, A. G. (1958) Common and distinctive traits in disturbances of the neurodynamics in various neuropsychiatric diseases. (Rus.) Tr. Inst. vyss. nerv. Dejat. Ser. Patofiziol. 5, 3-18.

379. Jackson, Hughlings, J. (1932) Selected writings. London.

380. Jacobsen, E., H. Kehlet, V. Larsen, I. Munkvad & K. Skinhöj (1955) Investigations into autonomic responses during emotion. Acta psychiat. scand. 30, 607-625.

381. Jacobsen, E. & E. Sonne (1956) The effect of benactyzine on the conditional responses in the rat. Acta pharmacol. (Kbh.) 12, 310-320.

382. Jaroszynski, J., E. Brozkiewicz, K. Gerard & T. Kolakowska (1955) Some data on the dynamics of catatonic stupor. (Pol.) Neurol. Neurochir. Psychiat. pol. 5, 149-159.

383. Jolly, P. (1920) Assoziationsversuche bei Debilen. Arch. Psychiat. Nervenkr. 61, 117-131.

384. Jones, H. G. (1956) The application of conditioning and learning techniques to the treatment of a psychiatric patient. J. abnorm. soc. Psychol. 52, 414-419.

385. Jong, H. de (1921) Die Hauptgesetze einiger wichtigen köperlichen Erscheinungen beim psychischen Geschehen von Normalen und Geisteskranken. Z. ges. Neurol. Psychiat. 69, 61-141.

386. Jong, H. de & J. Prakken (1929) Vergleichende plethysmographische (psychophysiologische) Versuche bei Normalen und Tabes-patienten. Acta psychiat. (Kbh.) 4, 65-73.

387. Jung, C. G. (1907) Über die Psychologie der Dementia praecox. Halle.

388. Jung, C. G. (1918) Reaction-time in association experiments. In. Jung. C. G. (edit.) Studies in word-association. London.

389. Jung, C. G. & F. Riklin (1918) The associations of normal subjects. In. Jung, C. G. (edit.) Studies in word-association. London.

390. Jung, C. G. (1918) Analysis of the associations of an epileptic. In. Jung, C. G. (edit.) Studies in word-association. London.

391. Jung, C. G. (1918) On disturbances in reproduction in association experiments. In. Jung, C. G. (edit.) Studies in word-association. London.

392. Jung, C. G. (1959) Die Schizophrenie. II internat. Cong. Psychiat. Zurich. 1, 187-188.

393. Jung, R. & E. A. Carmichael (1937) Über vasomotorische Reaktionen und Wärmeregulation im katatonen Stupor. Arch. Psychiat. Nervenkr. 107, 300-338.

394. Jus, A. (1955) Bioelectrical researches on the pathophysiological mechanisms of catatonic stupor. (Pol.) Neurol. Neurochir. Psychiat. pol. 5, 501-532.

395. Jus, A. & K. Jus. (1957) The significance of electroencephalographic conditional reactions for pathophysiological investigations in neurology and psychiatry. (Rus.) Z. Nevropat. Psihiat. (Korsakoff.) 57, 1363-1372.

396. Jus, A. (1957) Bioelectrical studies of the pathophysiological mechanisms in catatonic stupor. (Rus.) Z. Nevropat. Psihiat. (Korsakoff.) 57, 67-81.

397. Jus, A. (1959) Recherches bioélectriques sur la pathophysiologie de la schizophrénie. II internat. Cong. Psychiat. Zurich. 1, 189-195.

398. Kabelyanskaya, L. G. (1955) Experimental studies of the auditory analyser in patients with sensory aphasia. (Rus.) Sov. Vopr. Fiziol. Patol. Leningrad. 15.

399. Kameneva, N. N. (1956) Disturbances of the speech activity in schizophrenics. (Rus.) Vopr. Psihiat. Moscow. 174-175.

400. Kameneva, N. N. (1957) Schizophrenia. The clinic and pathophysiological mechanisms of schizophrenic delusions. (Rus.) Moscow.

401. Kamenskaya, V. M. (1952) Physiological investigations of the cortical activity in sequelae after head injury. (Rus.) Z. Nevropat. Psihiat. (Korsakoff.) 52, 11-20.

402. Kaminsky, S. D. & V. I. Savchuk (1951) New data about the functional conditions of the higher nervous system in various stages of hypertonia. (Rus.) Z. vyss. nerv. Dejat. Pavlova. 1, 703-715.

403. Kaminsky, S. D. & V. I. Savchuk (1956) The effect of aminazine on the higher nervous activity of dogs. (Rus.) Z. Nevropat. Psihiat. (Korsakoff.) 56, 104-115.

404. Kantorvich, N. V. & A. M. Lukina (1926) The formation of associative reflexes in progressive paralysis. (Rus.) Nov. Refl. Fiziol. nerv. Sist. Leningrad. 2, 369-382.

405. Karapetjan, E. A. (1958) Studies of the higher nervous activity in patients with narcolepsy and other diseases with sleep disturbances. (Rus.) Tr. Inst. Fiziol. Im. I. P. Pavlov. 7, 128-134.

406. Kashkarova, T. K. (1954) The problems of the pathophysiological foundations of the hypochondriacal delusions. (Rus.) Tes. Dokl. Inst. nauch. Konf. Leningrad. 37-40.

407. Kashkarova, T. K. (1956) Problems concerning the pathophysiological basis of hypochondriacal syndromes. (Rus.) Psihiat. klin. Probl. Pathol. vyss. nerv. Dejat. 1, 70-94.

408. Kashkarova, T. K. (1957) The pathophysiological basis of depersonalization. (Rus.) Psihiat. klin. Probl. Patol. vyss. nerv. Dejat. 2, 104-109.

409. Kaufman, D. A. (1954) Zur Frage der Pathologie des schizophrenen Defektes. Psychiat. Neurol. med. Psychol. (Lpz.) 6, 157-163.

410. Kaufman, D. A. (1956) Studies on the problems of the pathophysiology of the schizophrenic defect. (Rus.) Leningrad. Diss.

411. Kaufman, D. A. (1957) Pathophysiological data and the problems of the state of consciousness in schizophrenic defects. (Rus.) Nauch. Konf. Dejat. Sign. Sist. Norm. i Patol. 56-56.

412. Kaufman, D. A. (1957) Some characteristics of the disturbances of the higher nervous activity in patients with schizophrenic defect. (Rus.) 3 nauch. Sov. vozrast. Fiziol. Patol. Leningrad. 27-29.

413. Kaufman, D. A. (1958) The characteristics of the higher nervous activity in acute psychoses with schizophrenic symptoms. (Rus.) Tes. 18 Sov. Probl. vyss. nerv. Dejat. 2, 163-165.

414. Kaufman, D. A. (1958) Comparative pathophysiological studies of patients with schizophrenic and epileptic deterioration. (Rus.) Z. Nevropat. Psihiat. (Korsakoff.) 58, 964-970.

415. Kaufman, D. A. (1958) Pathophysiological data on the state of consciousness in schizophrenic deterioration. (Rus.) Z. Nevropat. Psihiat. (Korsakoff.) 58, 699-702.

416. Kaufman, D. A. (1959) Some characteristics of speech disturbances in schizophrenic deterioration. (Rus.) Z. Nevropat. Psihiat. (Korsakoff.) 59, 422-427.

417. Kazakov, P. M. (1957) Changes of respiratory movements in schizophrenia. (Rus.) Tr. Kuibyshev. med. Inst. 227-237.

418. Kent, G. H. & A. J. Rosanoff (1910) A study of association in insanity. Amer. J. Insan. 67, 37-96 & 317-390.

419. Kerbikov, O. V. & D. N. Krylov (1953) Studies of ultraparadoxical phases in psychogenic reactions. (Rus.) Z. vyss. nerv. Dejat. Pavlova. 3, 369-380.

420. Kerbikov, O. V., N. I. Ozeretsky, E. A. Popov & A. V. Snezhnevsky (1958) Textbook of Psychiatry. (Rus.) Moscow.

421. Khaletsky, A. M. (1956) Problems of infectious psychoses in the contemporary psychiatric literature. (Rus.) Z. Nevropat. Psihiat. (Korsakoff.) 56, 395-400.

422. Khira, K. A. (1958) Experimental studies of the higher nervous activity in patients with anancastic neuroses. (Rus.) Konf. Vopr. Patofiziol. vyss. nerv. Dejat. Moscow. 146-148.

423. Khomutov, A. V. (1957) About the investigation methods of conditional speech reflexes. (Rus.) Z. vyss. nerv. Dejat. Pavlova. 7, 775-779.

424. Khomutov, A. V. (1958) Characteristics of the conditional speech reflexes in neurasthenia and the clinical-physiological evaluation during treatment. (Rus.) Konf. Vopr. Patofiziol. vyss. nerv. Dejat. Moscow. 148-149.

425. Khromov, N. A. (1958) Disturbances of the higher nervous activity in penetrating cranial injury. (Rus.) Leningrad.

426. Khromov, N. A. (1958) The physiological understanding of the hysteric pseudodementia. (Rus.) Z. Nevropat. Psihiat. (Korsakoff.) 58, 1304-1311.

427. Khruleva, L. N. (1960) The effects of aminazine on the higher nervous activity of dogs. (Rus.) Z. Nevropat. Psihiat. (Korsakoff.) 60, 577-584.

428. Kilian, K. (1911) Zur Untersuchung der Assoziationen bei Maniakalischen. Klin. psych. nerv. Krank. 6, 28-82.

429. King, H. E. (1954) Psychomotor aspects of mental disease. An experimental study. Cambridge, Massachusetts.

430. Kirillova, Z. A. (1955) The neurodynamics of the higher nervous activity in schizophrenics treated with electrosleep. (Rus.) Tr. nauch. Konf. posv. loo Let. S. S. Korsakoff. 417-421.

431. Kleist, K. & W. Driest (1937) Die Katatonie auf Grund katamnestischer Untersuchungen. 1 Teil. Die als Katatonien verkannten Degenerationspsychosen. Z. ges. Neurol. Psychiat. 157, 479-556.

432. Kleist, K., K. Leonhard & H. Schwab (1940) Die Katatonie auf Grund katamnestischer Untersuchungen. 3 Teil. Formen und Verläufe der eigentlichen Katatonie. Z. ges. Neurol. Psychiat. 168, 535-586.

433. Kleist, K. & H. Schwab (1950) Die verworrenen Schizophrenien auf Grund katamnestischer Untersuchungen. Teil 2. Die denkverwirrten Schizophrenien. Arch. Psychiat. Nervenkr. 184, 28-79.

434. Kleist, K., K. Leonhard & E. Faust (1950) Die Hebephrenien auf Grund von katamnestischen Untersuchungen. Teil 1. Arch. Psychiat. Nervenkr. 185, 773-798.

435. Kleist, K., K. Leonhard & E. Faust (1951) Die Hebephrenien auf Grund von katamnestischen Untersuchungen. Teil 2. Arch. Psychiat. Nervenkr. 186, 1-12.

436. Kleist, K. (1953) Die Gliederung der neuropsychischen Erkrankungen. Mschr. Psychiat. Neurol. 125, 539-544.

437. Klepper, G. (1911) Die Unterscheidung von epileptischen und katatonischen Zuständen, speziell aus den Assoziationen. Klin. psych. nerv. Krank. 6, 1-27.

438. Klepzowa, M. K. (1957) Über die Wechselbeziehungen zwischen erstem und zweitem Signalsystem bei Hypertoniekranken im neurogenen Stadium. Dtsch. Gesundh.-Wes. 12, 58-64.

439. Klevtsur, E. I. (1958) An attempt to treat disturbances of the cortical dynamics in patients with chronic alcoholism. (Rus.) Konf. Vopr Patofiziol. vyss. nerv. Dejat. Moscow. 57-59.

440. Klochov, A. M. (1958) The effects of insulin on alimentary and motor-defensive conditional and unconditional reflexes. (Rus.) 4. Konf. molod. Uchen. Moscow. 18-21.

441. Klukan, B. (1955) The formation of conditional reflexes in general paralysis of the insane. (Chek.) Neurol. Psychiat. česk. 18, 215-218.

442. Knauff, H. W. (1950) Die Formen der Schizophrenien von Kleist und Leonhard nachgeprüft in einer Anstalt für chronisch Kranke. Z. menschl. Vererb.-u. Konstit.-Lehre. 29, 695-781.

443. Kogan, S. I. (1953) Some disturbances of the vascular reactions in the so-called hypochondriacal psychoses. (Rus.) Z. Nevropat. Psihiat. (Korsakoff.) 53, 922-934.

444. Kogan, S. I. (1957) Disturbances of the neurodynamics in some hypochondriacal syndromes. (Rus.) 3. nauch. Sov. vozrast. Fiziol. Patol. Leningrad. 31-33.

445. Kogan, S. I. (1958) Clinical-pathophysiological characteristics of hypochondriacal syndromes of various etiology. (Rus.) Tes. 18 Sov. Probl. vyss. nerv. Dejat. 2, 172-174.

446. Koganov, N. N. & E. S. Ermakova (1954) The characteristics of the cortical dynamics in schizophrenics during remissions and in defect states. Sb. Tes. Rostov. med. Inst. 105-107.

447. Kok, E. P. (1957) Deficiency of visual perception in amnestic aphasia. (Rus.) Z. Nevropat. Psihiat. (Korsakoff.) 57, 1121-1129.

448. Kok, E. P. & N. A. Kryshova (1958) The relation between the dynamics of the higher nervous activity and speech defects in aphasia. (Rus.) Tr. Inst. Fiziol. Im. I. P. Pavlov. 7, 159-165.

449. Kok, E. P. (1959) Study of the process of generalization in patients with motor and sensory aphasia. (Rus.) Z. vyss. nerv. Dejat. Pavlova. 9, 14-21.

450. Kolakowska, T. (1956) On defensive and orientative reactions in the course of catatonic stupor. (Pol.) Neurol. Neurochir. Psychiat. pol. 6, 853-863.

451. Kolesnichenko, N. S. (1958) Disturbances of abstract thinking in schizophrenic patients in various conditions. (Rus.) Konf. Vopr. Patofiziol. vyss. nerv. Dejat. Moscow. 62-63.

452. Koltsova, M. M. (1958) The formation of the higher nervous activity in children. (Rus.) Leningrad.

453. Kondratskaya, E. M. (1955) The disturbances of interaction of the signaling systems in schizophrenics. (Rus.) Uchen. Zapisk. 1. Leningrad. Inst. 2, 218-222.

454. Kononjachenko, V. A. (1953) Vascular unconditional and conditional reflexes in hypertensive disease. (Rus.) Z. vyss. nerv. Dejat. Pavlova. 3, 680-688.

455. Kononjachenko, V. A. (1954) Studies of the higher nervous activity by the method of conditional vascular reflexes in patients with hypertensive disease. (Rus.) Z. vyss. nerv. Dejat. Pavlova. 4, 620-628.

456. Kononjachenko, V. A. (1959) Analysis of the disturbances of higher nervous activity in hypertension. (Rus.) Z. vyss. nerv. Dejat. Pavlova. 9, 641-648.

457. Konovalov, N. V. (1955) Vascular disturbances in hepaticolenticular degeneration and other diseases of the liver. (Rus.) Z. Nevropat. Psihiat. (Korsakoff.) 55, 269-281.

458. Kornetov, A. N. (1954) Disturbances of the cortical dynamics in the paranoid form of schizophrenia. (Rus.) Odessa. Diss.

459. Kornetov, A. N. (1957) The role of ultraparadoxical phases in paranoid syndromes with feelings of passivity. (Rus.) Nauch. Konf. Dejat. Sign. Sist. Norm. i Patol. 57-58.

460. Korotkin, I. I. & M. M. Suslova (1951) Studies of the higher nervous activity in man in the somnambulic stage of hypnosis. (Rus.) Z. vyss. nerv. Dejat. Pavlova. 1, 617-622.

461. Korotkin, I. I. (1952) The effects of word stimuli as conditional inhibition in alert and hypnotic states. (Rus.) Tr. Inst. Fiziol. Im. I. P. Pavlov. 1, 345-355.

462. Korotkin, I. I. & M. M. Suslova (1955) Characteristics of the reciprocal influence of signaling systems in hypnotic and posthypnotic states. (Rus.) Z. vyss. nerv. Dejat. Pavlova. 5, 511-519.

463. Korotkin, I. I. & M. M. Suslova (1955) The physiological mechanisms of inhibitory action on stimuli inhibited by hypnotic suggestion. (Rus.) Dokl. Akad. Nauk. SSSR. no. 1, 189-192.

464. Korotkin, I. I. & M. M. Suslova (1957) Investigation of posthypnotic changes in conditional and unconditional reflexes resulting from suggestions made in the first phase of the hypnosis. (Rus.) Z. vyss. nerv. Dejat. Pavlova. 7, 889-897.

465. Korotkin, I. I. & M. M. Suslova (1958) Study of a hypnotically suggested conditional inhibition to words of known and unknown meaning. (Rus.) Z. vyss. nerv. Dejat. Pavlova. 8, 820-827.

466. Korotkin, I. I. & M. M. Suslova (1958) On the physiological study of suggestibility. (Rus.) Tes. 18 Sov. Probl. vyss. nerv. Dejat. 2, 189-191.

467. Korotkin, I. I. & T. V. Pleshkova (1958) On difficulties of elaborating conditional inhibition in patients with phobic neuroses. (Rus.) Tr. Inst. Fiziol. Im. I. P. Pavlov, 7, 185-191.

468. Koshkareva, K. I. (1958) Disturbances of thought and speech in schizophrenics, and their pathophysiological basis. (Rus.) Vopr. klin. org. Psikonevrol. Tomsk. 14-15.

469. Kostandov, E. A. (1954) Disturbances of the cortical dynamics with special regard to the interaction of the first and second signaling systems in schizophrenia. (Rus.) Moscow. Diss.

470. Kostandov, E. A. (1955) Disturbances of the neurodynamics, and especially the interaction of the signaling systems in the paranoid form of schizophrenia. (Rus.) Tr. Inst. vyss. nerv. Dejat. Ser. Patofiziol. 1, 26-47.

471. Kostandov, E. A. (1957) Disturbances of the higher nervous activity in patients with involutional psychoses. (Rus.) Nauch. Konf. Dejat. Sign. Sist. Norm. i Patol. 61-63.

472. Kostandov, E. A. (1957) Comparative characteristics of the disturbances of cortical dynamics in paranoid and catatonic schizophrenia. (Rus.) Nauch. Konf. Dejat. Sign. Sist. Norm. i Patol. 63-65.

473. Kostandov, E. A. (1957) The dynamics of restoration of cortical connections in catatonic schizophrenics going out of deep stupor. (Rus.) Nauch. Konf. Dejat. Sign. Sist. Norm. i Patol. 65-66.

474. Kostandov, E. A. (1958) Disturbances in the mobility of the nervous processes in patients with involutional psychoses. (Rus.) Konf. Vopr. Patofizol. nerv. Dejat. Moscow. 65-66.

475. Kostandov, E. A. (1958) Disturbances of the analytic-synthetic activity of the cerebral cortex in involutional depression and the influence of single doses of aminazine on these disturbances. (Rus.) Konf. Itog. nauch. issl. Rab. 1957. Moscow. 33-34.

476. Kostandov, E. A. (1958) The study of the synthetic activity of the cerebral cortex in involutional depression. (Rus.) Tes. 18 Sov. Probl. vyss. nerv. Dejat. 2, 192-193.

477. Kostandov, E. A. (1958) Disturbances of interaction of the first and second signaling systems in the catatonic form of schizophrenia. (Rus.) Tr. Inst. vyss. nerv. Dejat. Ser. Patofizol. 5, 101-120.

478. Kostandova, Z. A. (1958) Some data on the association experiment in schizophrenics. (Rus.) Sb. nauch. Inst. M. Asatiani. Tiflis. 5, 83-84.

479. Kovalev, V. V. (1955) Disturbances of the cortical dynamics in the Korsakoff syndrome. (Rus.) Z. Nevropat. Psihiat. (Korsakoff.) 55, 765-769.

480. Kovalev, V. V. (1955) Disturbances of the cortical dynamics in the Korsakoff syndrome. (Rus.) Tr. nauch. Konf. posv. loo Let. S. S. Korsakoff. 62-65.

481. Kovsharova, T. V. (1936) An experimental investigation of analytic psychotherapy . (Rus.) Nevropat. i Psihiat. 5, 1148-1162.

482. Kozlov, Y. G. (1953) Pathophysiological mechanisms of the hypochon-driacal delusions. (Rus.) Z. Nevropat. Psihiat. (Korsakoff.) 53, 935-941.
483. Kozlov, Y. G. (1954) Pathophysiological mechanisms of the hypochon-driacal delusions. (Rus.) Leningrad. Diss.
484. Kozlov, Y. G. (1958) The influence of aminazine on the basic processes of the higher nervous activity. (Rus.) Z. vyss. nerv. Dejat. Pavlova. 8, 904-910.
485. Kraepelin, E. (1892) Über die Beeinflussung einfacher psychischer Vor-gänge durch einige Arzneimittel. Jena.
486. Kraepelin, E. (1910) Psychiatrie. 8 Aufl. Leipzig.
487. Krajevsky, J. M. (1957) Unconditional and conditional vascular reflexes in patients with brain lesions and sleep treatment. (Rus.) Z. Nevropat. Psihiat. (Korsakoff.) Suppl. 57, 7-7.
488. Krasnogorsky, N. I. (1952) The physiology of speech development in children. (Rus.) Z. vyss. nerv. Dejat. Pavlova. 2, 474-480.
489. Krasnogorsky, N. I. (1954) Studies of higher nervous activity in men and animals. (Rus.) Moscow.
490. Krasnogorsky, N. I. (1956) New data on the physiology of speech activity. (Rus.) Z. vyss. nerv. Dejat. Pavlova. 6, 513-524.
491. Kreindler, A. (1947) Les réflexes conditionnels. Les Lois de leur forma-tion et leur domaine d'application. Bucharest.
492. Kreindler, A., G. Dabija, I. Poilici & A. Fradis (1956) Méthode complexe pour l 'étude de l'activité nerveuse supérieure chez l'homme. Rev. Sci. Méd. (Roum.) 1, 95-119.
493. Kreindler, A. & A. Fradis (1957) Studies on the neurodynamics of aphasia. (Rus.) Z. Nevropat. Psihiat. (Korsakoff.) 57, 929-940.
494. Krushinsky, L. V., V. A. Korzhov & L. N. Molodkina (1958) The in-fluence of ECT on pathological states produced by auditory stimulation in rats. (Rus.) Z. vyss. nerv. Dejat. Pavlova 8, 95-102.
495. Krylov, D. N. (1957) Studies of the disturbances of the activity of the cortical signaling systems and the interaction with some subcortical func-tions in the early period after closed head injury. (Rus.) Nauch. Konf. Dejat. Sign. Sist. Norm. i Patol. 67-69.
496. Krylov, D. N. (1958) Experimental studies of the strength, equilibrium and mobility of nervous processes in patients with closed head injury. (Rus.) Konf. Vopr. Patofiziol. vyss. nerv. Dejat. Moscow. 68-69.
497. Kryshova, N. A., E. P. Kok & V. M. Smirnov (1954) Clinical-physiological studies of patients with aphasia. (Rus.) Z. Nevropat. Psihiat. (Korsa-koff.) 54, 979-986.
498. Kryshova, N. A. (1958) Pathophysiological mechanisms of disturbances of speech in aphasia and means of rehabilitation. (Rus.) Konf. Vopr. Patofiziol. vyss. nerv. Dejat. Moscow. 71-71.
499. Kulikova, V. S., A. T. Pshonik & J. E. Segal (1952) About the vascular reactions in hypochondriacal syndromes. (Rus.) Probl. kort. viz. Patol. Leningrad. 289-300.
500. Kulchitskaya, G. P. (1956) Some characteristics of the disturbances of the higher nervous activity in the course of longstanding infectious psy-choses. (Rus.) Tr. voj. mor. med. Akad. Leningrad 155-165,

501. Küppers, E. (1928) Puls. Blutdruck. Vasomotorische Störungen. Blut-verteilung. In. Bumke, O. (edit.) Hb. Geisteskr. Teil 3. Berlin.

502. Kurapova, G. M. & S. M. Pavlenko (1958) Clinical and pathophysiological characteristics of schizophrenic patients during treatment with aminazine and serpasil combined with narcotics. (Rus.) Konf. Vopr. Patofiziol. vyss. nerv. Dejat. Moscow. 76-77.

503. Kurshev, V. A. (1958) Disinhibition in the joint activity of signaling systems in patients suffering from aphasia. (Rus.) Z. vyss. nerv. Dejat. Pavlova. 8, 814-819.

504. Kutin, V. P. (1956) The problem of pathophysiological characteristics of chronic states of schizophrenia. (Rus.) Z. vyss. nerv. Dejat. Pavlova. 6, 251-259.

505. Kuznetsova, A. S. (1957) Disturbances of the respiratory rhythms in vascular brain disease. (Rus.) Z. Nevropat. Psihiat. (Korsakoff.) 57, 950-954.

506. Lakosina, N. D. (1958) Studies of the psychogalvanic skin reaction in schizophrenic patients. (Rus.) Z. Nevropat. Psihiat. (Korsakoff.) 58, 1477-1483.

507. Landis, C. & H. DeWick (1929) The electrical phenomena of the skin (psychogalvanic reflex). Psychol. Bull. 26, 64-119.

508. Landis, C. (1932) Electrical phenomena of the skin (galvanic skin response). Psychol. Bull. 29, 693-752.

509. Landkof, B. L. (1938) Unconditional and conditional vascular reflexes in schizophrenia. (Rus.) Probl. Patofiziol. Ter. Schiz. Charkow. 37-63.

510. Landkof, B. L. & A. A. Shifrina (1938) The condition of the plethysmo-graphic curve in schizophrenics. Probl. Patofiziol. Ter. Schiz. Charkow. 26-36.

511. Lang-Belonogova, N. S. (1954) The use of speech reactions in evaluation of typological pecularities and the functional condition of the nervous system in patients with hypertension and gastric ulcer. (Rus.) Z. vyss. nerv. Dejat. Pavlova. 4, 781-790.

512. Langfeldt, G. (1926) The endocrine glands and autonomic systems in dementia praecox. Bergen. Diss.

513. Langfeldt, G. (1937) The prognosis in schizophrenia and the factors influencing the course of the disease. Copenhagen.

514. Langfeldt, G. (1939) The schizophreniform states. Copenhagen.

515. Langfeldt, G. (1953) Some points regarding symptomatology and diagnosis of schizophrenia. Acta psychiat. scand. Suppl. 80, 7-26.

516. Langfeldt, G. (1956) The prognosis in schizophrenia. Acta psychiat. scand. Suppl. 110.

517. Laranov, V. P. (1958) Unconditional vascular reactions during insulin coma in schizophrenics. (Rus.) Nauch. Rab. Psikonevrol. Uchpr. RSFSR. 49-50.

518. Last, S. L. & R. Ström-Olsen (1936) Chronaximetric studies in catatonia. J. ment. Sci. 82, 763-772.

519. Lastovetsky, V. V. & N. Podkamenny (1957) The pathology of the interaction of the first and second signaling systems in schizophrenics. (Rus.) Sb. Ref. med. Fak. Uzhgor. Lemberg. 109-111.

520. Lazarova, A. K. (1955) Experimental studies of the disturbances of the higher nervous activity in Korsakoff's amnestic syndrome. (Rus.) Tr. nauch. Konf. posv. 100 Let. S. S. Korsakoff. 73-74.

521. Lebedev, B. A. (1959) The clinical and pathophysiological basis of involutional psychoses. Vopr. Psikonevrol. Leningrad. 13-16.

522. Lebedinsky, M. S. (1958) Problems of psychotherapy. (Rus.) Moscow.

523. Leder, S. (1955) Dynamics of unconditional and conditional vegetative reflexes in the course of catatonic stupor. (Pol.) Neurol. Neurochir. Psychiat. pol. 5, 171-176.

524. Lehmann, A. (1899) Die körperlichen Äusserungen psychischer Zustände. I. Teil. Plethysmographische Untersuchungen. Leipzig.

525. Lenz. A. K. (1928) The higher reflex activity in general paralysis. (Rus.) Minsk.

526. Leonhard, K. (1936) Die Defektschizophrenen Krankheitsbilder. Leipzig.

527. Leonhard, K. (1942) Zur Unterteilung und Erbbilogie der Schizophrenien. I. Mitt. Die "typischen" Unterformen der Katatonie. Allg. Z. Psychiat. 120, 1-23.

528. Leonhard, K. (1942) Zur Unterteilung und Erbbiologie der Schizophrenien. 2 Mitt. Kombiniert-systematische und periodische Katatonien. Allg. Z. Psychiat. 121, 1-35.

529. Leonhard, K. (1943) Zur Unterteilung und Erbbiologie der Schizophrenien. 3 Mitt. Erbbiologie der Katatonien. Allg. Z. Psychiat. 122, 39-86.

530. Leonhard, K. (1943) Zur Unterteilung und Erbbiologie der Schizophrenien. 4 Mitt. Die paranoiden und verworrenen Schizophrenien typischer und kombiniert-systematischer Art. Allg. Z. Psychiat. 122, 194-231.

531. Leonhard, K. (1944) Zur Unterteilung und Erbbiologie der Schizophrenien. 5 Mitt. Die periodischen und phantastisch fortschreitenden paranoiden Schizophrenien mit ihrem Sippenbild. Allg. Z. Psychiat. 123, 9-25.

532. Leonhard, K. (1944) Zur Unterteilung und Erbbiologie der Schizophrenien. 6 Mitt. Erbbiologie der paranoiden und verworrenen Formen von Schizophrenie. Allg. Z. Psychiat. 123, 177-204.

533. Leonhard, K. (1945) Zur Unterteilung und Erbbiologie der Schizophrenien. 7 Mitt. Die hebephrenen Krankheitsformen und ihr. Erbbild. Psychiat.-neurol. Wschr. 23.

534. Leonhard, K. (1949) Einige kombiniert-systematische Schizophrenien. Allg. Z. Psychiat. 124, 409-432.

535. Leonhard, K. (1950) Eine Sippe affektvoller Paraphrenie. Arch. Psychiat. Nervenkr. 184, 291-356.

536. Leonhard, K. (1952) Formen und Verläufe der Schizophrenien. Mschr. Psychiat. Neurol. 124, 169-191.

537. Leonhard, K. (1957) Aufteilung der endogenen Psychosen. Berlin.

538. Levin, S. L. (1953) Attempt at physiological analysis of the depersonalization phenomena in schizophrenia. (Rus.) Z. Nevropat. Psihiat. (Korsakoff.) 53, 847-853.

539. Levitsky, L. M., A. I. Makarychev & L. F. Roshtina (1957) Characteristics of the cortical activity in corpulent patients. (Rus.) Nauch. Konf, Dejat. Sign. Sist. Norm. i Patol. 71-72,

540. Liberman, A. E. & N. I. Strelzova (1952) Some characteristics of the pupillary component of the orienting reflex. (Rus.) Z. vyss. nerv. Dejat. Pavlova. 2, 886-893.

541. Lichko, A. E. (1952) On the characteristics of the conditional and unconditional defensive and orienting reflexes in acute infectious psychoses. (Rus.) Tr. Inst. Fiziol. Im. I. P. Pavlov. 1, 406-412.

542. Lichko, A. E. (1953) The study of the orienting and defensive reflexes in the course of some infectious psychoses. (Rus.) Leningrad. Diss.

543. Lichko, A. E. (1956) The dynamics of some conditional and unconditional reflexes during insulin coma in the treatment of psychiatric patients. (Rus.) Nauch. Sess. vozrast. Fiziol. Chel. Moscow. Leningrad. 22-23.

544. Lichko, A. E. (1956) The study of rudimentary reflexes in man. (Rus.) Sov. Vopr. evolut. Fiziol. nerv. Sist. Leningrad. 96-97.

545. Lichko, A. E. (1957) Clinical-physiological characteristics of the insulin coma. (Rus.) Z. Nevropat. Psihiat. (Korsakoff.) 57, 1509-1516.

546. Lichko, A. E. (1957) Clinical-physiological characteristics of syndromes with disturbed consciousness. (Rus.) 3 nauch. Sov. vozrast. Fiziol. Patol. Leningrad. 48-50.

547. Lichko, A. E. (1958) The dynamics of rudimentary reflexes in man, during insulin coma. (Rus.) Material. evolut. Fiziol. Leningrad. 3, 140-148.

548. Lichko, A. E. (1958) Contribution to the physiological study of amnesia in cases of insulin shocks. (Rus.) Z. vyss. nerv. Dejat. Pavlova. 8, 793-803.

549. Lichko, A. E. (1959) Subcortical hyperkinesis and other motor symptom complexes in man during insulin coma. (Rus.) 2. nauch. Sov. evolut. Fiziol. Leningrad. 111-112.

550. Lifshits, A. E. (1957) Studies on the dynamics of vascular reactions during remission in juvenile schizophrenics. (Rus.) 3. nauch. Sov. vozrast. Fiziol. Patol. Leningrad. 47-48.

551. Lindsley, O. R. (1956) Operant conditioning methods applied to research in chronic schizophrenia. Psychiat. Res. Rep. Amer. psychiat. Ass. 5, 118-153.

552. Linsky, V. P. (1954) The problem of developing conditional reflexes in patients with Korsakoff syndromes. (Rus.) Z. vyss. nerv. Dejat. Pavlova. 4, 791-798.

553. Linsky, V. P. (1955) The pathophysiology of Korsakoff's syndrome. (Rus.) Tr. nauch. Konf. posv. 100 Let. S. S. Korsakoff. 56-59.

554. Linsky, V. P. (1955) The dynamics of some unconditional and conditional reflexes in schizophrenics. (Rus.) Psikonevrol. Konf. Probl. Schiz. Simferopol. 44-45.

555. Linsky, V. P. (1955) The dynamics of some unconditional and conditional reflexes in schizophrenia. (Rus.) Tes. Kharkov. med. Inst. posv. 150 Let. 225-227.

556. Linsky, V. P. (1956) Some unconditional and conditional reflexes in schizophrenics. (Rus.) Tes. Dokl. 20 Ukrain. psikonevrol. Inst. Charkow. 62-63.

557. Lipskaya, L. A. (1958) Problems of the pathogenesis of reactive psychoses. (Rus.) Tr. Inst. Fiziol. Im. I. P. Pavlov. 7, 211-216.

558. Litvinova, V. E. (1955) Motor chronaxy in schizophrenics in changes of the fundamental dynamics of cortical processes. (Rus.) Z. Nevropat. Psihiat. (Korsakoff.) 55, 259-265.

559. Löwenbach, H. & H. W. Gantt (1940) Conditional vestibular reactions. J. Neurophysiol. 3, 43-48.

560. Löwenstein, O. & A. Westphal (1933) Experimentelle und klinische Studien zur Physiologie und Pathologie der Pupillenbewegungen mit besonderer Berücksichtigung der Schizophrenie. Berlin.

561. Lubovsky, V. I. (1955) Some characteristics of the interaction of the two signaling systems and the formation of motor reactions in oligophrenic children. (Rus.) Moscow. Diss.

562. Lubovsky, V. I. (1958) A cause of disturbance of elaboration of new connections in oligophrenics. (Rus.) Tes. 18 Sov. Probl. vyss. nerv. Dejat. 3, 10-10.

563. Lukina, A. M. & S. A. Mashusova (1929) Characteristics of conditioning in epileptics. (Rus.) Nov. Refl. Fiziol. nerv. Sist. Leningrad. 3, 419-435.

564. Lunn, V. (1951) The position of reflexology in psychiatry. (Dan.) Bibl. Läger 143, 69-96.

565. Lunn, V. (1958) About the influence of electro-shock on the conditional withdrawal-reflex in man. (Dan.) Nord. psykiat. Medlemsbl. Suppl. 1, 249-260.

566. Luria, A. R. (1932) The nature of human conflicts. New York.

567. Luria, A. R. (1956) The regulating role of speech in forming voluntary movements. (Rus.) Z. vyss. nerv. Dejat. Pavlova. 6, 645-662.

568. Lurje, J. L. (1958) The state of the higher nervous activity in rheumatic patients. (Rus.) Klin. Med. (Mosk.) 5, 84-87.

569. Maiorov, F. P. (1950) The physiologic characteristics of somnambulism. (Rus.) Fiziol. Z. (Mosk.) 36, 649-652.

570. Maiorov, F. P. & M. M. Suslova (1951) Studies of the experimental speech regression in hypnosis. (Rus.) Z. vyss nerv. Dejat. Pavlova. 1, 479-484.

571. Maiorov, F. P. (1952) Studies of the higher nervous activity in hypnotic conditions. (Rus.) Tr. 15 Sov. posv. 50 Let. I. P. Pavlov. 262-276.

572. Makarychev. A. I., L. M. Levitsky & L. F. Roshtina (1958) The dynamics of cortical activity in obesity. (Rus.) Tes. 18 Sov. Probl. vyss. nerv. Dejat. 3, 13-13.

573. Makhinko, V. I. (1954) The Pavlovian theories of the two signaling systems. (Rus.) Charkow.

574. Malikin, R. Y., A. I. Sokolin, A. V. Braitsev & N. V. Rakhmanova (1954) The higher nervous activity in patients with latent syphilitic meningitis. (Rus.) Z. vyss. nerv. Dejat. Pavlova. 4, 629-641.

575. Malkina, M. G. & A. I. Kuznetsov (1958) Studies of disturbances of termoregulating reflexes in schizophrenia. (Rus.) Z. vyss. nerv. Dejat. Pavlova. 8, 36-41.

576. Malmo, R. B. & C. Shagass (1940) Physiologic studies of reaction to stress in anxiety and early schizophrenia. Psychosom. Med. 11, 9-24.

577. Malmo, R. B., C. Shagass, J. F. David & M. Engh (1951) Electromyographic studies of muscular tension in psychiatric patients under stress. J. clin. exp. Psychopath. 12, 45-66.

578. Malmo, R. B., C. Shagass & A. A. Smith (1951) Responsiveness in chronic schizophrenia. J. Personality. 19, 359-375.
579. Marinesco, G., A. Kreindler & L. Copelman (1935) Le test de Rorschach et la dynamique de l'écorce cérébrale d'après les lois des réflexes conditionnels de Pavlov. Ann. méd.-psychol. 93, 614-623.
580. Marinesco, G. & A. Kreindler (1935) Des réflexes conditionnels. Paris.
581. Marinesco, G. (1937) Contribution à l'étude des troubles sensitifs hystériques et le rôle des réflexes conditionnels dans la physio-pathologie de l'hystérie. Rev. neurol. 68, 585-600.
582. Markova, E. D. (1956) Characteristics of the disturbances of neurodynamics in amnestic aphasia. (Rus.) Moscow. Diss.
583. Markova, E. D. (1957) Characteristics of the disturbances of the neurodynamics in amnestic aphasia. (Rus.) Z. vyss. nerv. Dejat. Pavlova. 7, 344-353.
584. Markus, O. (1911) Über Assoziationen bei Dementia praecox. Arch. Psychiat. Nervenkr. 48, 344-393.
585. Martin, A. (1945) A study of types of word-association in dementia praecox and manic-depressives. J. gen. Psychol. 33, 257-264.
586. Martsinovskaya, E. N. (1955) Disturbances of the generalizing functions of speech and the formation of temporal connections in oligophrenic children. (Rus.) Moscow. Diss.
587. Mashkovsky, M. D. (1956) Pharmacological characteristics of aminazine and other phenothiazine derivatives. (Rus.) Z. Nevropat. Psihiat. (Korsakoff.) 56, 81-93.
588. Maslova, N. P. (1958) Changes of EEG in neurotic patients (neurasthenia) awake, asleep and awakening. (Rus.) Z. vyss. nerv. Dejat. Pavlova. 8, 517-523.
589. Masserman, J. H. (1943) Behavior and neurosis. Chicago.
590. Masserman, J. H. (1946) Principles of dynamic psychiatry. Philadelphia and London.
591. Mayer, W. (1921) Über paraphrene Psychosen. Z. ges. Neurol. Psychiat. 71, 187-206.
592. Melekhov, D. E. & V. M. Kamenskaya (1953) Clinical and pathophysiological investigations of sequelae after closed head injury. (Rus.) Z. Nevropat. Psihiat. (Korsakoff.) 53, 595-606.
593. Melekhov, D. E. & V. M. Kamenskaya (1955) Clinical and pathophysiological investigations of sequelae after closed head injury. (Rus.) Z. Nevropat. Psihiat. (Korsakoff.) 55, 641-649.
594. Melekhov, D. E. & V. M. Kamenskaya (1957) Clinical and pathophysiological investigations of the mental disturbances after closed head injury. (Rus.) Z. Nevropat. Psihiat. (Korsakoff.) 57, 1185-1194.
595. Melekhova, A. M. & I. V. Strelchuk (1958) Electrophysiological studies of the cerebral cortex of healthy men and chronic alcoholics. Observations of the first and second signaling systems in alert and hypnotic conditions. (Rus.) Konf. Vopr. Patofiziol. vyss. nerv. Dejat. Moscow. 89-91.
596. Merlin, V. S. (1954) The characteristics of conditional psychogalvanic reflexes in man. (Rus.) Fiziol. Z. (Mosk.) 40, 155-161.

597. Meshjerjakov, A. I. (1953) Disturbances of interaction of the two signaling systems in the formation of simple motor reactions after local brain lesions. (Rus.) Moscow. Diss.

598. Meskhi, R. G. (1956) The dynamics of the schizophasic syndrome. (Rus.) Tes. Dokl. Sess. Inst. M. Asatiani. Tiflis. 24-24.

599. Meskhi, R. G. (1958) The dynamics of the syndrome of schizophasia. (Rus.) Sb. nauch. Inst. M. Asatiani. Tiflis. 5, 95-97.

600. Mette, A. (1953) Bemerkungen zur Frage der Entstehung von Spracheigentümlichkeiten im Initialstadium der Schizophrenie auf dem Boden der Lehre I. P. Pawlows. Psychiat. Neurol. med. Psychol. (Lpz.) 5, 383-391.

601. Mette, A. (1955) Bemerkungen zur Symptomatik und Theorie der Sprachverwirrtheit bei Schizophrenie. Psychiat. Neurol. med. Psychol. (Lpz.) 7, 65-75.

602. Meyer, A. (1910) The dynamic interpretation of dementia praecox. Amer. J. Psychol. 21, 385-403.

603. Meyer, G., K. Leonhard & K. Kleist (1943) Die paranoiden Schizophrenien auf Grund katamnestischer Untersuchungen. 4 Teil. Die paranoide Demenz. (Progressive Auto-und Somatopsychosen.) Z. ges. Neurol. Psychiat. 177, 114-172.

604. Miasnikov, A. L. (1953) The pathogenesis and the treatment of hypertensive disease according to Pavlovian theories. (Rus.) Z. vyss. nerv. Dejat. Pavlova. 3, 55-70.

605. Mikhelson, M. J. (1957) The physiological role of acetylcholine and the selection of therapeutic drugs. (Rus.) Leningrad.

606. Milev, V. (1958) The clinical and experimental method in the study of hallucinations. (Rus.) Z. Nevropat. Psihiat. (Korsakoff.) 58, 1465-1469.

607. Miljutin, V. N. (1955) Disturbances in the dynamics of the cortical processes by hallucinations. (Rus.) Z. Nevropat. Psihiat. (Korsakoff.) 55, 182-186.

608. Minski, L. (1937) A note on some vasomotor disturbances in schizophrenia. J. ment. Sci. 83, 437-439.

609. Mirelson, L. A. & P. G. Nikiforova (1955) On conditional speech reactions in schizophrenics. (Rus.) Psikonevrol. Konf. Probl. Schiz. Simferopol. 46-47.

610. Mirelson, L. A. & A. N. Kornetov (1957) Disturbances of the cortical dynamics in schizophrenics with speech incoherence. (Rus.) Vopr. Rastroist. Krovoob. Schiz. Odessa. 205-210.

611. Mirelson, L. A. & A. N. Kornetov (1957) Disturbances of the cortical dynamics in incoherent schizophrenics. (Rus.) Tes. Dokl. Nauch.Sess. 50 Let. Revolut. Odessa. 81-82.

612. Mirelson, L. A. & A. N. Kornetov (1957) Disturbances of the cortical dynamics by speech incoherence in schizophrenics. (Rus.) Nauch. Konf. Dejat. Sign. Sist. Norm. i Patol. 77-78.

613. Mirelson, L. A. & A. N. Kornetov (1957) Some peculiarities of the neurodynamics of schizophrenics with incoherent speech. (Rus.) Z. Nevropat. Psihiat. (Korsakoff.) Suppl. 57, 66-66.

614. Mirolyubov, N. G. & N. B. Ugol (1933) The problem of the state of the process of excitation in schizophrenia. (Rus.) Sovetsk. Psikonevrol. 3, 68-82.

615. Mirolyubov, N. G. (1947) Derangement of interaction of first and second signaling systems of the cerebral cortex after closed head injury. (Rus.) Ref. nauch. issl. Rab. med. biol. Nauk. SSSR. 153-154.

616. Mirolyubov, N. G. (1949) Disturbances of interaction of the first and second signaling systems in patients with open head injury. (Rus.) Ref. nauch. issl. Rab. med. biol. Nauk. SSSR. 141-142.

617. Mishtenko, M. N. & A. S. Poznansky (1938) The relation between the strength of stimuli and the strength of reactions in schizophrenia. (Rus.) Probl. Patofiziol. Ter. Schiz. Charkow. 91-103.

618. Mitchell, I., I. R. Rosanoff & A. J. Rosanoff (1919) A study of association in Negro children. Psychol. Rev. 26, 354-359.

619. Molakhaltsev, A. P. & E. J. Rappeport (1957) Attempts at clinical-physiological investigation of the higher nervous activity in patients with presenile psychoses. (Rus.) Z. Nevropat. Psihiat. (Korsakoff.) Suppl. 57, 72-73.

620. Molakhaltsev, A. P. & E. J. Rappeport (1958) Clinical-physiological studies of the higher nervous activity in some types of presenile psychoses. (Rus.) Konf. Vopr. Patofiziol. vyss. nerv. Dejat. Moscow. 94-96.

621. Molotkova, I. A. (1953) Changes of the higher nervous activity in oligophrenics under the influence of bromides and prolonged sleep. (Rus.) Leningrad. Diss.

622. Molotkova, I. A. (1954) The development of conditional reflexes to synthetic stimuli in oligophrenics. (Rus.) Konf. po Itog. Rab. 1953 IEM. Leningrad. 15-17.

623. Molotkova, I. A. (1956) The characteristics of conditional reflexes on simultaneous complex stimuli in oligophrenics. (Rus.) Annot. nauch. Rab. Akad. Nauk. 47-49.

624. Molotkova, I. A. (1957) Conditional reflexes to successive complex stimuli in oligophrenic patients. (Rus.) Z. vyss. nerv. Dejat. Pavlova. 7, 58-62.

625. Molotkova, I. A. (1957) Studies of complex analytic-synthetic activity in oligophrenic patients. (Rus.) 3. nauch. Sov. vozrast. Fiziol. Patol. Leningrad. 60-61.

626. Molotkova, I. A. (1958) On characteristics of the interaction of speech reactions and motor reflexes studied with various unconditional reinforcements in old age. (Rus.) Konf. Vopr. Patofiziol. vyss. nerv. Dejat. Moscow. 96-96.

627. Monakhov, K. K. (1957) The problems of the significance of the second signaling system in the elaboration of motor conditional reflexes in anancastic neuroses with a cardiophobic syndrome. (Rus.) Nauch. Konf. Dejat. Sign. Sist. Norm. i Patol. 82-83.

628. Monakhov, K. K. (1958) Characteristics of the higher nervous activity in anancastic syndromes with cardiophobic syndromes (Rus.) Moscow. Diss.

629. Monakhov, K. K. (1958) Some characteristics of the higher nervous activity in anancastic neuroses with cardiophobic syndromes and functional disturbances of the cardiovascular activity. (Rus.) Tr. Inst. vyss. nerv. Dejat. Ser. Patofiziol. 5, 250-269.

630. Moravcsik, E. E. (1911) Diagnostische Assoziationsuntersuchungen. Allg. Z. Psychiat. 68, 626-673.

631. Morozov, G. V. (1953) Conditional reflexes of the heart in schizophrenics. (Rus.) Z. Nevropat. Psihiat. (Korsakoff.) 53, 191-196.
632. Müller-Hegemann, D. (1942) Assoziationsversuche mittels Silbenergänzung. Nervenarzt. 15, 389-396.
633. Müller-Hegemann, D. (1957) Psychotherapie. Berlin.
634. Murphy, G. (1921) A comparison of manic-depressive and dementia praecox cases by the free-association method. Amer. J. Insan. 77, 545-558.
635. Murphy, G. (1923) Types of word-association in dementia praecox, manic depressives, and normal persons, Amer. J. Psychiat. 2, 539-571.
636. Murphy, G. (1948) An historical introduction to modern psychology. London.
637. Narbutovich, I. O. & D. S. Svetlov (1934) Investigations into certain simple unconditional reflexes (orienting and defensive) in schizophrenia. (Rus.) Ark. biol. Nauk. Ser. B. 36, 183-227.
638. Narbutovich, I. O. (1938) Studies of some simple unconditional reflexes in schizophrenics. (Rus.) Tes. Dokl. 3 Sov. Fiziol. posv. I. P. Pavlov. 70-71.
639. Narbutovich, I. O. (1948) The neurodynamics of schizophrenia. (Rus.) Tes. Dokl. Sess. Stalingrad. med. Inst. 71-72.
640. Narbutovich, I. O. (1952) Pathological derangement of the combined activity of the first and second signaling systems in states of illusions and hallucinations. (Rus.) Tr. 15 Sov. posv. 50 Let. I. P. Pavlov. 277-284.
641. Nasonov, B. A. (1957) The signaling systems in Korsakoff's syndrome. (Rus.) Nauch. Sess. 40 Let. Revolut. Kieff. 24-25.
642. Nathan, E. W. (1909) Über die Assoziationen von Imbezillen und ihre diagnostische Verwertbarkeit. Klin. psych. nerv. Krank. 4, 320-379.
643. Naumova, V. V. (1956) The influence of phenamine on speech disturbances of schizophrenics. (Rus.) Tes. Konf. Ukrain. psikonevrol. Inst. 54-55.
644. Nazarov, K. N. (1955) Complex investigations of the motor reactions in schizophrenics with the syndrome of Kandinsky. (Rus.) Tes. nauch. Sess. posv. Vedenskogo. Odessa. 59-60.
645. Neele, E. & K. Kleist (1942) Die paranoiden Schizophrenien auf Grund katamnestischer Untersuchungen. 3 Teil. Die progressiven Beiziehungspsychosen. Z. ges. Neurol. Psychiat. 175, 4-67.
646. Nikiforova, P. G. (1955) The clinic and the disturbances of the higher nervous activity in chronic schizophrenics. (Rus.) Tes. Dokl. nauch. Sess. 50 Let. Revolut. Odessa. 33-34.
647. Noschenko, G. V. (1956) An attempt to influence by suggestion in hypnosis the functional interrelations between the first and second signaling systems in cases of hysteria. (Rus.) Z. vyss. nerv. Dejat. Pavlova. 6, 672-679.
648. Novikov, A. N. (1952) Unconditional vascular reflexes after closed head injury (in the acute stage.) (Rus.) Z. Nevropat. Psihiat. (Korsakoff.) 52, 18-24.
649. Novikov, A. N. (1953) The pathogenesis, clinic and treatment of cerebral concussion. (Rus.) Moscow. Diss.
650. Novikov, A. N. (1957) Vasomotor reactions during intellectual work in normals and persons with a past head injury. (Rus.) Z. Nevropat. Psihiat. (Korsakoff.) Suppl. 57, 56-57.

651. Novitskaya, A. I. (1956) Changes of vestibular unconditional reflexes in schizophrenics. (Rus.) Tes. Konf. Ukrain. psikonevrol. Inst. 65-65.
652. Novlyanskaya, K. A. (1957) Diagnostical and prognostical criteria of the periods between epileptic seizures. (Rus.) Z. Nevropat. Psihiat. (Korsakoff.) 57, 865-870.
653. Nuller, J. B. (1955) Hebephrenic states in schizophrenia. (Rus.) Tr. nauch. Konf. posv. 100 Let. S. S. Korsakoff. 170-174.
654. O'Connor, N. & K. Rawnsley (1959) Two types of conditioning in psychotics and normals. J. abnorm. soc. Psychol. 58, 157-161.
655. O'Connor, N. & J. P. Das (1959) Lability in schizophrenia. Brit. J. Psychol. 50, 333-337.
656. Ödegård, Ö. (1930) The psychogalvanic reactivity in normals and in various psychopathic conditions. Acta psychiat. (Kbh.) 5, 55-103.
657. Ödegård, Ö. (1932) The psychogalvanic reactivity in affective disorders. Brit. J. med. Psychol. 12, 132-150.
658. Ogienko, F. F. (1956) Vascular reactions in patients with various lesions of the central and peripheral nervous system. (Rus.) Z. vyss. nerv. Dejat. Pavlova. 6, 690-696.
659. Okhnyanskaya, L. G. (1955) Unconditional and conditional vascular reflexes in patients with silicosis. (Rus.) Z. vyss. nerv. Dejat. Pavlova. 5, 660-664.
660. Orbeli, L. A. (1949) Problems of the higher nervous activity. (Rus.) Moscow & Leningrad.
661. Osberg, I. J. (1956) The dynamics of vascular reactions and bioelectric activity in schizophrenics treated with aminazine. (Rus.) Avtoref. Dokl. Konf. issl. Psihiat. MZSSR. 54-56.
662. Otis, M. (1915) A study of association in defectives. J. educ. Psychol. 6, 271-288.
663. Pankov, D. V. (1958) Disturbances of the neurodynamics, and in particular the interaction of the signaling systems in arteriosclerosis of the brain. (Rus.) Konf. Itog. nauch. issl. Rab. 1957. Moscow. 35-36.
664. Pankov, D. V. (1958) Disturbances of the neurodynamics in cerebral arteriosclerosis and a pathogenetically based therapy. (Rus.) Tes. 18 Sov. Probl. vyss. nerv. Dejat. 3, 61-62.
665. Papandopulos, T. F. (1958) Plethysmographic studies of schizophrenic patients during remission after the first schizophrenic attack. (Rus.) Konf. Vopr. Patofiziol. vyss. nerv. Dejat. Moscow. 98-99.
666. Parkhon-Shtefanesku, K. & E. Tomorug (1958) The study of the mechanisms of the Kandinsky syndrome. (Rus.) Tes. Dokl. Jub. Stolet. Kaf. Psihiat. Leningrad. 60-61.
667. Paramonova, N. P. (1957) Age peculiarities of interaction of the two signaling systems. (Rus.) Z. vyss. nerv. Dejat. Pavlova. 7, 651-658.
668. Paschenkov, S. Z. (1952) Problems of hypochondriacal delusions. (Rus.) Z. Nevropat. Psihiat. (Korsakoff.) 52, 8-17.
669. Paschenkov, S. Z. (1958) Hypochondriacal conditions. (Rus.) Moscow.
670. Pavlov, B. V. & J. A. Povorinsky (1953) The interaction of the first and second signaling systems in the somnambulic phase of hypnosis. (Rus.) Z. vyss. nerv. Dejat. Pavlova. 3, 381-392.

671. Pavlov, B. V., J. A. Povorinsky & V. V. Bobkova (1955) The interaction of the first and second signaling systems in the somnambulic phase of hypnosis. (Rus.) Z. vyss. nerv. Dejat. Pavlova. 5, 11-18.
672. Pavlov, I. P. (1941) Lectures on conditional reflexes. (2nd. ed.) New York.
673. Pavlov, I. P. (1941) Lectures on conditional reflexes: Conditional reflexes and psychiatry. New York.
674. Pavlov, I. P. (1949) Pavlovian wednesdays. (Rus.) Moscow & Leningrad.
675. Pavlova, T. N. (1954) Changes in the higher nervous activity in operators of calculation machines during the working days. (Rus.) Z. vyss. nerv. Dejat. Pavlova. 4, 166-176.
676. Peimer, I. A., M. B. Umarov & N. A. Khromov (1954) Electrophysiological studies of psychasthenia and hysteria. (Rus.) Z. Nevropat. Psihiat. (Korsakoff.) 54, 903-914.
677. Pen. R. M. & M. A. Dzhagarov (1936) The formation of conditional connections in hypnotic sleep. (Rus.) Ark. biol. Nauk. 42, 77-88.
678. Perelman, A. A. & K. I. Koshkareva (1952) Conditional speech reactions in schizophrenics. (Rus.) Tr. 2 Pavlov. Konf. Tomsk. 188-192.
679. Perelman, A. A. & K. I. Koshkareva (1954) Disturbances of the first and second signaling systems in various types and stages of the schizophrenic process. (Rus.) Tr. 4 Pavlov. Konf. Tomsk. 207-212.
680. Perelman, L. B. (1952) The methods of anlysing the functional conditions of the vasoregulating mechanisms in hypertensive disease (Rus.) Z. Nevropat. Psihiat. (Korsakoff.) 52, 11-21.
681. Perminova, I. D. (1953) The pseudohallucionatory syndrome of Kandinsky. (Rus.) Z. Nevropat. Psihiat. (Korsakoff.) 53, 203-208.
682. Perminova, I. D. (1956) The role of neurodynamic disturbances in the production of hallucination. (Rus.) Gorki. Diss.
683. Pervomaisky, B. J. (1954) Speech disturbances in the manic phase of manic-depressive psychosis and the theories of the interaction of the signaling systems. (Rus.) Leningrad. Diss.
684. Pervomaisky, B. J. (1956) The types of speech reactions in the manic phase of manic-depressive psychosis. (Rus.) Sb. Tes. Dokl. Stalino. 177-178.
685. Pervomaisky, B. J. (1956) The interaction of the signaling systems in the manic phase of the manic-depressive psychosis. (Rus.) Psihiat. klin. Probl. Patol. vyss. nerv. Dejat. 1, 132-151.
686. Pervomaisky, B. J. (1957) Some data on the study of schizophrenic patients and the pathophysiological basis. (Rus.) Nauch. Konf. Dejat. Sign. Sist. Norm. i Patol. 89-90.
687. Pervov, L. G. (1953) Studies of the higher nervous activity in neuroses with a new variation of the association experiment. (Rus.) Tes. 16 Sov. Probl. vyss. nerv. Dejat. 173-174.
688. Pervov, L. G. (1956) Verbal method of determining the condition of higher nervous activity in man. (Rus.) Z. vyss. nerv. Dejat. Pavlova. 6, 329-332.
689. Pervov, L. G. (1957) Study of the higher nervous activity in hysterics with a new method of investigation. (Rus.) 3 nauch. Sov. vozrast. Fiziol. Patol. Leningrad. 63-65.

690. Pervov, L. G. (1958) The higher nervous activity and the type of nervous system in hysteria studied with three experimental methods. (Rus.) Tr. Inst. Fiziol. Im. I. P. Pavlov. 7, 217-224.

691. Pervov, L. G. (1958) Complex studies of the higher nervous activity in hysteric patients. (Rus.) Tr. Inst. Fiziol. Im. I. P. Pavlov. 7, 225-231.

692. Pervov, L. G. (1958) Study of the higher nervous activity in patients suffering from hysteria. (Rus.) Z. vyss. nerv. Dejat. Pavlova. 8, 654-658.

693. Peskova, M. V. (1957) Studies of some unconditional reflexes in schizophrenics. (Rus.) Aktual. Probl. Nevropat. Psihiat. Kuibyshev. 259-264.

694. Peters, H. N. & O. D. Murphree (1954) The conditional reflex in the chronic schizophrenic. J. clin. Psychol. 10, 126-130.

695. Pfaffmann, C. & H. Schlosberg (1936) The conditional knee jerk in psychotic and normal individuals. J. Psychol. 1, 201-206.

696. Pfeiffer, C. C., A. J. Riopelle, R. P. Smith, E. H. Jenney & H. L. Williams (1957) Comparative study of the effect of meprobamate on the conditioned response, on strychnine and pentylenetetrazol thresholds, on the normal electroencephalogram, and on polysynaptic reflexes. Ann. N. Y. Acad. Sci. 67, 734-745.

697. Pfeiffer, C. C. & E. H. Jenney (1957) The inhibition of the conditional response and the counteraction of schizophrenia by muscarinic stimulation of the brain. Ann. N. Y. Acad. Sci. 66, 753-764.

698. Piatkowski, F. (1955) Dynamics of vasomotor reflexes in the course of catatonic stupor. (Pol.) Neurol. Neurochir. Psychiat. pol. 5, 161-169.

699. Platonov, K. I. (1956) Psychotherapy of disturbed stereotypes of the higher nervous activity. (Rus.) Z. Nevropat. Psihiat. (Korsakoff.) 56, 854-857.

700. Platonov, K. I. (1958) La palabra como factor fisiológico y terapéutico. Moscow.

701. Pleshkova, T. V. (1952) Investigations of conditional and unconditional inhibition in hysteric neuroses. (Rus.) Tr. Inst. Fiziol. Im. I. P. Pavlov. 1, 356-368.

702. Pleshkova, T. V. (1953) Investigations of delayed conditional reflexes in hysteric neuroses. (Rus.) Tes. 16 Sov. Probl. vyss. nerv. Dejat. 177-178.

703. Pleshkova, T. V. (1955) Conditional inhibition of the first and second signaling systems in hysteric neuroses. (Rus.) Bjul. eksp. Biol. Med. 39, 36-39.

704. Pleshkova, T. V. (1957) Investigation of trace conditional inhibition in healthy persons and in patients suffering from neurasthenia. (Rus.) Z. vyss. nerv. Dejat. Pavlova. 7, 510-518.

705. Pleshkova, T. V. (1958) Conditional traced inhibition in hysteric neuroses. (Rus.) Tes. 18 Sov. Probl. vyss. nerv. Dejat. 3, 69-70.

706. Ploticher, A. I. (1955) Methodological variations in the study of conditional speech reactions of psychiatric patients. (Rus.) Z. vyss. nerv. Dejat. Pavlova. 5, 832-843.

707. Poljakov, V. P. (1956) The pathophysiological mechanisms in disturbances of the higher nervous activity in psychopaths with affective lability. (Rus.) Leningrad.

708. Popov, E. A. (1937) The pathophysiological mechanisms of motor disturbances in catatonia. (Rus.) Tr. tsent. psikonevrol. Inst. 190-199.

709. Popov, E. A. (1941)   The clinic and pathogenesis of hallucinations. (Rus.) Charkow. Diss.

710. Popov, E. A. (1948)   Material on the pathophysiology of schizophrenia (especially catatonia). Jub. Sb. Giliarovsky. 106-112.

711. Popov, E. A. (1949)   Characteristics of schizophrenic thinking and patho-physiological mechanisms. (Rus.) Tr. Sess. Ukrain. psikonevrol. Inst. 24, 121-126.

712. Popov, E. A. (1955)   The significance of the inhibitory phenomena in the clinic of psychiatric diseases. (Rus.) Z. vyss. nerv. Dejat. Pavlova. 5, 329-335.

713. Popov, E. A. (1957)   The application of the Pavlovian theories in psychiatry. (Rus.) Z. Nevropat. Psihiat. (Korsakoff.) 57, 673-680.

714. Popov, E. A. (1957)   Problems in the pathogenesis of schizophrenia. (Rus.) Z. Nevropat. Psihiat. (Korsakoff.) 57, 545-555.

715. Popova, M. S. (1958)   Comparative characteristics of the higher nervous activity in paranoid schizophrenics with various duration of the disease. (Rus.) Konf. Itog. nauch. issl. Rab. 1957. Moscow. 36-38.

716. Popper, E. (1920)   Über Schmerzgefühle bei Oligophrenen. Neurol. Zbl. 39, 13-21.

717. Portsija, L. I. (1958)   Disturbances of the higher nervous activity in morons (Rus.) Konf. Vopr. Patofiziol. vyss. nerv. Dejat. Moscow. 102-103.

718. Povorinsky, J. A. & N. N. Traugott (1937)   Some characteristics of the cortical dynamics in hypnotic sleep. (Rus.) Ark. biol. Nauk. 44, 5-22.

719. Povorinsky, J. A. & V. K. Faddeyeva (1940)   Experimental investigations of the cortical dynamics in hysteria. (Rus.) Tes. Dokl. 7 Sov. Fiziol. posv. I. P. Pavlov. 51-52.

720. Povorinsky, J. A. (1953)   Changes in the cutaneous and vascular reactions in hypnosis by the actions of words and direct stimuli. (Rus.) Z. Nevro-pat. Psihiat. (Korsakoff.) 53, 854-860.

721. Povorinsky, J. A. (1956)   Untersuchungsmethodik motorischer bedingter Reflexe bei verbaler Bekräftigung. Berlin.

722. Povorinsky, J. A. (1959)   Studies of the nervous mechanisms in schizo-phrenia and schizophreniform psychoses during treatment with ataraxic drugs. (Rus.) Vopr. Psikonevrol. Leningrad. 95-97.

723. Pravdina-Vinorskaya, E. N. (1957)   The neurological characteristics of the oligophrenic syndrome. (Rus.) Moscow.

724. Prokhorova, E. S. (1954)   Some pathophysiological mechanisms of the hys-teric paralysis. (Rus.) Z. vyss. nerv. Dejat. Pavlova. 4, 773-780.

725. Prokhorova, E. S. (1956)   Experimental studies of the motor-kinesthetic analyser in patients with hysteric paralyses and pareses. (Rus.) Tr. Konf. Probl. Nevros. Petrozavodsk. 179-185.

726. Propp, M. V. (1953)   Changes of vascular conditional and unconditional reflexes in functional and organic disturbances of the central nervous system. (Rus.) Leningrad. Diss.

727. Protopopov, V. P. (1909)   Combined motor reactions on auditory stimuli. (Rus.) Leningrad. Diss.

728. Protopopov, V. P. (1938)   Pathophysiological characteristics of the func-tions of the central nervous system in schizophrenia. (Rus.) Probl. Patofiziol. Ter. Schiz. Charkow. 14-25.

729. Protopopov, V. P. (1946) Pathophysiological foundations of a rational treatment of schizophrenia. (Rus.) Kieff.

730. Protopopov, V. P. (1948) The somatic characteristics of manic-depressive psychoses. (Rus.) Nevropat. i Psihiat. 17, 57-64.

731. Protopopov, V. P. & E. A. Rushkevich (1956) Studies of the disturbances of abstract thinking and physiological characteristics in psychiatric patients. (Rus.) Kieff.

732. Protopopov, V. P. (1957) Problems of the manic-depressive psychosis. (Rus.) Z. Nevropat. Psihiat. (Korsakoff.) 57, 1355-1362.

733. Prusenko, A. (1925) Conditional connections in schizophrenics. (Rus.) Ukrain. Vestn. Refleksol. eksp. Pedagog. 1, 144-162.

734. Pshonik, A. T. (1956) Hirnrinde und rezeptorische Funktion des Organismus. Berlin.

735. Pshonik, A. T. & R. A. Felberbaum (1957) Changes in the higher nervous activity in women during menstruation. (Rus.) Z. Nevropat. Psihiat. (Korsakoff.) Suppl. 57, 74-74.

736. Rabin, A. I., G. F. King, & J. C. Ehrmann (1955) Vocabulary performance of short-term and long-term schizophrenics. J. abnorm. soc. Psychol. 50, 255-258.

737. Rajeva, S. N. (1954) Disturbances of the neurodynamics with special reference to the interaction of the signaling systems in hysteric neuroses. (Rus.) Moscow. Diss.

738. Rajeva, S. N. (1955) Some disturbances of the interaction of the signaling systems in hysteria. (Rus.) Tr. Inst. vyss. nerv. Dejat. Ser. Patofizol. 1, 48-66.

739. Rajeva, S. N. (1955) The influence of prolonged sleep on some disturbances of the cortical dynamics in hysteria. (Rus.) Tr. Inst. vyss. nerv. Dejat. Ser. Patofiziol. 1, 230-249.

740. Rajeva, S. N. (1957) Some experimental clinical studies of "sore points" in hysteric patients. (Rus.) Nauch. Konf. Dejat. Sign. Sist. Norm. i Patol. 91-93.

741. Rajeva, S. N. (1957) The effect of activating delirious pathodynamic structures in patients with paranoid schizophrenia. (Rus.) Nauch. Konf. Dejat. Sign. Sist. Norm. i Patol. 93-95.

742. Rajeva, S. N. (1958) The influences of various doses of ACTH on the higher nervous activity of paranoid schizophrenics. (Rus.) Konf. Itog. nauch. issl. Rab. 1957. Moscow. 38-39.

743. Rajeva, S. N. (1958) Studies of complex dynamic structures in patients with paranoid schizophrenia. (Rus.) Tes. 18 Sov. Probl. vyss. nerv. Dejat. 3, 90-92.

744. Rajeva, S. N. (1958) Influences of word stimuli related to "sore points" on the combined activity of the first and second signaling systems and some autonomic functions in hysteric patients. (Rus.) Tr. Inst. vyss. nerv. Dejat. Ser. Patofiziol. 5, 157-176.

745. Rajeva, S. N. (1958) Characteristics of the interaction of the first and second signaling systems by the activation of pathodynamic structures in patients with paranoid schizophrenia. (Rus.) Tr. Inst. vyss. nerv. Dejat. Ser. Patofiziol. 5, 55-84.

746. Ranschburg, P. & E. Bálint (1900) Über quantitative und qualitative Veränderungen geistiger Vorgänge im hohen Greisenalter. Allg. Z. Psychiat. 57, 689-718.

747. Rapaport, D. (1942) Emotions and memory. Baltimore.

748. Rapaport, D., M. Gill & R. Schafer (1946) Diagnostic psychological testing. II. Chicago.

749. Raymond, M. J. (1956) Case of fetishism treated by aversion therapy. Brit. med. J. 7, 854-857.

750. Razran, G. H. S. (1933) Conditional responses in animals other than dogs. Psychol. Bull. 30, 261-324.

751. Razran, G. H. S. (1934) Conditional withdrawal response with shock as the conditioning stimulus in adult human subjects. Psychol. Bull. 31, 111-143.

752. Reese, W. G., R. Doss & W. H. Gantt (1953) Autonomic responses in differential diagnosis of organic and psychogenic psychoses. A.M.A. Arch. Neurol. Psychiat. 70, 778-793.

753. Reese, W. G. (1953) Certain aspects of conditioning in the human. Ann. N. Y. Acad. Sci. 56, 330-341.

754. Reimann, W. (1955) Die Lehre Pawlows vom 1. und 2. Signalsystem. Leipzig.

755. Reiser, L. A. (1953) Experimental studies of the interaction of the first and second signaling systems in the late stages after head injury. (Rus.) Tes. 16 Sov. Probl. vyss. nerv. Dejat. 182-183.

756. Reiser, L. A. (1955) Some peculiarities of the higher nervous activity in psychiatric patients studied by plethysmography. (Rus.) Z. vyss. nerv. Dejat. Pavlova. 5, 520-523.

757. Reiser, L. A. (1957) Some clinical experimental studies of the higher nervous activity in schizophrenics. (Rus.) Vitebsk. Diss.

758. Renard, E. (1942) Le docteur G. Clérambault. Sa vie et son oeuvre. Paris. Diss.

759. Richter, D. (1957) Schizophrenia: Somatic aspects. London.

760. Riklin, F. (1918) Cases illustrating the phenomena of association in hysteria. In. Jung. C. G. (edit.) Studies in word-association. London.

761. Rittershaus, E. (1910) Zur psychologischen Differentialdiagnose der einzelnen Epilepsieformen. Arch. Psychiat. Nervenkr. 46, 1-93 & 465-545.

762. Robinson, J. & W. H. Gantt (1947) The orienting reflex (questioning reaction): Cardiac, respiratory, salivary and motor components. Bull. Johns Hopk. Hosp. 80, 231-253.

763. Roger, A. & H. Gastaut (1957) Les méchanismes neurophysiologiques du conditionnement et leurs modifications sous l 'effet des médicaments psychotropes. In. Garattini, S. & V. Ghetti (edit.) Psychotropic drugs. Amsterdam, London, New York & Princeton.

764. Rogov, A. A. (1951) Vascular conditional and unconditional reflexes in man. (Rus.) Moscow & Leningrad.

765. Rohde, M. (1909) Assoziationsvorgänge nach der Methode Fuhrmann bei Dementia hebephrenica s. praecox. Berlin. Diss.

766. Rohde, M. (1911) Assoziationsvorgange bei Defektpsychosen. Mschr. Psychiat. Neurol. 30, 272-321 & 384-411 & 519-544.

767. Rokotova, N. A. (1954) Methods for studying types of nervous functions in man. (Rus.) Fiziol. Z. (Mosk.) 40, 726-729.
768. Romanov, V. I. (1958) Changes of the higher nervous activity in patients with neurasthenia during complex treatment. (Rus.) Leningrad. Diss.
769. Ronchevsky, S. P. (1928) Study on salivary secretory conditional reflexes of catatonics. (Rus.) Nevropat. i Psihiat. 21, 340-351.
770. Rosanoff, A. J. (1938) Manual of psychiatry. New York.
771. Rosanoff, I. R. & A. J. Rosanoff (1913) A study of association in children. Psychol. Rev. 20, 43-89.
772. Rosen, V. H. & W. H. Gantt (1943) Effect of metrazol convulsions on conditional reflexes in dogs. Arch. Neurol. Psychiat. (Chicago) 50, 8-17.
773. Roth, G. (1955) Die zerebralen Anfallsleiden im Elektroencephalogramm und im Jung ' schen Assoziationstest. Wien. Arch. Psychol. Psychiat. Neurol. 5, 206-212.
774. Rozhnov, V. E. (1956) Some data on the condition of the olfactory analyser in schizophrenic patients with olfactory hallucinations. (Rus.) Vopr. Psihiat. Moscow. 193-195.
775. Rudakova, T. A. (1958) The pathophysiological analysis of phantom pain after amputation. (Rus.) Tr. Inst. Fiziol. Im. I. P. Pavlov. 7, 232-238.
776. Rusinov, V. S. (1957) Electrophysiological investigations of the higher nervous activity. (Rus.) Z. vyss. nerv. Dejat. Pavlova. 7, 855-867.
777. Rushkevich, E. A. (1954) Some signs of insufficient active inhibition and inertia of the nervous processes in schizophrenic patients. (Rus.) Z. Nevropat. Psihiat. (Korsakoff.) 54, 158-163.
778. Rushkevich, E. A. (1956) Method of elaborating motor reactions by means of verbal instruction and additional stimulation. (Rus.) Z. vyss. nerv. Dejat. Pavlova. 6, 913-918.
779. Rutledge, L. T. & R. W. Doty (1955) Differential action of chlorpromazine on conditional responses to peripheral versus direct cortical stimuli. Federat. Proc. 14, 126-126.
780. Rutledge, L. T. & R. W. Doty (1957) Differential action of chlorpromazine on reflexes conditioned to central and peripheral stimulation. Amer. J. Physiol. 191, 189-192.
781. Saarma, J. M. (1955) Changes of the neurodynamics in schizophrenic patients during insulin treatment. (Rus.) Tr. nauch. Konf. posv. 100 Let. S. S. Korsakoff. 380-388.
782. Saarma, J. M. (1956) Elementary disturbances of the interaction of the signaling systems in schizophrenics. (Rus.) Tr. med. Fak. Tartu. Tallin. 86-88.
783. Saimov, K. A. (1955) The interaction of the two signaling systems in phasic conditions. (Rus.) Z. Nevropat. Psihiat. (Korsakoff.) 55, 176-181.
784. Sakharova, O. S. & A. K. Anufriev (1955) The pathophysiological mechanisms of hypochondriasis in schizophrenics. (Rus.) Psikonevrol. Konf. Probl. Schiz. Simferopol. 38-39.
785. Salter, A. (1949) Conditional reflex therapy. New York.
786. Samoilova, Z. T. (1952) The influence of pharmacological and toxicological substances on conditional reflex activity. (survey of studies of Soviet authors). (Rus.) Z. vyss. nerv. Dejat. Pavlova. 2, 258-288.

787. Sandomirsky, M. I. (1952) The clinical use of chronaximetry in psychiatric disorders. (Rus.) Z. Nevropat. Psihiat. (Korsakoff.) 52, 24-30.
788. Sandomirsky, M. I. (1955) Unconditional and conditional changes of the peripheral chronaxy in patients with infectious psychoses. (Rus.) Z. Nevropat. Psihiat. (Korsakoff.) 55, 759-764.
789. Sargant, W. & H. J. Shorvon (1947) Excitatory abreaction: With special reference to its mechanism and the use of ether. J. ment. Sci. 93, 709-732.
790. Sarró Burbano, R. & R. O. 'Shannahan Bravo (1950) Estado finales de la esquizofrénia. Cong. de Valencia. Mayo-Junio 1950.
791. Sarró Burbano, R. (1959) Desmembración de la esquizofrénia. II. Internat. Cong. Psychiat. Zurich. 310-311.
792. Savaneli, N. A. (1956) The interaction of the signaling systems in hypochondriacal syndromes. (Rus.) Tr. Sess. Armjan. Nevropat. Psihiat. Erevan. 141-146.
793. Savaneli, N. A. (1956) The characteristics of the higher nervous activity in schizophrenics with hypochondriacal syndromes. (Rus.) Tes. Dokl. 20 Ukrain. Psikonevrol. Inst. Charkow. 61-61.
794. Savaneli, N. A. (1957) Disturbances of the activity of the first and second signaling systems in schizophrenics with hypochondriacal syndromes. (Rus.) Nauch. Konf. Dejat. Sign. Sist. Norm. i Patol. 96-97.
795. Savaneli, N. A. (1957) The pathodynamics of the hypochondriacal syndromes in schizophrenia and neuroses. (Rus.) Tiflis. Diss.
796. Savaneli, N. A. (1958) The neurodynamics of hypochondriacal syndromes in psychoneuroses. (Rus.) Sb. nauch. Inst. M. Asatiani. Tiflis. 5, 247-250.
797. Savchuk, V. I. (1958) Unconditional vascular reflexes under various functional conditions of the cerebral cortex. (Rus.) Z. vyss. nerv. Dejat. Pavlova. 8, 804-813.
798. Schafer, R. (1944) A study of thought processes in a word association test. Charact. & Personal. 13, 212-227.
799. Schafer, R. (1945) Clinical evaluation of word association test. Bull. Menninger Clin. 9, 84-88.
800. Schilder, P. & E. Stengel (1931) Asymbolia for pain. Arch. Neurol. Psychiat. (Chicago.) 25, 598-600.
801. Schnabl, S. (1955) Untersuchung allgemeiner und typologischer Besonderheiten der höheren Nerventätigkeit des Menschen mit einer Komplexmethode. Leipzig. Diss.
802. Schneider, C. (1930) Die Psychologie der Schizophrenen. Leipzig.
803. Schneider, C. (1942) Die schizophrenen Symptomverbände. Berlin.
804. Schneider, F. W. (1955) Klinisch-katamnestische Untersuchungen an Schizophrenen eines Nervenlazarettes des Zweiten Weltkrieges. Schweiz. Arch. Neurol. Psychiat. 75, 227-272.
805. Schnitzler, J. G. (1909) Experimentelle Beiträge zur Tatbestandsdiagnostik. Z. angew. Psychol. 2, 51-91.
806. Scholl, K. (1909) Versuche über die Einführung von Komplexen in die Assoziation von Gesunden und Geisteskranken. Klin. psych. nerv. Krank. 3, 197-233.

807. Schrammova, H. (1956) Investigations on the formation of the new temporary associations during consciousness disorders following electric shock. (Pol.) Neurol. Neurochir. Psychiat. pol. 6, 527-533.

808. Schulte-von der Stein, C. (1955) Nachprüfung der Kleist-Leonhardschen Schizophrenieformen in den Frauenabteilungen einer Heil-und Pflegeanstalt. Arch. Psychiat. Nervenkr. 193, 303-336.

809. Schulz, B. & K. Leonard (1940) Erbbiologisch-klinische Untersuchungen an insgesamt 99 im Sinne Leonhards typischen bzw. atypischen Schizophrenien. Z. ges. Neurol. Psychiat. 168, 587-613.

810. Schunk, J. G. (1954) Aufmerksamkeit und bedingte Reaktion. Leipzig. Diss.

811. Schwab, H. (1938) Die Katatonie auf Grund katamnestischer Untersuchungen. 2 Teil. Die Erblichkeit der eigentlichen Katatonie. Z. ges. Neurol. Psychiat. 163, 441-506.

812. Schwab, H. (1942) Die paranoiden Schizophrenien auf Grund katamnestischer Untersuchungen. 2 Teil. Phantasiophrenie und progressive Konfabulose. Z. ges. Neurol. Psychiat. 173, 38-108.

813. Schwab, H. (1949) Die verworrenen Schizophrenien auf Grund katamnestischer Untersuchungen. 1 Teil. Die Schizophasien. Arch. Psychiat. Nervenkr. 182, 333-399.

814. Segal, J. E. (1949) The pathophysiological structure of the hypochondriacal syndrome. (Rus.) Probl. kort. viz. Patol. Leningrad. 229-236.

815. Segal, J. E. (1953) The neurodynamics of vascular reactions in the hallucinatory-paranoid form of schizophrenia. (Rus.) Z. Nevropat. Psihiat. (Korsakoff.) 53, 182-190.

816. Segal, J. E. (1955) The neurodynamics of vascular reactions in the hallucinatory-paranoid form of schizophrenia. (Rus.) Z. Nevropat. Psihiat. (Korsakoff.) 55, 249-258.

817. Segal, J. E. (1955) Clinical-physiological investigations of the disturbances of the interoceptors in schizophrenia. (Rus.) Tr. nauch. Konf. posv. 100 Let. S. S. Korsakoff. 317-322.

818. Segal, J. E. (1956) The pathophysiological analysis of interoceptive hallucinations in schizophrenia. (Rus.) Vopr. Psihiat. Moscow. 196-198.

819. Segal, J. E. (1956) The pathophysiological analysis of the Kandinsky syndrome in schizophrenics. (Rus.) Vopr. Psihiat. Moscow. 198-200.

820. Segal, J. E. (1956) The dynamics of vascular reactions and respiration during treatment of schizophrenics. (Rus.) Tes. Dokl. 20 Ukrain. Psikonevrol. Inst. Charkow. 55-56.

821. Segal, J. E. (1956) Pathophysiological studies of interoceptive hallucinations in schizophrenia. (Rus.) Avtoref. Dokl. issl. Psihiat. MZSSR. 62-64.

822. Segal, J. E. (1956) The dynamics of some physiological reactions during insulin coma in the treatment of schizophrenia. (Rus.) Avtoref. Dokl. issl. Psihiat. MZSSR. 61-62.

823. Segal, J. K. (1927) The elaboration of conditional reflexes and differentiation in oligophrenics. (Rus.) Nevropat. i Psihiat. 20, 535-540.

824. Semenov, S. F. (1955) The problems of the pathology of analysers in schizophrenia. (Rus.) Psikonevrol. Konf. Probl. Schiz. Simferopol. 12-13.

825. Semenova, K. A. (1957) Pathophysiological mechanisms of transcortical aphasia. (Rus.) Z. Nevropat. Psihiat. (Korsakoff.) Suppl. 57, 41-41.

826. Sem-Jacobsen, C. W., M. C. Petersen, J. A. Lazarte, H. W. Dodge & C. B. Holman (1955) Intracerebral electrographic recordings from psychotic patients during hallucinations and agitation. Amer. J. Psychiat. 112, 278-288.

827. Serebryakova, Z. N. (1954) The neurodynamics of vascular reactions in anancastic neuroses. (Rus.) Z. vyss. nerv. Dejat. Pavlova. 4, 348-354.

828. Seredina, M. I. (1941) Experimental studies of the neurodynamics of epileptic seizures in children. (Rus.) Tes. Dokl. 9 Sov. Fiziol. posv. I. P. Pavlov. 77-78.

829. Seredina, M. I. (1947) On disturbances of the higher nervous activity in hysteric neuroses. (Rus.) Ref. nauch. issl. Rab. med. biol. Nauk. SSSR. 154-155.

830. Seredina, M. I. (1947) Experimental investigations of the functions of the cerebral cortex in general paresis. (Rus.) Ref. nauch. iss. Rab. med. biol. Nauk. SSSR. 81-82.

831. Seredina, M. I. (1949) Disturbances of the neurodynamics of anancastic conditions. (Rus.) Ref. nauch. issl. Rab. med. biol. Nauk. SSSR. 142-143.

832. Seredina, M. I. (1952) The influence of epileptic seizures on the conditional reactions of the first and second signaling systems. (Rus.) Z. vyss. nerv. Dejat. Pavlova. 2, 652-667.

833. Seredina, M. I. (1953) Experimental and clinical studies of the interaction of the first and second signaling systems in delirium tremens. (Rus.) Z. vyss. nerv. Dejat. Pavlova. 3, 99-118.

834. Seredina, M. I. (1953) Disturbances of the first and second signaling systems in chronic alcoholic hallucinosis. (Rus.) Z. vyss. nerv. Dejat. Pavlova. 3, 849-864.

835. Seredina, M. I. (1955) Disturbances of the neurodynamics in anancastic neuroses. (Rus.) Tr. Inst. vyss. nerv. Dejat. Ser. Patofiziol. 1, 67-80.

836. Seredina, M. I. (1955) Disturbances of the higher nervous activity in general paresis. (Rus.) Tr. Inst. vyss. nerv. Dejat. Ser. Patofiziol. 1, 137-149.

837. Seredina, M. I. (1955) Disturbances of the first and second signaling systems in some forms of alcoholic hallucinations. (Rus.) Tr. Inst. vyss. nerv. Dejat. Ser. Patofiziol. 1, 150-169.

838. Seredina, M. I. (1955) The influence of caffein on the interaction of the first and second signaling systems in chronic alcoholic hallucinosis. (Rus.) Tr. Inst. vyss. nerv. Dejat. Ser. Patofiziol. 1, 212-229.

839. Seredina, M. I. (1955) Experiences with pathogenetically based combined treatment of anancastic neuroses. (Rus.) Tr. Inst. vyss. nerv. Dejat. Ser. Patofiziol. 1, 330-349.

840. Seredina, M. I. (1955) J. A. Povorinsky. The methods of studying motor conditional reflexes with verbal reinforcement. (Rus.) Z. Nevropat. Psihiat. (Korsakoff.) 55, 871-871.

841. Seredina, M. I. (1957) The influence of sleep treatment on the activity of the first and second signaling systems in patients with delirium tremens. (Rus.) Nauch. Konf. Dejat. Sign. Sist. Norm. i Patol. 101-102.

842. Seredina, M. I. (1957) Disturbances of the combined activity of the signaling systems in acute alcoholic hallucinosis. (Rus.) Nauch. Konf. Dejat. Sign. Sist. Norm. i Patol. 102-104.

843. Seredina, M. I. (1958) The effect of various doses of serpasil on the higher nervous activity of patients with circular depression. (Rus.) Konf. Itog. nauch. issl. Rab. 1957. Moscow. 39-40.

844. Seredina, M. I. (1958) Effect of sleep treatment on the combined activity of the first and second signaling systems in patients with delirium tremens. (Rus.) Tr. Inst. vyss. nerv. Dejat. Ser. Patofiziol. 5, 293-308.

845. Seredina, M. I. (1958) Disturbances of the combined activity of the signaling systems in acute alcoholic hallucinosis. (Rus.) Tr. Inst. vyss. nerv. Dejat. Ser. Patofiziol. 5, 141-156.

846. Sergejeva, K. A. (1953) Vascular conditional and unconditional reflexes in patients with obliterating endarteritis. (Rus.) Z. vyss. nerv. Dejat. Pavlova. 3, 865-872.

847. Servit, Z. (1955) Problems of the interaction of excitation and inhibition in the pathophysiology of epileptic seizures. (Rus.) Z. vyss. nerv. Dejat. Pavlova. 5, 474-479.

848. Shakhnovich, A. R. & V. R. Shakhnovich (1954) The study of conditional pupillary reflexes in men without previous training. (Rus.) Z. Nevropat. Psihiat. (Korsakoff.) 54, 313-316.

849. Shakow, D. (1946) The nature of deterioration in schizophrenic conditions. Nerv. Ment. Dis. Monogr. no. 70. New York.

850. Shapiro, M. B. & E. N. Nelson (1955) An investigation of the nature of cognitive impairment in co-operative psychiatric patients. Brit. J. med. Psychol. 28, 239-256.

851. Shargorodsky, L. J. (1955) Some problems concerning the investigation methods and the pathophysiology of unconditional vascular reflexes. (Rus.) Z. Nevropat. Psihiat. (Korsakoff.) 55, 430-437.

852. Shattock, F. M. (1950) The somatic manifestations of schizophrenia. J ment. Sci. 96, 32-142.

853. Shelest, E. N. (1955) The motor inhibition in schizophrenia. (Rus.) Psikonevrol. Konf. Probl. Schiz. Simferopol. 14-16.

854. Shelest, E. N. (1955) The problems of motor inhibition in schizophrenia. (Rus.) Tes. Konf. Rjazan. Inst. I. P. Pavlov. 166-169.

855. Shevaleva, E. N. (1948) An attempt at pathophysiological analysis of schizophrenic syndromes. (Rus.) Nevropat. i Psihiat. 17, 49-54.

856. Shevaleva, E. N. (1949) An attempt to study experimentally the epileptic syndrome. (Rus.) Nevropat. i Psihiat. 18, 54-57.

857. Shevchenko, J. G. (1954) Sequelae of prefrontal leucotomy in schizophrenia. (Rus.) Moscow.

858. Shipkovenski, N. S. (1958) The colored spots method in the evaluation of the characteristics of temperament. (Rus.) Z. Nevropat. Psihiat. (Korsakoff.) 58, 1326-1331.

859. Shkurko, E. D. (1954) The problems of the pathophysiological basis of involutional psychoses. (Rus.) Tes. Dokl. Inst. nauch. Konf. Leningrad. 134-136.

860. Shkurko, E. D. (1956) Problems concerning the physiological basis of in-volutional psychoses. (Rus.) Psihiat. klin. Probl. Patol. vyss. nerv. Dejat. 1, 95-103.

861. Shmidt, E. V. & N. A. Sukhovskaya (1954) The pathophysiology of sensory aphasia. (Rus.) Z. Nevropat. Psihiat. (Korsakoff.) 54, 987-995.

862. Shpak, V. M., G. V. Noshtenko, E. A. Stjerbina & R. I. Kashenbaum (1956) The mobility of the nervous processes in hallucinatory-paranoid psychoses. (Rus.) Sb. Tes. Dokl. Stalino. 177-178.

863. Shraiber, J. L. (1947) Problems of the pathodynamics of phobia. (Rus.) Ref. nauch. issl. Rab. med. biol. Nauk. SSSR. 86-86.

864. Shterbakova, N. I. (1957) The problems of the interaction of the first and second signaling systems in involutional depression. (Rus.) Nauch. Konf. Dejat. Sign. Sist. Norm. i Patol. 137-137.

865. Shumilina, A. I. (1956) Characteristics of the conditional reflex activity of dogs receiving aminazine. (Rus.) Z. Nevropat. Psihiat. (Korsakoff.) 56, 116-120.

866. Shumsky, N. G. (1958) The clinic of paraphrenic (fantastic-paranoid) schizophrenia. (Rus.) Z. Nevropat. Psihiat. (Korsakoff.) 58, 462-470.

867. Shvedskaya, A. G. (1954) Characteristics of unconditional specific immunological reactions in schizophrenia. (Rus.) Z. Nevropat. Psihiat. (Korsakoff.) 54, 741-746.

868. Sikharulidze, A. I. (1958) The influence of plasma from schizophrenic patients and the effects of aminazine on conditional and unconditional salivary reflexes and gastric secretion in dogs. (Rus.) Tes. 18 Sov. Probl. vyss. nerv. Dejat. 3, 127-128.

869. Silverstein, A. & N. S. Kline (1956) Autonomic pharmacology in schizophrenia. Review of literature and report of preliminary investigations. A.M.A. Arch. Neurol. Psychiat. 75, 389-399.

870. Sinkevich, Z. L. (1951) Disturbances in interaction of the first and second signaling systems in chronic alcoholism. (Rus.) Z. vyss. nerv. Dejat. Pavlova. 1, 608-616.

871. Sinkevich, Z. (1953) The elaboration of conditional disinhibition. (Rus.) Moscow. Diss.

872. Sinkevich, Z. L. (1955) An attempt to investigate conditional inhibition in schizophrenics. (Rus.) Tr. Inst. vyss. nerv. Dejat. Ser. Patofiziol. 1, 13-25.

873. Sinkevich, Z. L. (1955) Disturbances of the interaction of the first and second signaling systems in chronic alcoholism. (Rus.) Tr. Inst. vyss. nerv. Dejat. Ser. Patofiziol. 1, 182-189.

874. Sinkevich, Z. L. (1957) Some characteristics of the changes in elective relations between direct and verbal stimuli in patients with chronic alcoholism. (Rus.) Nauch. Konf. Dejat. Sign. Sist. Norm. i Patol. 104-105.

875. Sinkevich, Z. L. (1957) The influence of different doses of alcohol on the interaction of the signaling systems. (Rus.) Nauch. Konf. Dejat. Sign. Sist. Norm. i Patol. 107-108.

876. Sinkevich, Z. L. (1958) New observations on the characteristics of severe alcoholism. (Rus.) Konf. Itog. nauch. issl. Rab. 1957. Moscow. 40-42.

877. Slezkova, V. A. (1957) The problems of "subclinical seizures" in severe epilepsy. (Rus.) Z. Nevropat. Psihiat. (Korsakoff.) 57, 876-880.
878. Sluchevsky, I. F. (1956) The theory of "sore points" and its significance for psychiatry. (Rus.) Psihiat. klin. Probl. Patol. vyss. nerv. Dejat. 1, 9-20.
879. Sluchevsky, I. F. (1956) Abnormal ideas in terms of theories of the higher nervous activity. (Rus.) Psihiat. klin. Probl. Patol. vyss. nerv. Dejat. 1, 21-31.
880. Smetannikov, P. G. (1954) The problems of the pathophysiological basis of the syndrome of amentia. (Rus.) Tes. Dokl. Inst. nauch. Konf. Leningrad. 109-112.
881. Smetannikov, P. G. (1954) The influence of caffein on the higher nervous activity of patients with syndromes of amentia in infections and intoxications. (Rus.) Tes. Dokl. Inst. nauch. Konf. Leningrad. 113-115.
882. Smetannikov, P. G. (1956) Problems concerning the pathophysiological basis of syndromes of amentia. (Rus.) Psihiat. klin. Probl. Patol. vyss. nerv. Dejat. 1, 121-131.
883. Smetannikov, P. G. (1957) On the influence of caffein on the higher nervous activity of patients with syndromes of amentia after infections and intoxications. (Rus.) Z. Nevropat. Psihiat. (Korsakoff.) Suppl. 57, 59-59.
884. Smetannikov, P. G. (1958) Disturbances of interaction of the signaling systems in involutional depression and the depressive stage of manic-depressive psychosis. (Rus.) Konf. Vopr. Patofiziol. vyss. nerv. Dejat. Moscow. 119-121.
885. Smetannikov, P. G. (1958) Comparative characteristics of the cortical dynamics and autonomic functions in various diseases with depressive syndromes. (Rus.) Konf. Itog. nauch. issl. Rab. 1957. Moscow. 42-43.
886. Smetannikov, P. G. (1958) Disturbances of the higher nervous activity with special regard to the interactions of cortex and subcortex in involutional depression. (Rus.) Tes. 18 Sov. Probl. vyss. nerv. Dejat. 3, 131-132.
887. Smirnov, D. A. (1953) The word experiment in medical practice. (Rus.) Z. vyss. nerv. Dejat. Pavlova. 3, 408-415.
888. Smyshljajev, E. B. (1958) Some characteristics of the pathophysiology of the higher nervous activity in demented epileptics. (Rus.) Konf. Vopr. Patofiziol. vyss. nerv. Dejat. Moscow. 121-123.
889. Smyshljajev, E. B. (1958) The pathophysiology of the brain in demented epileptics. (Rus.) Tes. 18 Sov. Probl. vyss. nerv. Dejat. 3, 133-135.
890. Snjakin, P. G. (1952) The visual analyser in hypertensive disease. (Rus.) Z. Nevropat. Psihiat. (Korsakoff.) 52, 22-27.
891. Sokolova, G. S. (1958) Conditional traced eyelid reflexes in neurotics with depressive syndromes. (Rus.) Tes. 18 Sov. Probl. vyss. nerv. Dejat. 3, 136-137.
892. Sokolova, G. S. (1958) Traced conditional eyelid reflexes in healthy persons and neurotic patients. (Rus.) Tr. Inst. Fiziol Im. I. P. Pavlov. 7, 239-249.

893. Sologub, N. M. (1958) Studies of the higher nervous activity in patients with traumatic epilepsy. (Rus.) Tes. 18 Sov. Probl. vyss. nerv. Dejat. 3, 138-139.

894. Sokolov, E. N. & N. P. Paramonova (1956) On the role of orientative reflexes in establishing motor conditional reactions in man. (Rus.) Z. vyss. nerv. Dejat. Pavlova. 6, 702-709.

895. Sokolov, E. N. (1958) Perception and conditional reflexes. (Rus.) Moscow.

896. Solokov, I. P. (1953) Pathophysiological and typological interpretation of psychasthenia and anancastic phenomena. (Rus.) Riga. Diss.

897. Sólyom, L. & E. Varga (1957) Neue experimentelle Angaben zur Pathophysiologie der Schizophrenie und der Psychasthenie. Psychiat. Neurol. med. Psychol. (Lpz.) 9, 73,78.

898. Sommer, R. (1899) Lehrbuch der psychopathologischen Untersuchungsmethoden. Berlin & Wien.

899. Sommer, R. (1901) Diagnostik der Geisteskrankheiten. Berlin & Wien.

900. Sosjura, B. J. & S. B. Aksentiev (1953) Vascular reflexes in regional hypotension. (Rus.) Z. Nevropat. Psihiat. (Korsakoff.) 53, 951-956.

901. Sosjura, B. J. & S. B. Aksentiev (1957) Vascular reflexes in regional cerebral hypotension. (Rus.) Z. Nevropat. Psihiat. (Korsakoff.) 57, Suppl. 8-8.

902. Spence, K. W. & J. Taylor (1951) Anxiety and strength of the U.C.S. as determiners of the amount of eyelid conditioning. J. exp. Psychol. 42, 183-188.

903. Spence, K. W. & J. Taylor (1953) The relation of conditional response strength to anxiety in normal, neurotic, and psychotic subjects. J. exp. Psychol. 45, 265-272.

904. Spence, K. W. (1956) Behavior theory and conditioning. New Haven & London.

905. Spirkin, A. G. & E. P. Brunowt (1953) Die Lehre I. P. Pawlows von den Signalsystemen. Berlin.

906. Spivak, L. I. (1953) Patellar reflex changes in depressive and hypomanic states. (Rus.) Z. Nevropat. Psihiat. (Korsakoff.) 53, 422-428.

907. Stanishevskaya, N. N. (1954) Clinical and pathophysiological studies of schizophrenics treated with tissue, sleep and insulin. (Rus.) Z. vyss. nerv. Dejat. Pavlova. 4, 184-193.

908. Stanishevskaya, N. N. (1955) Plethysmographic studies of patients with catatonic schizophrenia. (Rus.) Tr. nauch. Konf. posv. 100 Let. S. S. Korsakoff. 363-376.

909. Stanishevskaya, N. N. (1956) Studies of the vascular reactions of patients with hallucinatory-paranoid schizophrenia during complex treatment. (Rus.) Vopr. Psihiat. Moscow. 205-206.

910. Stanishevskaya, N. N. (1956) Plethysmographic and pneumographic studies of schizophrenic patients with catatonic symptoms. (Rus.) Vopr. Psihiat. Moscow. 207-208.

911. Stanishevskaya, N. N. (1956) Studies of conditional and unconditional reflexes in schizophrenics during sleep treatment. (Rus.) Avtoref. Dokl. issl. Psihiat. MZSSR. 75-77.

912. Stanishevskaya, N. N. (1957) Plethysmographic and pneumographic studies during sleep treatment of patients with hallucinatory-paranoid forms of schizophrenia. (Rus.) Z. Nevropat. Psihiat. (Korsakoff.) 57, Suppl. 68-69.

913. Stanishevskaya, N. N. (1957) Some peculiarities of the vascular, motor and respiratory components of reflex activity in patients suffering from schizophrenia. (Rus.) Z. vyss. nerv. Dejat. Pavlova. 7, 683-688.

914. Staritsin, A. S. (1958) Some data with kinestiometric and plethysmographic investigations of schizophrenics. (Rus.) Probl. Patol. Kinestes. nerv. psik. Zabol. Simferopol. 100-107.

915. Stashtuk, M. D. (1958) The immunological reactivity in schizophrenics. (Rus.) Tr. Chernovits. Obl. 27-33.

916. Stchastny, A. I. (1939) Modifications of the vegetative nervous activity in syndromes of protective inhibition in schizophrenics. (Rus.) Tes. Dokl. 5 Sov. Fiziol. posv. I. P. Pavlov. 78-78.

917. Stengel, E. & G. Fitzgerald (1945) Vestibular reactivity to caloric stimulation in schizophrenics. J. ment. Sci. 91, 93-100.

918. Stengel, E., A. J. Oldham & A. S. C. Ehrenberg (1955) Reactions to pain in various abnormal mental states. J. ment. Sci. 101, 52-69.

919. Stjerbina, E. A. (1957) The characteristics of remission and cure in schizophrenia. (Rus.) Z. Nevropat. Psihiat. (Korsakoff.) Suppl. 57, 69-70.

920. Stocker, A. (1953) La névrose considéré comme un réflexe conditionnel "sui generis". Encéphale. 42, 455-474.

921. Strelchuk, I. V. (1949) Disturbances of the neurodynamics in chronic alcoholics. (Rus.) Ref. nauch. issl. Rab. med. biol. Nauk. SSSR. 137-139

922. Strelchuk, I. V. (1951) Experiences with prolonged sleep in morphine addicts and its effect on the higher nervous activity. (Rus.) Z. vyss. nerv. Dejat. Pavlova. 1, 383-391.

923. Strelchuk, I. V. (1953) Experiences with hypnotherapy on the basis of the Pavlovian theories of the first and second signaling systems. (Rus.) Z. vyss. nerv. Dejat. Pavlova. 3, 353-368.

924. Strelchuk, I. V. (1955) An attempt to study the cortical dynamics of hypnosis and its therapeutic effect, on the basis of the Pavlovian theories of the first and second signaling systems. (Rus.) Tr. Inst. vyss. nerv. Dejat. Ser. Patofiziol. 1, 298-313.

925. Strelchuk, I. V. & Z. L. Sinkevich (1955) Disturbances of the cortical dynamics in chronic alcoholism. (Rus.) Tr. Inst. vyss. nerv. Dejat. Ser. Patofiziol 1, 170-181

926. Strelchuk, I. V. (1956) The clinic and treatment of drug addiction. (Rus.) Moscow.

927. Strelchuk, I. V. (1957) An attempt to study the influence of psychotherapy on the interaction of the first and second signaling systems. (Rus.) Nauch. Konf. Dejat. Sign. Sist. Norm. i Patol. 111-112.

928. Strelchuk, I. V. (1958) The disturbances of the neurodynamics in epileptic patients and the nervous mechanisms of therapeutic action. (Rus.) Konf. Itog. nauch. issl. Rab. 1957. Moscow. 43-45.

929. Strelchuk, I. V. (1958) Disturbances of the neurodynamics in hypertensive disease with neuropsychiatric symptoms, and a pathogentically based therapy. (Rus.) Tr. Inst. vyss. nerv. Dejat. Ser. Patofiziol. 5, 309-325.

930. Strelchuk, I. V. (1958) Studies of the nervous mechanisms of psychotherapeutic influence in neuroses. (Rus.) Tr. Inst. vyss. nerv. Dejat. Ser. Patofiziol. 5, 326-342.

931. Streljukhin, A. K. & N. I. Shterbakova (1957) The problems of the interaction of the signaling systems in manic-depressive psychosis. (Rus.) Nauch. Konf. Dejat. Sign. Sist. Norm. i Patol. 111-111.

932. Streltsova, N. I. (1954) The characteristics of some unconditional reflexes in schizophrenics. (Rus.) Charkow. Diss.

933. Streltsova, N. I. (1955) Characteristics of some unconditional reflexes in schizophrenic patients. (Rus.) Tr. nauch. Konf. posv. 100 Let. S. S. Korsakoff. 329-333.

934. Stroikova, K. V. (1959) The localization of the effect of aminazine in schizophrenic patients. (Rus.) Z. Nevropat. Psihiat. (Korsakoff.) 59, 402-409.

935. Strong, E. K. (1913) A comparison between experimental data and clinical results in manic-depressive insanity. Amer. J. Psychol. 24, 66-98.

936. Stürup, G. K. (1940) Visceral pain. Plethysmographic "pain-reactions". London & Copenhagen.

937. Sukharebsky, L. M. (1956) The diagnostic significance of psychogalvanic reactions in schizophrenic patients. (Rus.) Tes. Dokl. Sess. Inst. M. Asatiani. Tiflis. 54-56.

938. Sukharebsky, L. M. (1956) Psychogalvanic reactions during hallucinatory-paranoid emotions in schizophrenic patients. (Rus.) Avtoref. Dokl. issl. Psihiat. MZSSR. 80-81.

939. Sukharebsky, L. M. (1958) The diagnostic significance of psychogalvanic reflexes in schizophrenic patients. (Rus.) Sb. nauch. Inst. M. Asatiani. Tiflis. 251-255.

940. Surat, V. S. (1956) The effects of the functional state of the brain cortex on the motor aphasia syndrome. (Rus.) Z. vyss. nerv. Dejat. Pavlova. 6, 242-250.

941. Suslova, M. M. (1952) Studies of the cerebral activity in the somnambulic stage of hypnosis. (Rus.) Tr. Inst. Fiziol. Im. I. P. Pavlov. 1, 296-315.

942. Symonds, P. M. (1931) Diagnosing personality and conduct. New York.

943. Tadzhibaeva, M. M. (1956) Association experiments in chronic alcoholics before and after hypnosis. (Rus.) Sb. Rab. Vopr. Nevropat. Psihiat. Stalinabad. 131-138

944. Taranskaya, A. D. (1955) The influence of some pharmacological drugs on hallucinations in schizophrenia. (Rus.) Tr. nauch. Konf. posv. 100 Let. S. S. Korsakoff. 349-352.

945. Taranskaya, A. D. (1956) Effect of atropine and pilokarpine on the conditional reflexes in mentally deranged patients. (Rus.) Z. vyss. nerv. Dejat. Pavlova. 6, 100-107.

946. Tatarenko, N. P. (1928) Reflex mechanisms in schizophrenics. (Rus.) Vracheb. Delo. 3, 217-221.

947. Tatarenko, N. P. (1934) Disorders of the conditional reflex activity in patients with senile psychosis. (Rus.) Sovetsk. Psikonevrol. 1, 85-87.

948. Tatarenko, N. P. (1937) Problems of motor regulation in schizophrenia. (Rus.) Tr. tsent. psikonevrol. Inst. 8, 182-189.
949. Tatarenko, N. P. (1947) The pathophysiological foundation of schizophrenic states. (Rus.) Tr. 14 Sess. Ukrain. psikonevrol. Inst. 366-374.
950. Tatarenko, N. P. (1951) The psychopathology of syndromes resulting from inert excitation in the cerebral cortex. (Rus.) Z. vyss. nerv. Dejat. Pavlova. 1, 603-607.
951. Tatarenko, N. P. (1954) The pathophysiology of schizophrenia. (Rus.) Z. Nevropat. Psihiat. (Korsakoff.) 54, 710-714.
952. Tatarenko, N. P. (1954) The pupillary components of the orienting reaction and the aspects of its clinical use. (Rus.) Z. Nevropat. Psihiat. (Korsakoff.) 54, 153-157.
953. Tatarenko, N. P. (1955) Some controversial problems in the theories of schizophrenia. (Rus.) Z. Nevropat. Psihiat. (Korsakoff.) 55, 837-842.
954. Tatarenko, N. P. (1956) The significance of studying the orienting reflex in the psychiatric clinic. (Rus.) Z. vyss. nerv. Dejat. Pavlova. 6, 360-364.
955. Tatarenko, N. P. (1956) The pathophysiology of paranoia. (Rus.) Tes. Konf. Ukrain. psikonevrol. Inst. 45-46.
956. Tatarenko, N. P. (1957) The clinic and pathophysiology of hypochondriacal conditions. (Rus.) Aktual. Probl. Nevropat. Psihiat. Kuibyshev. 188-196.
957. Tatarenko, N. P. (1958) Principles and methods of evaluating the effects of treatment in schizophrenia. (Rus.) Z. Nevropat. Psihiat. (Korsakoff.) 58, 722-727.
958. Tendler, A. D. (1933) Associative tendencies in psychoneurotics. Psychol. Clin. 22, 108-116.
959. Tendler, A. D. (1945) Significant features of disturbance in free association. J. Psychol. 20, 65-89.
960. Tepina, M. M. (1956) Temperature reactions in schizophrenic patients. (Rus.) Psihiat. klin. Probl. Patol. vyss. nerv. Dejat. 1, 179-187.
961. Thenon, J. (1955) La esquizofrénia y el estado hipnoide. Acta neuropsiquiát. argent. 1, 369-379.
962. Thumb, A. & K. Marbe (1901) Experimentelle Untersuchungen über die psychologischen Grundlagen der sprachlichen Anlalogiebildung. Leipzig.
963. Tiganov, A. S., L. I. Golubykh, V. M. Kamenskaya & L. I. Lando (1958) Experiences with meratran and frenquel in patients with paranoid schizophrenia. (Rus.) Z. Nevropat. Psihiat. (Korsakoff.) 58, 600-615.
964. Timofejeva, A. I. (1953) The association experiment as a method for the study of the cortical dynamics in schizophrenics. (Rus.) Tes. 20 nauch. Sess. Saratov. med. 53-54.
965. Timofejeva, A. N. (1954) The problems of the pathophysiological basis of the manic-depressive psychosis. (Rus.) Tes. Dokl. Inst. nauch. Konf. Leningrad. 119-122.
966. Timofejeva, A. N. (1955) Hypnoid phases and some other disturbances of the higher nervous activity in manic-depressive psychosis. (Rus.) Eksp. issl. psihiat. nevrol. Klin. Leningrad.
967. Timofejeva, A. N. (1956) Problems concerning the pathophysiological basis of manic-depressive psychosis. (Rus.) Psihiat. klin. Probl. Patol. vyss. nerv. Dejat. 1, 152-159.

968. Timofejeva, A. N. (1956) Clinical experimental studies of thinking in manic patients. (Rus.) Psihiat. klin. Probl. Patol. vyss. nerv. Dejat. 1, 160-165.

969. Timofejeva, A. N. (1957) The dynamics of unconditional vascular reflexes in the manic and depressive phases of the manic-depressive psychosis (Rus.) Psihiat. klin. Probl. Patol. vyss. nerv. Dejat. 2, 198-207.

970. Tirkeltaub, J. A. (1958) Pathophysiological characteristics of the higher nervous activity in patients with pseudoneurotic schizophrenia treated with aminazine. (Rus.) Konf. Vopr. Patofiziol. vyss. nerv. Dejat. Moscow. 129-130.

971. Tonkonogy, I. M. (1955) About the disturbances of the higher nervous activity in motor aphasia. (Rus.) Z. vyss. nerv. Dejat. Pavlova. 5, 783-792.

972. Torchinskaya, V. A. (1954) Problems of the pathophysiology of manic-depressive psychosis. (Rus.) Z. Nevropat. Psihiat. (Korsakoff.) 54, 934-940.

973. Traugott, N. N. & A. S. Chistovich (1952) Problems concerning the higher nervous activity in chronic delusional states (paraphrenia). Tr. Inst. Fiziol. Im. I. P. Pavlov. 1, 413-424.

974. Traugott, N. N. (1952) The investigative methods of the interaction of the signaling systems in the psychiatric clinic. (Rus.) Z. Nevropat. Psihiat. (Korsakoff.) 52, 3-12.

975. Traugott, N. N., L. J. Balonov & A. E. Lichko (1953) The pathophysiological analysis of stuporous conditions in infectious psychoses. (Rus.) Tes. 16 Sov. Probl. vyss. nerv. Dejat. 215-216.

976. Traugott, N. N. (1954) Über den Einfluss der aktiven Therapie auf die Sprachreaktionen der Schizophrenen im Wortexperiment. Psychiat. Neurol. med. Psychol. (Lpz.) 6, 211-220.

977. Traugott, N. N. & A. S. Chistovich (1954) Probe eines physiologischen Verständnisses der Sprachverworrenheit bei der Schizophrenie. Psychiat. Neurol. med. Psychol. (Lpz.) 6, 153-156.

978. Traugott, N. N. (1954) The interactions of the signaling systems in some acute disturbances of cerebral functioning. (Rus.) Leningrad. Diss.

979. Traugott, N. N. & L. J. Balonov (1955) Characteristics of the higher nervous activity in longstanding infectious psychoses with schizophrenic symptomatology. (Rus.) Tr. nauch. Konf. posv. 100 Let. S. S. Korsakoff. 325-329.

980. Traugott, N. N. (1956) Two types of motor excitation in confusional states of infectious psychoses. (Rus.) Tr. voj. mor. med. Akad. Leningrad. 141-154.

981. Traugott, N. N. (1956) The pathophysiological analysis of disturbances of orientation in amnestic syndromes. (Rus.) Nauch. Sess. vozrast. Fiziol. Chel. Moscow & Leningrad. 31-31.

982. Traugott, N. N. (1956) The physiological analysis of schizophrenic symptoms. (Rus.) Tes. 17 Sov. Probl. vyss. nerv. Dejat. 122-123.

983. Traugott, N. N., L. J. Balonov, D. A. Kaufman & A. E. Lichko (1957) Zu einigen Fragen des Studiums der höheren Nerventätigkeit bei Psychosen. Psychiat. Neurol. med. Psychol. (Lpz.) 9, 325-332.

984. Traugott, N. N. (1957) The disturbances of the interactions of the signaling systems. (Rus.) Moscow & Leningrad.
985. Traugott, N. N., L. J. Balonov & A. E. Lichko (1957) The physiology of the higher nervous activity in man. (Rus.) Moscow.
986. Traugott, N. N. & L. J. Balonov (1957) The pathophysiology of some syndromes developing after ingestion of aminazine. (Rus.) 3 nauch. Sov. vozrast. Fiziol. Patol. Leningrad. 76-78.
987. Traugott, N. N. & L. J. Balonov (1958) Characteristics of "sore points" in depressive conditions. (Rus.) Konf. Vopr. Patofiziol. vyss. nerv. Dejat. Moscow. 131-133.
988. Traugott, N. N. (1958) Symposium on further ways of studying the pathology of the higher nervous activity in man. (Rus.) Tes. 18 Sov. Probl. vyss. nerv. Dejat. 1, 135-136.
989. Traugott, N. N. & L. J. Balonov (1958) Neurophysiological analysis of clinical states after aminazine injections. (Rus.) Z. Nevropat. Psihiat. (Korsakoff.) 58, 585-591.
990. Traugott, N. N. (1958) The evolutional physiological study of disturbances of the higher nervous activity in psychiatric diseases. (Rus.) Sb. posv. 75 Let. L. A. Orbeli. 206-221.
991. Traugott, N. N., L. J. Balonov & A. E. Lichko (1958) The problems of "sore points" in the pathology of the higher nervous activity in man. (Rus.) Material. evolut. Fiziol. Leningrad. 3, 166-191.
992. Traugott, N. N. (1959) The evolutional physiological approach in the study of speech functions. (Rus.) 2 nauch. Sov. evolut. Fiziol. Leningrad. 163-164.
993. Trautscholdt, M. (1882) Experimentelle Untersuchungen über die Association der Vorstellungen. Lepzig. Diss.
994. Travinskaya, M. A. (1957) The problems of disturbances of the first and second signaling systems in alcoholism. (Rus.) Nauch. Konf. Dejat. Sign. Sist. Norm. i Patol. 118-120.
995. Travinskaya, M. A. (1957) The dynamics of the disturbances of the conditional reflex activity of the signaling systems during treatment of alcoholics with antabus. (Rus.) Nauch. Konf. Dejat. Sign. Sist. Norm. i Patol. 120-121.
996. Travinskaya, M. A. (1957) Disturbances of interaction of the signaling systems in alcoholics with various degree of dementia. (Rus.) Sb. nauch. Tr. Rjazan. 3, 58-71.
997. Trofimov, N. M. (1953) The types of disturbances of the conditional reflex activity in various stages of oligophrenia. (Rus.) Tes. 16 Sov. Probl. vyss. nerv. Dejat. 217-218.
998. Trofimov, N. M. (1953) A complex investigation of the higher nervous activity in different stages of oligophrenia. (Rus.) Leningrad. Diss.
999. Trofimov, N. M. (1954) Some forms of pathological disturbances in the interaction of the signaling systems. (Rus.) Konf. po Itog. Rab. 1953. IEM. Leningrad. 23-24.
1000. Trofimov, N. M. (1955) Characteristics of the conditional reflex activity in different stages of mental deficiency. (Rus.) Z. vyss, nerv. Dejat. Pavlova. 5, 358-362,

1001. Trofimov, N. M. (1955)   The mechanisms of induced interrelations of the signaling systems. (Rus.) Z. vyss. nerv. Dejat. Pavlova. 5, 816-824.

1002. Trofimov, N. M. (1958)   The problems of the functional development of the higher nervous activity in oligophrenia. (Rus.) Konf. Vopr. Patofiziol. vyss. nerv. Dejat. Moscow. 133-133.

1003. Trunova, M. M. (1954)   Disturbances of the neurodynamics and especially the interaction of the first and second signaling systems in anancastic conditions. (Rus.) Moscow. Diss.

1004. Trunova, M. M. (1955)   Some characteristics of the interaction of the first and second signaling systems in anancastic neuroses. (Rus.) Tr. Inst. vyss. nerv. Dejat. Ser. Patofiziol. 1, 81-96.

1005. Trunova, M. M. (1957)   The influence of insulin on the higher nervous activity of schizophrenics. (Rus.) Nauch. konf. Dejat. Sign. Sist. Norm. i Patol. 126-127.

1006. Trunova, M. M. (1957)   Some characteristics of the interaction of the signaling systems in anancastic neuroses and psychasthenia. (Rus.) Nauch. Konf. Dejat. Sign. Sist. Norm. i Patol. 124-125.

1007. Trunova, M. M. (1958)   Changes of the pathodynamic structures during insulin hypoglycemia in patients with paranoid schizophrenia. (Rus.) Konf. Vopr. Patofiziol. vyss. nerv. Dejat. Moscow. 134-135.

1008. Trunova, M. M. (1958)   Some characteristics of the higher nervous activity in patients with general paresis. Konf. Itog. nauch. issl. Rab. 1957. Moscow. 45-46.

1009. Trunova, M. M. (1958)   Disturbances of the combined activity of the signaling systems in anancastic neuroses and psychasthenia. (Rus.) Tr. inst. vyss. nerv. Dejat. Ser. Patofiziol. 5, 177-195.

1010. Tscholakow, K. (1955)   Zur pathophysiologischen Analyse einiger Frühsymptome der Schizophrenie. Psychiat. Neurol. med. Psychol. (Lpz.) 7, 97-101.

1011. Tsukrovich-Zakshevskaya, F. A. (1952)   The dynamics of conditional and unconditional vascular reflexes in infectious psychoses. (Rus.) Leningrad. Diss.

1012. Tulubjeva, L. D. (1953)   The disturbances of the interaction of the signaling systems in schizophrenic defects. (Rus.) 2 nauch. Konf. KGMI Kishinev. 59-60.

1013. Turgijev, S. B. (1958)   The pathophysiology of some symptoms in alcoholic delirium. (Rus.) Konf. Vopr. Patofiziol. vyss. nerv. Dejat. Moscow. 135-136.

1014. Turova, Z. G. (1954)   Some disturbances of the interaction of the first and second signaling systems in the puerile syndrome. (Rus.) Z. vyss. nerv. Dejat. Pavlova. 4, 324-338.

1015. Tushinskaya, M. M. (1956)   Study of higher nervous activity in patients affected with neuroses of the neurasthenia type. (Rus.) Z. vyss. nerv. Dejat. Pavlova. 6, 108-112.

1016. Udaltsova, M. S. (1956)   Ultraparadoxical phases as the basis of various schizophrenic symptoms. (Rus.) Psihiat. klin. Probl. Patol. vyss. nerv. Dejat. 1, 104-120.

1017. Ugol. N. B. (1957)   An attempt at a pathophysiological analysis of senile dementia. (Rus.) Vopr. Psihiat. Nevropat. Leningrad. 15-26.

1018. Ukhtomsky, A. A. (1950) The theory of dominants. (Rus.) Leningrad.
1019. Umarov, M. B. (1953) Anancastic neuroses and psychasthenia. (Rus.) Leningrad. Diss.
1020. Unger, L. P. (1954) The significance of the types of higher nervous activity and exogenous factors for the course of schizophrenia. (Rus.) Tr. Kuibyshev. med. Inst. 66-72.
1021. Usievich, M. A., E. J. Shternberg & N. N. Stanishevskaya (1958) Clinical and pathophysiological characteristics of the higher nervous activity in schizophrenics with hypochondriacal syndromes. (Rus.) Tes. 18 Sov. Probl. vyss. nerv. Dejat. 3, 161-161.
1022. Usievich, M. A. & V. I. Redjanov (1958) Pathophysiological analysis of of the role of occupational therapy in some schizophrenic cases with asthenia and catatonia. (Rus.) Konf. Vopr. Patofiziol. vyss. nerv. Dejat. Moscow. 138-139.
1023. Usov, A. G. (1953) The characteristics of the excitatory processes in normal and pathological aging. (Rus.) Tes. 16 Sov. Probl. vyss. nerv. Dejat. 223-224.
1024. Usov, A. G. (1954) Simultaneous activity of the signaling systems in normal aging. (Rus.) 3 nauch. Konf. nauch. Rab. Leningrad. 61-62.
1025. Usov, A. G. (1955) A complex method for the study of the higher nervous activity in the normal and in the mentally sick. (Rus.) Z. vyss. nerv. Dejat. Pavlova. 5, 825-831.
1026. Usov, A. G. (1955) Experimental data on problems of the oxygen effect on the higher nervous activity of old persons. (Rus.) Z. vyss. nerv. Dejat. Pavlova. 5, 351-357.
1027. Usov, A. G. (1955) Studies of the induced interrelations of the signaling systems in healthy old persons and in patients with senile psychoses. (Rus.) Z. vyss. nerv. Dejat. Pavlova. 5, 807-815.
1028. Usov, A. G. (1956) Experimental data on the mechanism of delirium formation in senile psychoses. (Rus.) Z. vyss. nerv. Dejat. Pavlova. 6, 93-99.
1029. Usov, A. G. (1957) Changes of the functions of the signaling systems in complex reactions in normal and pathological aging. (Rus.) Nauch. Konf. Dejat. Sign. Sist. Norm. i Patol. 127-128.
1030. Usov, A. G. (1957) The problems of functional interaction between motor and autonomic centres in old persons. (Rus.) 3 nauch. Sov. vozrast. Fiziol. Patol. Leningrad. 80-81.
1031. Usov, A. G. (1958) Characteristics of the interaction of the motor, alimentary and defensive eyelid reflexes in persons of old age. (Rus.) Konf. Vopr. Patofiziol. vyss. nerv. Dejat. Moscow. 139-140.
1032. Varga, E. & L. Solyóm (1957) Die Anwendung der bedingten Lidreflexmethode an Hand neurophychiatrischen Krankenmaterials. Psychiat. Neurol. med. Psychol. (Lpz.) 9, 68-73.
1033. Vertogradova, O. P. (1955) Vascular conditional and unconditional reflexes in schizophrenia. (Rus.) Tr. nauch. Konf. posv. 100 Let. S. S. Korsakoff. 317-322.
1034. Veshapeli, N. G. (1957) Some clinical and neurodynamical data on severe forms of oligophrenia. (Rus.) Nauch. Konf. Dejat. Sign. Sist. Norm. i Patol. 18-19.

1035. Vikker, J. L. (1959) Prognosis based on pathophysiology in psychiatric diseases. (Rus.) Z. Nevropat. Psihiat. (Korsakoff.) 59, 78-82.

1036. Viktorov, I. T. (1957) Problems of the differential diagnosis of epilepsy in children and the plethysmographic method. (Rus.) Z. Nevropat. Psihiat. (Korsakoff.) 57, 889-896.

1037. Vinogradov, N. V. (1934) The paradoxical phase in catatonics. (Rus.) Ark. biol. Nauk. Ser. B. 36, 345-350.

1038. Vinogradov, N. V., V. P. Golovina, F. P. Maiorov & I. O. Narbutovich (1934) Observations on the natural sleep of catatonic schizophrenics. (Rus.) Ark. biol. Nauk. Ser. B. 36, 165-181.

1039. Vinogradov, N. V. (1936) The effect of an epileptic seizure on the higher nervous activity. (Rus.) Bjul. VIEM. no 3-4. 111-111.

1040. Vinogradov, N. V. & L. A. Reiser (1953) An attempt to analyse experimentally the interaction of the first and second signaling systems in schizophrenia in connection with the clinical course of the disease. (Rus.) Z. vyss. nerv. Dejat. Pavlova. 3, 77-91.

1041. Vinogradov, N. V. (1956) Study of changes of the internal inhibition in schizophrenics in connection with the clinical course of the disease. (Rus.) Z. vyss. nerv. Dejat. Pavlova. 6, 801-811.

1042. Vobin, R. J. (1959) The effect of ataraxic drugs on some types of delusions and the concomitant neurophysiological disturbances. (Rus.) Vopr. Psikonevrol. Leningrad. 105-107.

1043. Vogt, R. (1902) Plethysmographische Untersuchungen bei Geisteskranken. Centralbl. f. Nervenheilk. 25, 665-681.

1044. Volfovsky, O. I. (1955) Some characteristics of the higher nervous activity in chronic schizophrenics. (Rus.) Psikonevrol. Konf. Probl. Schiz. Simferopol. 48-49.

1045. Völgyesi, F. A. (1955) Entwicklung der Hypnose-Psychotherapie gemäss den Entdeckungen J. Braids und der Lehre I. P. Pawlows. Psychiat. Neurol. med. Psychol. (Lpz.) 7, 129-145.

1046. Volpert, I. E. (1958) The problems of the physiological basis of psychotherapy. (Rus.) Tr. Inst. Fiziol. Im. I. P. Pavlov. 7, 58-62.

1047. Vrono, M. S. (1957) Characteristics of the terminal phase of schizophrenia with speech incoherence. (Rus.) Z. Nevropat. Psihiat. (Korsakoff.) 57, 565-572.

1048. Walitzky, M. (1889) Contribution a l'étude des mensurations psychométriques chez les aliénés. Rev. Philos. 28, 583-595.

1049. Warren, H. C. (1921) A history of the association psychology. London.

1050. Wehrlin, K. (1918) The associations of imbeciles and idiots. In. Jung, C. G. (edit.) Studies in word-association. London.

1051. Welch, L., O. Diethelm & L. Long (1946) Measurement of hyper-associative activity during elation. J. Psychol. 21, 113-126.

1052. Wells, F. L. (1919) Autistic mechanisms in association reaction. Psychol. Rev. 26, 376-382.

1053. Wells, H. K. (1956) Pavlov and Freund: I. Ivan P. Pavlov. New York.

1054. Wendt, H. (1955) Dauerschlafbehandlung und Psychotherapie. Arb. tag. Kortiko. viz. Regulat. Berlin. 231-241.

1055. Wendt, H. (1956) Schlaftherapie und zweites Signalsystem. Z. psychosom. Med. 2, 215-219,

1056. Whipple, G. M. (1921) Manual of mental and physical tests. 3rd. ed. Baltimore.
1057. Wimmer, A. (1909) Über Assoziationsuntersuchungen, besonders schwachsinniger Kinder. Mschr. Phychiat. Neurol. 25, 169-182 & 268-284.
1058. Woodworth, R. S. (1937) Experimental psychology. New York.
1059. Wortis, J. (1950) Soviet psychiatry. Baltimore.
1060. Wreschner, A. (1900) Eine experimentelle Studie über die Association in einem Falle von Idiotie. Allg. Z. Psychiat. 57, 241-339.
1061. Wreschner, A. (1909) Die Reproduktion und Assoziation von Vorstellungen. Z. Psychol. Physiol. d. Sinnes. Ergbd. 3.
1062. Yakovleva, E. A. (1939) Motor chronaxy in paranoid and catatonic forms of schizophrenia. (Rus.) Ark. biol. Nauk. 55, 9-16.
1063. Yakovleva, E. A. (1940) Modifications of chronaxy in schizophrenics caused by prolonged sleep. (Rus.) Tr. Psihiat. Klin. I. P. Pavlov. 2, 149-157.
1064. Yakovleva, E. A. (1940) Some central-peripheral changes of the nervous system in schizophrenic and depressive states. (Rus.) Bjul. eksp. Biol. Med. 10, 376-379.
1065. Yakovleva, E. A. (1953) Intersignal interactions of the cerebral cortex. (Rus.) Moscow.
1066. Yakovleva, E. A. (1957) The problem of experimental neuroses. (Rus.) Z. vyss. nerv. Dejat. Pavlova. 7, 841-854.
1067. Yakovleva, E. K. (1952) Characteristics of the electrical activity of the cerebral cortex in anancastic neuroses. (Rus.) Z. Nevropat. Psihiat. (Korsakoff.) 52, 20-23.
1068. Yakovleva, E. K. (1958) The pathogenesis and treatment of anancastic neuroses and psychasthenia. (Rus.) Leningrad.
1069. Yapontsev, P. A. (1939) The elaboration of positive and inhibitory conditional connections in general paresis. (Rus.) Ark. biol. Nauk. 53, 9-22.
1070. Yapontsev, P. A. (1940) A neuro-dynamic interpretation of certain neurological disorders observed under different forms of active therapy of schizophrenia. (Rus.) Tes. Dokl. 7 Sov. Fiziol. posv. I. P. Pavlov. 80-81.
1071. Yarotsky, A. I. (1954) Characteristics of the formation of vestibular conditional reflexes. (Rus.) Z. vyss. nerv. Dejat. Pavlova. 4, 381-386.
1072. Yashvili, V. E. (1956) Problems of the neurodynamics of the visual and cutaneous analysers in schizophrenia. (Rus.) Tes. Dokl. Sess. Inst. M. Asatiani. Tiflis. 58-59.
1073. Yashvili, V. E. (1956) The interaction of the signaling systems in some types of psychopathy. (Rus.) Tr. Tbilis, med. Inst. Tiflis. 9, 245-251.
1074. Zachepitsky, R. A. (1954) Combinations of sleep and psychotherapy in the treatment of neuroses. (Rus.) Z. Nevropat. Psihiat. (Korsakoff.) 54, 431-435.
1075. Zakharova, N. N.: (1957) Studies of the cortical dynamics, and especially the interaction of the signaling systems, in mutistic schizophrenics. (Rus.) Nauch. Konf. Dejat. Sign. Sist. Norm. i Patol. 44-46.
1076. Zakharova, N. N. (1958) Studies of the neurodynamics of schizophrenic patients with electromyography. (Rus.) Konf. Vopr. Patofiziol. vyss. nerv. Dejat. Moscow. 48-49.

1077. Zakharova, N. N. (1958) Ultraparadoxical phases in the cerebral cortex of schizophrenic patients with speech disturbances. (Rus.) Konf. Vopr. Patofiziol. vyss. nerv. Dejat. Moscow. 50-51.

1078. Zakharova, N. N. (1958) Investigations of the cortical dynamics, especially the interaction of the signaling systems, in schizophrenics with severe disturbances of speech. (Rus.) Tr. Inst. vyss. nerv. Dejat. Ser. Patofiziol. 5, 121-137.

1079. Zakrzewska, F. (1953) Unconditional and conditional vasomotor reflexes to cold in schizophrenia in defect state. (Pol.) Neurol. Neurochir. Psychiat. pol. 3, 581-593.

1080. Zakrzewska, F. (1955) Studies on the pathophysiological analysis of the states of catatonic stupor. (Pol.) Neurol. Neurochir. Psychiat. pol. 5, 177-184.

1081. Zaltsman, G. I. (1954) Experimental investigations of conditional connections of the first and second signaling systems in schizophrenics. (Rus.) Alma-Ata. Diss.

1082. Zaltsman, G. I. (1956) Some characteristics of conditional connections in the first and second signaling systems in schizophrenics. (Rus.) Sb. Uzbek. Sov. Vopr. Psihiat. Tashkent. 278-289.

1083. Zamakhover, S. M. (1957) Characteristics of conditional connections of the first and second signaling systems in schizophrenic patients. (Rus.) Nauch. Konf. Dejat. Sign. Sist. Norm. i Patol. 42-43.

1084. Zamakhover, S. M. (1958) Two types of disturbances of the neurodynamics in schizophrenic patients. (Rus.) Konf. Vopr. Patofiziol. vyss. nerv. Dejat. Moscow. 46-48.

1085. Zborovsky, A. B. (1957) Disturbances of the first and second signaling systems in patients with rheumatism. (Rus.) Z. vyss. nerv. Dejat. Pavlova. 7, 374-380.

1086. Zharikov, N. M., J. A. Iliynsky, O. V. Kerbikov & L. S. Matvejets (1956) Immunological reactivity in schizophrenia. (Rus.) Z. Nevropat. Psihiat. (Korsakoff.) 56, 612-621.

1087. Zharikov, N. M. (1956) The characteristics of disturbances of the dynamics of simple motor performances in schizophrenics. (Rus.) Vopr. Psihiat. Moscow. 167-170.

1088. Zhudro, E. M. (1958) Disturbances of the interaction of the first and second signaling systems in severe types of chronic alcoholism. (Rus.) Konf. Vopr. Patofiziol. vyss. nerv. Dejat. Moscow. 44-46.

1089. Zhurikova, N. A. (1939) Changes of cortical dynamics in hypoglycemic states during insulin treatment of schizophrenics. (Rus.) Tes. Dokl. 5 Sov. Fisziol. posv. I. P. Pavlov. 33-34.

1090. Zhurikova, N. A. (1940) Changes in the unconditional reflex activity in insulin hypoglycemia in man. (Rus.) Tes. Dokl. 7 Sov. Fiziol. posv. I. P. Pavlov. 29-29.

1091. Ziehen, T. (1896) Über Messungen der Associationsegschwindigkeit bei Geisteskranken, namentlich bei circulärem Irresein. Neurol. Zbl. 15, 290-307

1092. Zimukova, L. I. (1958) Clinic and neurodynamic aspects of involutional psychoses during treatment. (Rus.) Vopr. Psihiat. Nevropat. Leningrad. 172-184.

1093. Zimukova, L. I. (1958) Some data on the neurodynamics of patients with involutional psychoses. (Rus.) Konf. Vopr. Patofiziol. vyss. nerv. Dejat. Moscow. 52-53.

1094. Zimukova, L. I. (1959) Disturbances of the higher nervous activity in paranoid syndromes in schizophrenia, involutional psychoses and other psychiatric diseases. (Rus.) Vopr. Psikonevrol. Leningrad. 97-99.

1095. Zitovich, I. S. (1918) About vasomotor psychoreflexes. (Rus.) Russki. fiziol. Z. 1, 113-127.

1096. Zjuzin, I. K. (1954) Functional lability of the motor analysers in epilepsy. (Rus.) Z. Nevropat. Psihiat. (Korsakoff.) 54, 543-548.

1097. Zlatoverov, A. I. (1955) Cortical influence on symptoms resulting from organic lesions of the central nervous system. (Rus.) Z. Nevropat. Psihiat. (Korsakoff.) 55, 916-918.

1098. Zmanovsky, J. F. (1958) The characteristics of the higher nervous activity in patients with climacteric disturbances. (Rus.) Konf. Vopr. Patofiziol. vyss. nerv. Dejat. Moscow. 53-55.

1099. Znamensky, V. V. (1953) The problems of the strength of reactivity in schizophrenia. (Rus.) Z. Nevropat. Psihiat. (Korsakoff.) 53, 753-758.

1100. Zurabashvili, A. D. (1952) The neurodynamic analysis of psychopathological phenomena. (Rus.) Z. vyss. nerv. Dejat. Pavlova. 2, 393-407.

1101. Zurabashvili, A. D. (1953) About the significance of the word experiment in the psychiatric clinic. (Rus.) Z. vyss. nerv. Dejat. Pavlova. 3, 393-407.

1102. Zurabashvili, A. D. (1955) Some data about the word signalization. (Rus.) Z. Nevropat. Psihiat. (Korsakoff.) 55, 805-810.

1103. Zurabashvili, A. D. (1958) The contemporary theories of schizophrenia. (Rus.) Tiflis.

1104. Zykhar, V. P. (1953) Physiological characteristics of various stages of hypnosis based on studies of unconditional and conditional vascular reactions. (Rus.) Tes. Sov. Probl. kort. viz. Fiziol. Leningrad. 72-73.

1105. Zykhar, V. P. (1957) Changes of cortical dynamics in hypnotic sleep. (Rus.) Z. Nevropat. Psihiat. (Korsakoff.) 57, Suppl. 55-56.

INDEX OF RUSSIAN JOURNALS AND CONGRESS REPORTS

The majority of the cited Russian journals and congress reports are not found in the WHO and Unesco publications of abbreviations of the titles of medical periodicals. Therefore, I had to make my own abbreviations. It would be advisable for the libraries also to give the Russian text of the index.

1. Aktual. Probl. Nevropat. Psihiat. Kuibyshev.

   Актуальные проблемы невропатологии и психиатрии, Куйбышев

2. Annot. nauch. Rab. Akad. Nauk.

   Аннотации научных работ Академии медицинских наук СССР

3. Ark. biol. Nauk.

   Архив биологических наук

4. Avtoref. Dokl. issl. Psihiat. MZSSR.

   Авторефераты докладов годичной конференции Института психиатрии МЗ СССР, Москва

5. Bjul. eksp. Biol. Med.

   Бюллетень экспериментальной биологии и медицины (СССР)

6. Bjul. VIEM.

   Бюллетень ВИЭМ (Всесоюзный Институт экспериментальной медицины)

7. Dokl. Akad. Nauk. SSSR.

   Доклады Академии наук СССР

8. Eksp. issl. psihiat. nevrol. Klin. Leningrad.

   Зкспериментальные исследования в психиатрической и неврологической клиниках. Минздрав РСФСР. Годичные научные исследования Психо-неврологического Института им.В.М.Бехтерева, Ленинград

9. Fiziol. Z. (Mosk.)

   Физиологический Журнал СССР им.Сеченова, Москва

10. Jub. Sb. Giliarovsky.

    Юбилейный сборник, посвященный 70-летию со дня рождения проф. В.А.Гиляровского. Проблемы современной психиатрии, Москва

11. Klin. Med. (Mosk.)

Клиническая медицина (СССР), Москва

12. Konf. Itog. nauch. issl. Rab. 1957. Moscow.

Конференция по итогам научно-исследовательской работы Института высшей нервной деятельности АН СССР эа 1957 г.

13. 4 Konf. molod. Uchen. Moscow.

Четвертая конференция молодых ученых Академии медицинских наук СССР. Институт нормальной и патологической фиэиологии, Москва

14. Konf. po Itog. Rab. 1953. IEM. Leningrad.

Конференция по итогам научно-исследовательской работы Института экспериментальной медицины эа 1953 г., Ленинград

15. Konf. Vopr. Patofiziol. vyss. nerv. Dejat. Moscow.

Конференция по вопросам патофиэиологии высшей нервной деятельности человека применительно к эадачам психиатрической и нервной клиник, Москва

16. Material. evolut. Fiziol. Leningrad.

Материалы по эволюционной физиологии, Ленинград

17. Nauch. Konf. Dejat. Sign. Sist. Norm. i Patol.

Научная конференция по вопросам совместной деятельности первой и второй сигнальных систем в норме и патологии, Москва

18. 2 nauch. Konf. KGMI. Kishinev.

2 научная конференция молодых ученых Государственного медицинского Института, Кишинев. Теэисы докладов

19. 3 nauch. Konf. nauch. Rab. Leningrad.

3 научная конференция научных работников, Ленинград

20. Nauch. Rab. Psikonevrol. Uchpr. RSFSR.

Научные работы врачей психо-неврологических учреждений РСФСР, Научно-исследовательский Институт психиатрии Минэдрава РСФСР

21. Nauch. Sess. 40 Let. Revolut. Kieff.

Научная сессия, посвященная 40-летию Великой Октябрьской социалистической революции, Киевская психо-неврологическая больница им. ак. И.П. Павлова, Киев

22. Nauch. Sess. vozrast. Fiziol. Chel. Moscow & Leningrad.

Научная сессия по вопросам возрастной физиологии человека, Москва и Ленинград

23. 2 nauch. Sov. evolut. Fiziol. Leningrad.

2 научный совет по вопросам эволюционной физиологии, Ленинград

24. 3 nauch. Sov. vozrast. Fiziol. Patol. Leningrad.

Третье научное совещание по возрастной физиологии и патологии высшей нервной деятельности человека, Ленинград

25. Nevropat. i Psihiat.

Невропатология и психиатрия

26. Nov. Refl. Fiziol. nerv. Sist. Leningrad.

Новое в рефлексологии и физиологии нервной системы. Сборник, Ленинград

27. Probl. Fiziol. tsent. nerv. Sist. posv. 70 Let. K. M. Bykov.

Проблемы физиологии центральной нервной системы. Сборник, посвященный 70-летию со дня рождения акад. К.М.Быкова, Ленинград

28. Probl. klin. eksp. Nevropat. Psihiat. Charkow.

Проблемы клинической экспериментальной невропатологии и психиатрии, Харьков

29. Probl. kort. viz. Patol. Leningrad.

Проблемы кортико-висцеральной патологии, Ленинград

30. Probl. Patofiziol. Ter. Schiz. Charkow.

Проблемы патофизиологии и терапии шизофрении. Центральный психо-неврологический Институт, Харьков

31. Probl. Patofiziol. Ter. Schiz. Kieff.

Проблемы патофизиологии и терапии шизофрении, Киев

32. Probl. Patol. Kinestes. nerv. psik. Zabol. Simferopol.

Проблемы патологии кинестезии и движения в клинике нервных и психических заболеваний, Симферополь

33. Psihiat. klin. Probl. Patol. vyss. nerv. Dejat.

Психиатрическая клиника и проблемы патологии высшей нервной деятельности, Ленинград. Государственный Институт для усовершенствования врачей им.С.М.Кирова

34. Psihiat. Nevropat. eksp. Psikol.

Психиатрия, невропатология и экспериментальная психология

35. Psikonevrol. Konf. Probl. Schiz. Simferopol.

Психо-неврологическая научно-практическая конференция, посвященная проблемам шизофрении и опухолей головного мозга, Тезисы докладов

36. Ref. nauch. issl. Rab. med. biol. Nauk. SSSR.

Рефераты научно-исследовательских работ медико-биологических наук Академии медицинских наук СССР

37. Russki fiziol. Z.

Русский физиологический журнал.

38. Sb. nauch. Inst. M. Asatiani. Tiflis.

Сборник трудов научно-исследовательского психиатрического Института им.Асатиани, Тбилиси

39. Sb. nauch. Tr. Rjazan.

Сборник научных трудов Рязанского медицинского Института им. И.П.Павлова, том 3

40. Sb. Nevropat. Psihiat. Riga.

Сборник научных работ по невропатологии и психиатрии, Рига Латв. ССР

41. Sb. posv. 75 Let. L. A. Orbeli.

Сборник, посвященный 75-летию акад. Л.А.Орбели. Проблемы эволюц. функций, Москва и Ленинград

42. Sb. Rab. Vopr. Nevropat. Psihiat. Stalinabad.

Сборник работ по невропатологии и психиатрии, Сталинабад

43. Sb. Ref. med. Fak. Uzhgor. Lemberg.

Сборник рефератов научных работ медицинского факультета Ужгородского Униреситета, Львов

44. Sb. Tes. Dokl. Stalino.

Сборник тезисов докладов. Юбил. 29 научн. конференц. Сталинского Государственного медицинского Института им.Горького

45. Sb. Tes. Rostov. med. Inst.

Сборник тезисов реф. отчет. науч. сессии Ростовского Госуд. Медицинского Института

46. Sb. Tr. Boln. Im. Balinskogo. Leningrad.

Сборник трудов психиатрической больницы им.Балинского

47. Sb. Uzbek. Sov. Vopr. Psihiat. Tashkent.

Сборник материалов Узбексого Республ. совещания по актуальным вопросам психиатрии

48. Sov. Vopr. evolut. Fiziol. nerv. Sist. Leningrad.

Современные вопросы эволюционной физиологии нервной системы

49. Sov. Vopr. Fiziol. Patol. Leningrad.

Совещание по вопросам физиологии и патологии речевой деятельности Акад. наук СССР Инстит. физиологии им.Павлова

50. Sovetsk. Med.

Советская медицина

51. Sovetsk. Psikonevrol.

Советск. психоневрология

52. Sovr. Probl. Schiz.

Современная проблема шизофрении, Москва-Ленинград

53. Sovr. Psikonevrol.

Современная психоневрология

54. Tes. Dokl. Inst. nauch. Konf. Leningrad.

Тезисы докл. Институт. науч. конф. Ленинград Институт усоверш. врачей им.Кирова

55. Tes. Dokl. Jub. Stolet. Kaf. Psihiat. Leningrad.

Тезисы докладов юбилейной конференции, посвященной 100-летию кафедры психиатрии

56. Tes. Dokl. nauch. Sess. 50 Let. Revolut. Odessa.

Тезисы докладов научной сессии, посвященной 50 лет русской революции, Одесского медицинского Института

57. Tes. Dokl. Sess. Inst. M. Asatiani. Tiflis.

Тезисы докладов рассирен. конференции научно-исследоват. института психиатрии им.Асатиани, посвящ. пробл. клинич. патофизиол. и терапии шизофрении.

58. Tes. Dokl. Sess. Stalingrad. med. Inst.

Тезисы докладов 8 научн. сесс. Сталинградского медиц. инстит.

59. Tes. Dokl. (3-13) Sov. Fiziol. posv. I. P. Pavlov.

Тезисы докладов (3- 13) совещ. по проблем. высшей нервной деятельпости, посвященного И.П.Павлову

60. Tes. Dokl. 20. Ukrain. Psikonevrol. Inst. Charkow.

Тезисы докладов 20 научн. сессии Украинск. научно-исслед. психо-неврологич. института

61. Tes. Kharkov. med. Inst. posv. 150 Let.

Тезисы доклад. научн. сесс., посвящ. 150-летию Харьковского медицин. института

62. Tes. Konf. Rjazan. Inst. I. P. Pavlov.

Тезисы докл. конференции Рязанского мед. института им.Павлова

63. Tes. Konf. Ukrain. psikonevrol. Inst.

Тезисы и рефераты докладов на годичной конференц. Украинск. научно-исслед. психо-неврологического Института, Харьков

64. Tes. nauch. Sess. posv. Vedenskogo. Odessa.

Тезисы докладов науч. сессии, посвящ. вопросам применения учения Н.Е.Введенского в клинической практике

65. Tes. (10-20) nauch. Sess. Saratov. med.

Тезисы (10-20) научной сессии Саратовского мед. института

66. Tes. Sov. Probl. kort. viz. Fiziol. Leningrad.

Тезисы совещания по проблем. кортико-висцеральн. физиолог. и патолог. Института физиологии им.Павлова АН СССР, Ленинград

67. Tes. (16-18) Sov. Probl. vyss. nerv. Dejat.

Тезисы (16-18) совещания по пробл. высшей нервной деятельности

68. Tr. Chernovits. Obl.

Труды Черновицкой областн. психо-невролог. больницы Минздрава УССР.

69. Tr. Inst. Fiziol. Im. I. P. Pavlov.

Труды института физиологии им.Павлова

70. Tr. Inst. vyss. nerv. Dejat. Ser. Patofiziol.

Труды института высшей нервной деятельности, серия пато физиологич.

71. Tr. Konf. Probl. Nevros. Petrozavodsk.

Труды конференции по проблеме невроз Петрозаводск.

72. Tr. Kuibyshev. med. Inst.

Труды Куйбышевского медицин. института

73. Tr. med. Fak. Tartu. Tallin.

Труды мединского факультета Тартусского Университета, Таллин

74. Tr. 1 Moskov. psihiat. Boln.

Труды I Московской психиатрической больницы

75. Tr. nauch. Konf. posv. 100 Let. S. S. Korsakoff.

Труды научной конференции, посвящен. 100-летию со дня рождения С.С.Корсакова

76. Tr. (2-4) Pavlov. Konf. Tomsk.

Труды (2-4) Павловской конференции, Томск

77. Tr. Psihiat. Klin. I. P. Pavlov.

Труды психиатрической клиники им.Павлова

78. Tr. Sess. Armjan. Nevropat. Psihiat. Erevan.

Труды первой науч. сессии Армянского общества невропатологов и психиатров

79. Tr. (14-20) Sess. Ukrain. psikonevrol. Inst.

Труды (14-20) научной сессии Укр. психо-неврологическ. институт

80. Tr. 15 Sov. posv. 50 Let. I. P. Pavlov.

Труды 15 совещания, посвящен. 50-летию учения И.П.Павлова, Москва-Ленинград

81. Tr. Tbilis. med. Inst. Tiflis.

Труды Тбилисского госуд. медиц. института, Тбилиси

82. Tr. tsent. psikonevrol. Inst.

Труды центрального психо-невролог. института УССР, Харьков

83. Tr. voj. mor. med. Akad. Leningrad.

Труды военно-морск. медицин. Академии, Ленинград

84. Tr. vsesoj. Sjesd. Nevropat. Psihiat. Moscow.

Труды Всесоюзного съезда невропатологов и психиатров, Москва

85. Uchen. Zapisk. 1 Leningrad. Inst.

Ученый записки 1 Ленинградского медицин. института им.Павлова

86. Ukrain. Vestn. Reflexol. eksp. Pedagog.

Украинский вестник рефлексологии и экспериментальной педагогики

87. Vopr. Klin. Nevropat. Psihiat.

Вопросы клинической невропатологии и психиатрии. Сб. науч. трудов Виин. госуд. медиц. института и Винн. клинич. психо-неврол. больницы, том 10

88. Vopr. klin. org. Psikonevrol. Tomsk.

Вопросы клинич. и организац. психоневрологии. Межобл. науч.сесс. психиатр. и невропатол. в г.Томске, посвящен. 50 летию больницы

89. Vopr. Klin. Patogenez. Schiz. Moscow.

Вопросы клиники, лечения и патогенеза шизофрении и психич. наруш. сосудист. забол. Гос. науч.-иссл. инстит. психиатрии Минздрава РСФСР

90. Vopr. Psihiat. Moscow.

Вопросы психиатрии, Автореф. Москва

91. Vopr. Psihiat. Nevropat. Leningrad.

Вопросы психиатрии и неврологии, Ленинград

92. Vopr. Psikonevrol. Leningrad.

Вопросы психоневрологии, Институт им.Ъехтерева, Ленинград

93. Vopr. Rastroist. Krovoob. Schiz. Odessa.

Вопросы расстройства мозгового кровообращения при шизофрении

94. Vracheb. Delo.

Врачебное дело (СССР), Киев

95. Z. Nevropat. Psihiat. (Korsakoff.)

Журнал невропатологии и психиатрии им.Корсакова

96. Z. vyss. nerv. Dejat. Pavlova.

Журнал высшей нервной деятельности

SUBJECT INDEX

In this subject index, "Conditioning" gives the page numbers which deal with studies of various psychiatric diseases and normals. On these listed pages, references will be found.

AUTHOR INDEX

Abramson, D. I., 43, 96
Ackner, B., 43
Altschule, M. D., 43, 100
Angyal, A., 99
Apter, I. M., 66
Arieti, S., 85
Arnold, O. H., 103
Ås, A., 11
Aschaffenburg, G., 17, 20, 75
Aslanov, A. S., 83
Asratyan, E. A., 7
Astrup, C., 18, 19, 22, 23, 25, 26, 58, 60, 61, 62, 63, 64, 65, 66, 68, 69, 74, 76, 78, 88, 92, 97, 102

Balonov, L. J., 46, 53, 72, 83
Bambas, B. S., 53
Baruk, M. H., 96
Baskina, N. F., 83
Batsha, T., 67
Bekhterev, V. M., 3
Bell, J. E., 15, 91
Bellak, L., 102
Belousova, M. T., 59
Bender, L., 94
Binswanger, L., 105
Birnbaum, K., 75
Blackman, N., 99
Bleuler, E., 23, 67, 68, 88, 89, 104
Bleuler, M., 105, 109
Bridger, W. H., 81
Brozek, J., 96
Brunnschweiler, H., 23, 66, 67, 68
Bumke, O., 95, 100
Bykov, K. M., 10, 44

Carmichael, E. A., 95, 97
Chapman, W. P., 60
Chistovich, A. S., 39, 40, 49, 72, 81, 84, 92, 93
Chuchmareva, N. I., 87

Clausen, J., 42
Clérambault, G., 46, 83, 103, 104, 266
Crown, S., 17, 28

Dahl, N. L., 110
De, B., 15, 17, 23, 27, 28, 90
Dobrzhanskaya, A. K., 84, 86

Elizarova, K. A., 59, 66
Ey, H., 3, 107
Eysenck, H. J., 13
Eysenck, S. B. G., 17, 27

Faddeyeva, V. K., 58, 76
Faust, E., 181
Feilbach, W., 66
Finesinger, J. E., 11
Fish, F. J., 107
Fossum, A., 61, 102
Funkenstein, D. H., 99

Gakkel, L. B., 18, 22, 23, 66
Galton, F., 15
Gantt, W. H., 3, 4, 6, 9, 10, 37, 39, 60, 62, 68, 70, 81, 99, 231, 267
Gellhorn, E., 93, 99, 100
Giliarovsky, V. A., 82
Gill, M., 90
Gjessing, G., 6
Golovina, V. P., 66, 85

Hall, K. R. L., 94
Harzstein, N. G., 23, 62, 76
Henschel, A., 96
Hilgard, E. R., 3, 10
Hill, D., 100
Holmboe, R., 61, 102
Holzinger, J., 66
Hoskins, R. G., 99
Huston, P. E., 95

Igersheimer, W. W., 93

343

Indiana University
Northwest Campus Library